The Perfect Complement to Chenier's Prac

Unique Features why it's the only book of its kind in America

- Table of Content has: *Page Numbers*, *Task Numbers*, and *Pictures*.

- *Self Checking Techniques* – Unique to this book. Helps build on-the-job confidence.

- All *Trig Formulas are Illustrated*.

- How *Metric Conversion Factors* are determined.

- Many *Trade Tricks* left out of traditional math books.

- Lay Out *Geometric Figures, 3 to 8 sides and ellipses*.

- Only *Illustrated Appendix*.

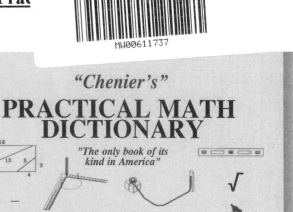

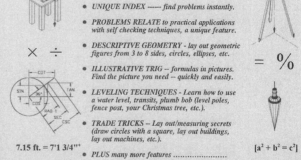

"Chenier's"

PRACTICAL MATH DICTIONARY

"The only book of its kind in America"

- *ILLUSTRATIVE Table of Contents & English/ Metric Appendix ------ found only in this book.*
- *UNIQUE INDEX ------ find problems instantly.*
- *PROBLEMS RELATE to practical applications with self checking techniques, a unique feature.*
- *DESCRIPTIVE GEOMETRY - lay out geometric figures from 3 to 8 sides, circles, ellipses, etc.*
- *ILLUSTRATIVE TRIG -- formulas in pictures. Find the picture you need -- quickly and easily.*
- *LEVELING TECHNIQUES - Learn how to use a water level, transits, plumb bob (level poles, fence post, your Christmas tree, etc.).*
- *TRADE TRICKS - Lay out/measuring secrets (draw circles with a square, lay out buildings, lay out machines, etc.).*
- *PLUS many more features ....*

"A BOOK FOR EVERYONE"

406 Pages, 6″× 7-1/2″ ISBN: O-962-60611-1
[Perfect size for your tool box]

   This is the PERFECT book for all trades personnel and the do-it-yourself person. The book is a spin-off of 40 years of technical on-the-job experience in many different trades and occupations, including 30 plus years of teaching experiences. It has over **400 pages, "Packed"** with unique information.

   This book includes many trade tricks left out of traditional math books, and useful (economical) practical math concepts.

For Further Information Contact: **Chenier's Educational Enterprises, Inc.**
3999 Co. 416 – 20th Rd.
Gladstone, MI 49837

Phone: 906-786-1630
Fax: 906-786-8088
www.cheniermath.com

Chenier's

Practical Math Application Guide

For: Do-It-Yourselfers, Trades people, Students, etc.

• *Featuring an Illustrative Table of Contents, pages 9 - 16*

- **Basic Mathematical Skills**
- **Measuring Techniques**
- **Squaring Techniques**
- **Leveling Techniques**
- **Calculate and Lay Out Angles**
- **Calculate and Lay Out Stairs**
- **Calculate and Lay Out Rafters**
- **One & Two Point Sketching**
- **Plus** many, many, many, more unique features ....

"A BOOK FOR EVERYONE"

BY
NORMAN J. CHENIER

Gladstone, Michigan
CHENIER EDUCATIONAL ENTERPRISES, INC.
PUBLISHERS

Acknowledgements

I would like to thank my Lord and Savior, Jesus Christ, for giving me the talents, courage, and health to finish this project. I do it all for His honor and glory.

I would also like to extend my appreciation and sincere thanks to my wife, Joanne who helped with the secretarial work and stuck by me every step of the way.

I am especially grateful for my editor George Strandness, a retired Air Force pilot who went out of his way to help me edit this project. I would also like to acknowledge my investors and friends: Jim Almonroeder, marketing chairman, and colleague; Al Atwood, my retired Editor, and his wife Clare; Gary and Annis Bengston; Clayton and Dorlene Carlson, David and Carol Carlson (sister); Ronald and Patricia Carlson; Betty Chenier (sister), Donald Chenier (brother); Robert and Kathy LaRoche; Vicki Meyer; Gary Olsen, Corporate lawyer; Paul Paulson, CPA, and Thomas and Dorothy Srock.

Grateful appreciation and thanks are also extended to the Stanley Tools Division of the Stanley Works, New Britain, Connecticut; The L.S. Starrett Company, Athol, Massachusetts; The Hydrolevel Co., Ocean Springs, Mississippi; The General Tools MFG Co., LLC New York, New York; and Texas Instruments, Dallas, Texas.

I would also like to extend my appreciation and sincere thanks to my mother, Jeanette (Chenier) Frazer, for her guidance and encouragement throughout my life; to James Mitchell, our copyright lawyer; to Gerard Mogilka our salesman; and to Karen Meiers our CPA.

Introduction

This is a practical math program that will enhance your practical math skills. The beauty of practical math is that you can build anything to plus or minus (±) 1/16 (which is equivalent to 1/32 of an inch accuracy) with very little difficulty. "To build anything, it must be **measured correctly** (true in dimension), it must be **square** (uniform geometrically), and it must be **level** (oriented with the horizon)". Norman J. Chenier.

How to get Started:

It is important to take the "PRETEST" in module #1, so you (and your instructor, if in a class) will know where you stand, as far as basic math skills go. Take the pretest now, then take the post test after you've studied the material. Hopefully, the results will surprise you.

The "Fun Part" of the math program:

Every math concept presented in this book is demonstrated and made easy for you to practice. Some examples are listed below:

Measurement:

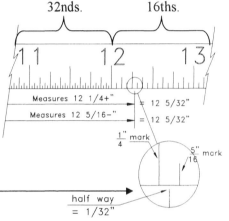

1st: Most American English tape measures do not have 1/32″ increments after 12 inches, as the tape measure on the right shows.. ***But, many trades, such as, cabinetmaking, millwright work, machinist work, etc. need this accuracy***. To achieve more accuracy, and to keep it simple, this book addresses the problem by referring to the distance between two 1/16″ marks as ± 1/16 (plus or minus half the distance to the nearest 1/16 mark).

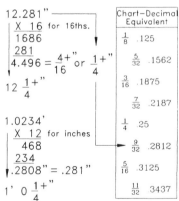

2nd: **The above concept can be proven mathematically** by converting (changing) decimals of inches to a fraction of an inch by multiplying by the desired denominator (lower number of the fraction). Example, the decimal 12.281″ can be changed to 16ths of an inch by multiplying the <u>decimal only</u> by 16 for 16ths., 32 for 32nds, 64 for 64ths, etc., and/or by verifying the decimal by using a decimal of an inch equivalent chart.

3rd: Convert decimals of feet to feet, inches, and ±1/16 of an inch accuracy by multiplying by the desired denominators and/or by using a decimals of a foot chart and a decimals of an inch chart.

Squaring:

1st: Square an object on a 11″ × 17″ sheet of paper without the use of a square. Accuracy must be ± 1/16 of an inch. Use a tape measure, pencil, and a straight edge.

2nd: Square an object on a concrete floor using a chalk line and two tape measures to ±1/16 of an inch accuracy using the same principal. Then you can square up a garage, 24 '- 0″ × 32' - 0″, a house, 28' - 0' × 48' - 0″, a trailer 6' - 0″ × 8' - 0″, etc. The possibilities are endless and easy to achieve ±1/16 of an inch.

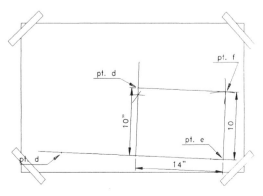

Introduction (Continued)

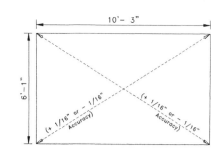

3rd: Measure to + 1/16 of an inch and -1/16 of an inch. ***This indicates a tolerance of 1/8"*** which is not very accurate for most practical applications. However a tolerance of 1/8" would be okay for squaring a large building (see page 93).

Leveling:

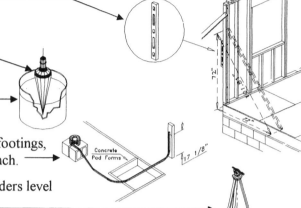

1st: Level an object with a spirit level. Level a wall, a door frame, pipe, footings, cabinets, etc. Check the level for accuracy (see page 347 in textbook).

2nd: Level a vertical object by using a plumb bob. Level poles, Christmas trees, pipes, tubing, etc.

3rd: Level a vertical object by using a plumb bob in oil. Level walls, motors, machines, etc.

4th: Level a horizontal object with a water level. Level footings, cabinets, garage doors, machines, etc. to ± 1/16th inch.

5th: Level a horizontal object with a transit and/or a builders level (in the textbook sold separately).

Angles:

1st: **Copy and Transfer Angles** with a Lay Out Square.

2nd: **Lay Out Angles** (from angle tangent) with a Lay Out Square.

3rd: **Measure Angles** (find degrees) with a Lay Out Square and the formula TOA.

4th: **Convert angles into degrees, minutes, and seconds**, for example, $27.396° = 27° \ 23 \ ' \ 45.6"$ (27 degrees 23 min. 45.6 sec.).

[Note if any of the basic math concepts found on these two pages are <u>not clear</u>, they will be addressed in detail within this book. Master these concepts and you will be able to build anything.]

Basic technical information included in this book and the textbook (sold separately):

- Basic algebra and formula manipulation, basic geometric, basic trig and the right triangle (sine, cosine, and tangent made easy with the scientific calculator). Plus many new applications approaches relevant to these math principles, found only in this book.

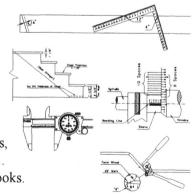

- **Other Unique Features** - Learn how to use the lay out and framing square to lay out stairs, rafters, octagons, braces, etc. Also learn how to use the lay out square to draw perfect circles.
  Learn how to read; micrometers marked in thousandths (.001") and ten thousandths (.0001"), vernier calipers, dial calipers, and digital calipers.
  Learn how to bend and level tubing, sketch, scribe, lay out pipe saddles, line-up fences, line-up walls, etc., and much, much, more ....

- **Trade Tricks** - Loaded with trade tricks left out of traditional math books.

Table of Contents

[Note, the Task Numbers correlate with the "Chenier's Practical Math Dictionary, sold separately. These Task Numbers are for instant reference to the textbook.]

TABLE OF CONTENTS

$Area = \pi r^2$ $Circumference = \pi d$

Math Training Module #6 (Continued):

TABLE OF CONTENTS

TABLE OF CONTENTS

Math Training Module #14 **(Continued)**

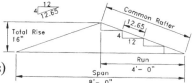
Math Training Module #15:

Math Training Module #16:

TABLE OF CONTENTS

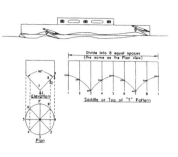
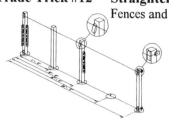
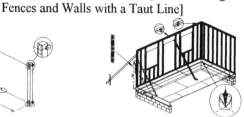

Appendices (Continued)

"This page intentionally blank."

Math Training Module #1

☐ **Introduction** – Whether this material is used in a classroom or individually, **it is very important to take the Pretest**. This will make it clear to you why this math program is so important. It will also illustrate to you how easy it can be to learn basic concepts to encompass your world of work or hobbies. The math program will be much more fun and meaningful with a solid foundation in basic math skills.

☐ <u>**The pretest**</u>. The best way to take the test is to do it all at once. This seems to be the hardest part of the math program. But, one of the most important parts of it, as you will know what your basic math skills are when you are completed. Also, you will know where your short comings are and what to study for.

☐ This workbook is designed to work in conjunction with the Practical Math Dictionary. From this point on the Practical Math Dictionary will be referred to as the **Textbook**. Also, and very important, is that no calculators should be used until you have obtained a solid foundation in these basic math skills. This will give you a better understanding of basic math and more confidence for on the job later.

☐ Use the blank copy of the pretest in the workbook to take notes after you completed the pretest. This will give you a fresh start. Refer to the Basic Math Study Notes below and the textbook to help you out.

☐ To use the **Practical Math Dictionary**, find the Task No. listed next to the problem in the pretest or module, then go to the Text Book and find that Task No. A similar problem will be demonstrated for you.

Objective Practice Problems: Calculate the practice problems on page 23 and 24. Use the Practical Math Dictionary to review the problems on your pretest. Use the blank pretest on page 25, 26, and 27 to correct any problems wrong, if needed. Do a little at a time and gradually you will become more proficient in basic math skills. The fun part is coming. However, if you fail to keep up, it will not be any fun.

<u>**Basic Math Study Notes for this Module**</u> – [These notes are for the 1st page of the pretest.]
<u>**(Whole Numbers, Common Fractions, Mixed Numbers, Denominate Numbers, and Decimal Fractions)**</u>:

<u>**Whole Numbers:**</u>

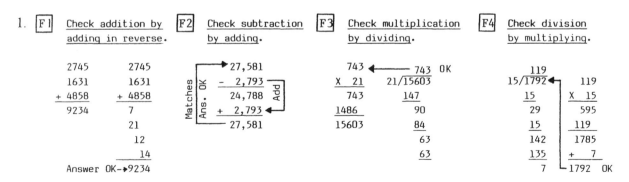

F1 ◄— Note the <u>**Number and the Letter**</u> in the box is a Task Number for quick reference in the textbook.

[Remember that on the job, chances are the answer to the problem that you are working on <u>will not</u> be in a book. Therefore, start self-checking each type of problem <u>now</u> to build confidence for the job later.]

Common Fractions:

2.   Check **common fraction** calculations by doing the opposite calculation.

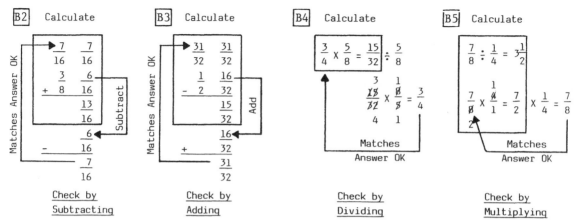

| | Check by Subtracting | Check by Adding | Check by Dividing | Check by Multiplying |

Mixed Numbers:

3.   Check **mixed number** calculations by doing the opposite calculation.

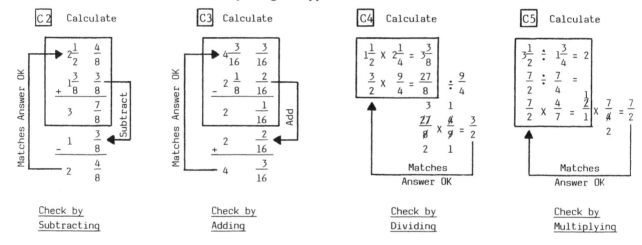

| | Check by Subtracting | Check by Adding | Check by Dividing | Check by Multiplying |

Denominate Numbers: (similar to mixed numbers, but apply to feet, inches, pounds, ounces, etc.)

4.   The two different methods of **multiplying denominate numbers**.   D4

a)   Square Measure (Area)

$$
\begin{array}{rcr}
2'9'' & = & 33'' \\
\times\ 1'6'' & = & \times\ 18'' \\
\hline
& & 264 \\
& & 33 \\
\hline
& & 594\ \text{sq. in.}
\end{array}
$$

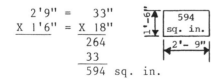

RULE 1

CHANGE NUMBERS TO THE SAME
DENOMINATION THEN MULTIPLY

b)   Linear Measure (Length)

$$
\begin{array}{r}
8'3'' \\
\times\ \ 3 \\
\hline
24'9''
\end{array}
$$

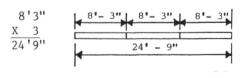

RULE 2

MULTIPLY EACH SPECIFIC DENOMINATION
BY THE WHOLE NUMBER

Basic Math Study Notes (Continued)

Denominate Numbers (Continued):

5.   Two different methods of **dividing denominate numbers**.

| D5 | Divide denominate numbers. Example: divide 7 ft. 3 in. by 4   [Use one method to check the other method]

| Method 1 | Method 2 |
| (Change to all inches then divide) | (Divide into each group) |

Method 1 (Change to all inches then divide)

$\underline{21}$ ¾″ = 1′ 9 3/4″

7 ft. 3 in. = 87″   4/87

[7 × 12 = 84″, and 3″ = 87″] $\underline{8}$

7

$\underline{4}$

3

Method 2 (Divide into each group)

$\underline{1\ ft.\quad 9\ ¾\ in.}$

4/7 ft.   3 in.

$\underline{4}$

3 = $\underline{+36}$

39

$\underline{36}$

3

Decimal Fractions:

6. | E2 | **Add** decimal fractions. Example: Add 7.8, 63, and .029. ⟶

7.800

63.000

$\underline{+\quad.029}$

70.829

[Note: Decimals must line up vertically in both addition and subtraction.]

| E3 | **Subtract** decimal fractions. Example: Subtract 762.9 from 2,714.08. ⟶

2,714.08

$\underline{-\quad762.90}$

1,951.18

| E4 | **Multiply** decimal fractions: Example: Multiply 1.25 × .023. ⟶

1.25   2 places

$\underline{\times\ .023}$ $\underline{+3}$ places

375   5

$\underline{250}$

.02875

[Note: Move the decimal point 5 places to the left in the product.]

| E5 | **Divide** decimal fractions: Example: Divide 48.9 ÷ .03.

.03./48.90.

[Note: Move the decimal point in the divisor (.03) two places to the right to make a whole number. Move the decimal point in the dividend (48.9) the same number of places.]

1630

3/4890.

$\underline{3}$

18

$\underline{18}$

9

$\underline{9}$

[Check the answers for decimal fractions the same way as with whole numbers.]

[Note: These notes are designed to give the reader a quick review of all the basic types of numbers included in the page 1 of the pretest. If more detailed information is needed, please refer to the textbook.]

Miscellaneous Math Notes:

- When dividing whole numbers │A5│ that don't come out even (have a remainder) show the answer
  with the remainder -- example:

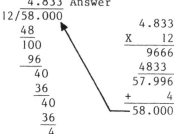

- When dividing decimal fractions │E5│ always carry the decimal point at least 3 places for most
  applications -- example:

```
            4.833 Answer
   12/58.000                    4.833
      48                     X     12
      ___                    _____
      100                     9666
       96                     4833
       ___                    _____
        40                   57.996
        36                  +     4
        ___                 _____
         40                 58.000
         36
         ___
          4
```

- When multiplying whole numbers │A4│ with zeros use either of the two methods shown below.

```
Examples:    652                          652
           X 707  ------- or -------     X 707
           _____                         _____
           4564                          4564
          45640                           000
          _____                         4564
          460964                         _____
                                         460964
          If you don't understand
          this method -------- use this method.
```

- <u>To round off a decimal a required number of places,</u> do not change the digit being rounded off if the next
  digit is below 5, or add 1 to the digit if the next digit is 5 or above. See the examples shown below.

  round off. 2.29 to one place (tenths) = 2.3 because 9 is greater than 5
  round off 2.298 to two places (hundredths) = 2.30 because 8 is greater than 5
  round off 2.2983 to three places (thousandths) = 2.298 because 3 is lower than 5
  round off 2.29835 to four places (ten-thousandths) = 2.2984 because at 5 the preceding number is raised 1

[Note: These notes cover most of the problems listed on page 1 of the pretest. However, the pretest was made
  so every problem on the pretest would work out even. This is done to measure, more accurately, student
  progress at the end of the math program. Realistically, these types of math problems will not come out
  even in the world of work. The modules coming will reflect on problems relevant to the real world.]

**This program is unique and the only one of it's kind in America. It will make you much more employable and
efficient in basic math skills. However, the outcome is entirely up to you.**

Objective Practice Problems for Module #1

A2 — Add and Check Whole Numbers

1.
```
    76
    84
+   25
```

2.
```
    385
    978
    272
+   846
```

A3 — Subtract and Check Whole Numbers

3.
```
    37
−   19
```

4.
```
    6,952
−     849
```

A4 — Multiply and Check Whole Numbers

5.
```
    67
×   34
```

6.
```
    385
×   509
```

A5 — Divide and Check Whole Numbers

7. $24\overline{)290}$

8. $105\overline{)31,290}$

B2 — Add and Check Common Fractions

9.
$$\frac{5}{32} + \frac{9}{16}$$

10.
$$\frac{17}{64} + \frac{1}{4}$$

B3 — Subtract and Check Common Fractions

11.
$$\frac{1}{2} - \frac{7}{32}$$

12.
$$\frac{5}{6} - \frac{1}{4}$$

B4 — Multiply and Check Common Fractions

13. $\dfrac{3}{16} \times \dfrac{1}{4} =$

14. $24 \times \dfrac{5}{16} =$

B5 — Divide and Check Common Fractions

15. $\dfrac{13}{16} \div \dfrac{1}{4} =$

16. $\dfrac{7}{8} \div 4 =$

C2 — Add and Check Mixed Numbers

17.
$$6\frac{1}{4} + 3\frac{5}{16}$$

18.
$$18\frac{3}{64} + 4\frac{3}{4}$$

C3 — Subtract and Check Mixed Numbers

19.
$$17\frac{13}{16} - 4\frac{5}{8}$$

20.
$$24\frac{1}{4} - 8\frac{3}{8}$$

Objective Practice Problems for Module #1

C4 — Multiply and Check Mixed Numbers

21.
22.

$2\frac{1}{2} \times 4\frac{1}{4} =$ $5\frac{1}{2} \times 7 =$

C5 — Divide and Check Mixed Numbers

23.
24.

$10\frac{1}{2} \div 2\frac{5}{8} =$ $4\frac{3}{8} \div 7 =$

D2 — Add and Check Denominate Numbers

25.
26.

$8'5\frac{3}{16}''$ $20'2\frac{1}{4}''$
$+\ 12'2\frac{1}{2}''$ $9\frac{7}{8}''$
$+\ 3'4\frac{7}{32}''$

D3 — Subtract and Check Denominate Numbers

27.
28.

$9'7\frac{3}{4}''$ $10'0''$
$-\ 4'6\frac{7}{8}''$ $-\ 3'3\frac{1}{2}''$

D4 — Multiply and Check Denominate Numbers

29.
30.

$7'2''$ $3'5''$
$\times\ 3'6''$ $\times\ 4$

D5 — Divide and Check Denominate Numbers

31.
32.

$8'6'' \div 6 =$ $7/\overline{9'\ \ 4''}$

E2 — Add and Check Decimal Fractions

33.
34. Add .0029, 6, 4.813
and .8762 =

32.0
7.7
+ 8.5

E3 — Subtract and Check Decimal Fractions

35.
36. Subtract 2.63
from 46 =

9.82
− 6.95

E4 — Multiply and Check Decimal Fractions

37.
38.

.38   3.07
× 7.5   × .805

E5 — Divide and Check Decimal Fractions

39.
40.

$6.6/\overline{26}$ $.43/\overline{7.095}$

DIRECTIONS: Calculate the problems listed below and reduce all fractions to their lowest terms.

WHOLE NUMBERS	

1. Task No.→ **A2**

$$\begin{array}{r} 447 \\ 962 \\ 851 \\ +\ 1084 \\ \hline \end{array}$$

2. **A3**

$$\begin{array}{r} 13{,}754 \\ -\ 4{,}875 \\ \hline \end{array}$$

3. **A4**

$$\begin{array}{r} 749 \\ \times\ 486 \\ \hline \end{array}$$

4. **A5**

$23/\overline{47{,}932}$

A1

COMMON FRACTIONS

5. **B2**

$$\begin{array}{r} \frac{7}{32} \\ \frac{5}{+\ 16} \\ \hline \end{array}$$

6. **B3**

$$\begin{array}{r} \frac{17}{32} \\ \frac{5}{-\ 16} \\ \hline \end{array}$$

7. **B4**

$\frac{15}{16} \times \frac{2}{3} =$

8. **B5**

$\frac{27}{64} \div \frac{3}{4} =$

B1

MIXED NUMBERS

9. **C2**

$$\begin{array}{r} 2\frac{1}{4} \\ 7\frac{3}{8} \\ +\ \ \ \\ \hline \end{array}$$

10. **C3**

$$\begin{array}{r} 10\ \frac{3}{8} \\ -\ 5\frac{7}{16} \\ \hline \end{array}$$

11. **C4**

$2\frac{1}{2} \times 3\frac{1}{5} =$

12. **C5**

$2\frac{1}{2} \div 3\frac{1}{5} =$

C1

DENOMINATE NUMBERS

13. **D2**

$$\begin{array}{r} 4 \text{ ft. } 1\ \frac{1}{8} \text{ in.} \\ +\ 3 \text{ ft. } 5\frac{3}{16} \text{ in.} \\ \hline \end{array}$$

14. **D3**

$$\begin{array}{r} 17 \text{ ft. } 5\ \frac{3}{4} \text{ in.} \\ -\ 2 \text{ ft. } 6\frac{7}{32} \text{ in.} \\ \hline \end{array}$$

15. **D4**

$$\begin{array}{r} 4 \text{ ft. } 9 \text{ in.} \\ \times\ 3 \text{ ft. } 4 \text{ in.} \\ \hline \end{array}$$

_____ sq. in.

_____ sq. ft.

16. **D5**

8 ft. 4 in. ÷ 5 =

D1

DECIMAL FRACTIONS

17. **E2**

$$\begin{array}{r} .05 \\ 1.07 \\ 25.31 \\ +\ 9.88 \\ \hline \end{array}$$

18. **E3**

$$\begin{array}{r} 150.04 \\ -\ 97.95 \\ \hline \end{array}$$

19. **E4**

$$\begin{array}{r} 72.13 \\ \times\ .089 \\ \hline \end{array}$$

20. **E5**

$.875/\overline{38.5}$

E1

COMPLEX FRACTIONS — B6 / Task No.

21.

$$\dfrac{\dfrac{7}{8} \times 24}{\dfrac{7}{16} \div \dfrac{5}{8}}$$

FIND AVERAGES — E8

22. Find the average of 81, 77, 102, and 68 = _____.

CHANGE FRACTIONS TO DECIMALS — E6

23. Change $\dfrac{3}{17}$ to a decimal fraction = _____.

24. Change $7\dfrac{1}{2}"$ to decimals of a foot = _____.

(Carry decimals 3 places)

CHANGE DECIMALS TO FRACTIONS — E7

Change the two figures below so you can read the dimensions on an American (English) tape measure.

25. 7.29 ft. = _____.

26. 4.625 in. = _____.

POWERS — H1

27. 3^5 = _____

SQUARE ROOTS — H2

28. $\sqrt{21{,}025}$

RATIO AND PROPORTION — I1

DIRECT PROPORTION | I3

29. 22:4 = 55:X

X = _____

PERCENTAGE — G1

30. Write 8 1/2% as a decimal = _____. | G1

31. Write 3/4% as a decimal = _____. | G1

32. Write .075 as a percent = _____. | G2

33. Write 1/4 as a percent = _____. | G3

34. Find 4% of $46.00 = _____. | G4

BASIC ALGEBRA — J1

ADDITION AND EQUATIONS | J2

35. X + 778 = 949

X = _____

MULTIPLICATIONS AND EQUATIONS | J4

36. 19A = 323

A = _____

© Copyright 2005 Chenier Educational Enterprises, Inc.

AREA OF A SQUARE OR RECTANGLE

K2 ← Task No.

37. How many <u>square feet</u> of material are needed to cover a rectangle 25 ft. by 34 ft.? _____

38. How many <u>square yards</u>? _____

25'- 0"

34'- 0"

Rule: Area = length x width
Formula: A = lw

VOLUME OF A CUBE OR RECTANGULAR SOLID

L2

39. How many <u>cubic feet</u> of material are needed to cover a rectangular solid 3 ft. by 9 ft. by 12 ft.? _____

40. How many <u>cubic yards</u>? _____

3'- 0"

9'- 0"

12'- 0"

Rule: Volume = length x width x height
Formula: V = lwh

ANGLES

K11 (and Page 71)

41. Angle C equals _____° (degrees).

C

?

90°

A

28°

B

43. Convert 22.375° to degrees, minutes, and seconds = _____.

42. The complement of an angle is the angle, which, when added to another angle, equals 90°. What is the complement of angle c below?

Angle b = _____°.

90°

?

37°

a   b   c

THE TAPE MEASURE

K2

44–50. Below is an American (English) tape measure. Fill in the missing dimensions below.

46. _____

45. _____

44. _____

1   2   3   4   5   6

47. _____

48. _____

49. _____

50. _____

MICROMETER (.001") — Task No. — **N2**

Fill in the missing micrometer readings below. Change the fraction to the nearest 64th inch.

1. _____ Thousandths

2. _____ Fraction of an inch

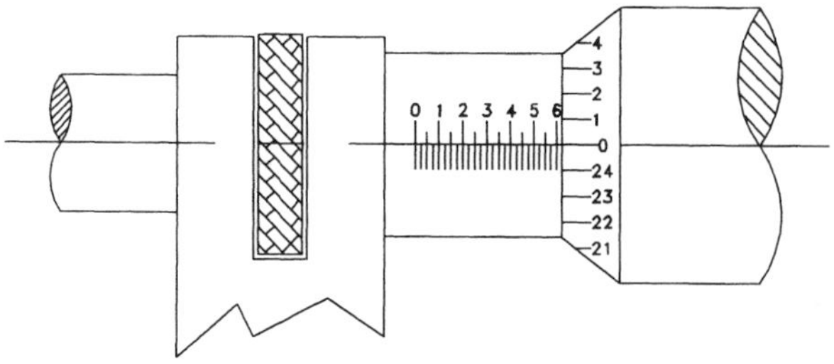

MICROMETER (.0001") — **N2A**

Fill in the missing micrometer readings below. Change the fraction to the nearest 64th inch.

3. _____ Thousandths

4. _____ Fraction of an inch

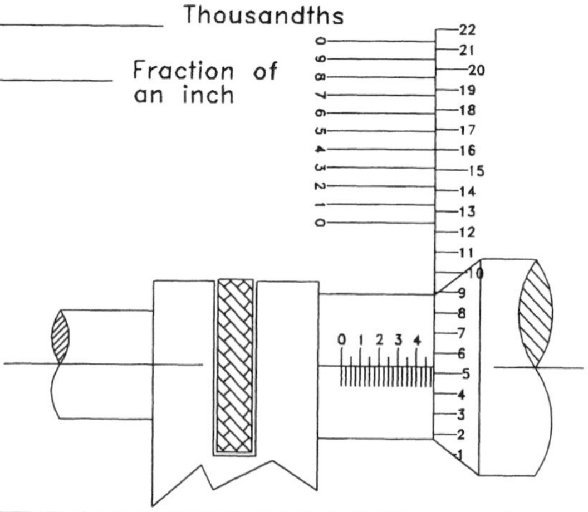

THE RULE OF PYTHAGORAS K5A and SOH–CAH–TOA FORMULAS: Page 179 (textbook) M1

Find the length of the missing right triangle <u>side a</u> shown on the right.

5. Side a = _____ (decimal 3 places)

_____ (ft., in., and ±16ths.)

6. Angle A = _____•.

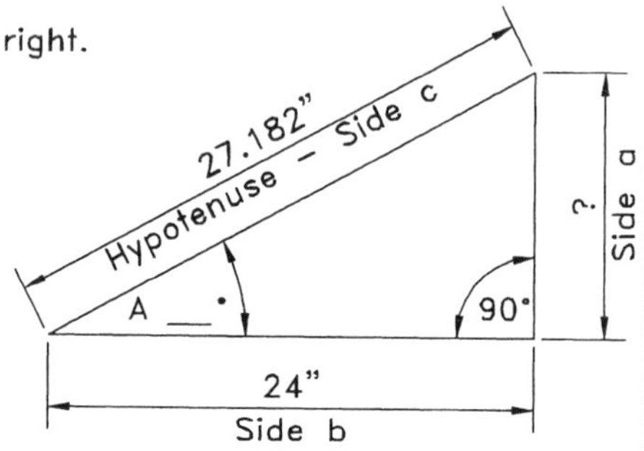

27.182" Hypotenuse – Side c
A ___•
90°
? Side a
24" Side b

Use a scientific calculator and/or the Trig Tables in the textbook to solve the unknown right triangle angles and sides shown on the right.

7. Hyp. = _____ (dec. 3 places) <u>or</u> _____ ft., in., & ±16ths.

8. Side Adj. = _____ (dec. 3 places) <u>or</u> _____ ft., in., & ±16ths.

? Hyp. (c)
25°
90°
7.5" Opp. (a)
? Adj. (b)

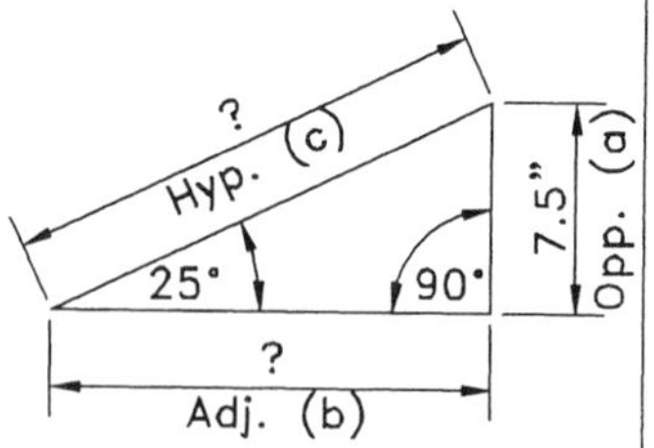

Calculate <u>angle A</u> and the <u>hypotenuse</u> of the right triangle on the right.

9. Angle A = _____•.

10. Hyp. = _____ (dec. 3 places) <u>or</u> _____ ft., in., & ±16ths.

? Hyp.
A ___•
90°
9 3/4" Opp.
15 1/2" Adj.

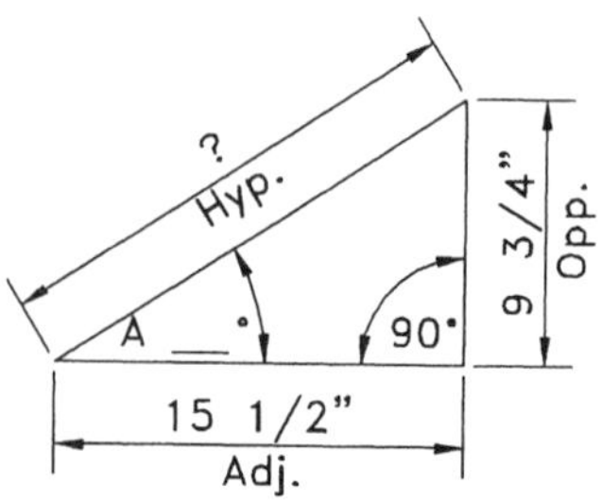

Formulas: $a^2 + b^2 = c^2$, and SOH–CAH–TOA (Use extra paper, if needed)

Math Training Module #2

Instructional Objectives: **Page No.**

☐ **Use the corrected pretest** and continue calculating and self-checking the problems on the 2nd page ... 26 of the pretest. Use the blank pretest found in the workbook. Use the textbook for self study.

☐ **Review the Basic Math Study Notes listed below** on complex fractions (as applied to measurement), how to change fractions to decimals, and vice versa, change decimals to fractions. Also, how to read a **Decimal of an Inch Equivalent Chart**.. **Inside Front Cover**

☐ **Info #1A - Convert Feet and Inches to Decimals** (Tape Measure in INCHES).................. 31, 32

☐ **Trade Trick #1 - Make a Story Pole,** Problem 1 and Problem 2: (24 3/4″ Stick) 33, 34

Hands On:

Basic Math Study Notes for this Module – (These notes are for the 1st half of page 2 of the Pretest) (Complex Fractions, Averages, Change Fractions to Decimal, and Change Decimals to Fractions):

Complex Fractions: (Practical Examples of Complex Fractions)

1. $\boxed{\text{B6}}$ Change a complex fraction to a decimal fraction.

$\boxed{\text{E6}}$ Example 1.   Change $3\frac{1}{2}''$ to decimals of a foot.

Remember 1 foot $= \frac{12''}{12}''$ therefore $3\frac{1}{2}''$ is $\dfrac{3\frac{1}{2}}{12}$ of a foot.

$$\frac{3\frac{1}{2}}{12} = \frac{3.5}{12} \quad \text{and} \quad 12\overline{)3.5}^{\,.292'} \qquad \text{Answer } 3\frac{1}{2}'' = .292'$$

$$\begin{array}{r} 2\ 4 \\ \hline 1\ 10 \\ 1\ 08 \\ \hline 20 \\ 12 \end{array}$$

$\boxed{\text{G1}}$ Example 2.   Change $\frac{3}{4}\%$ to a decimal.

Remember that $\frac{3}{4}\%$ equals $\dfrac{\frac{3}{4}}{100}$ or $\dfrac{.75}{100}$ or $100\overline{)\,.7500}^{\,.0075}$

Answer $\frac{3}{4}\% = .0075$ as a decimal

$$\begin{array}{r} 700 \\ \hline 500 \\ 500 \end{array}$$

The purpose of these notes is to focus in on a few of the types of problems that most people have trouble with and to serve as a review of material that is easily forgotten. These notes will build on each other and will help prepare you for quizzes, tests, and other modules that will follow. But most important, on the job.

29

Find Averages:

2. **E8** How to find the average of a group (two or more) of numbers. First, set up the numbers vertically in a column; second, add them up; and third, divide by the total number of numbers in the column.

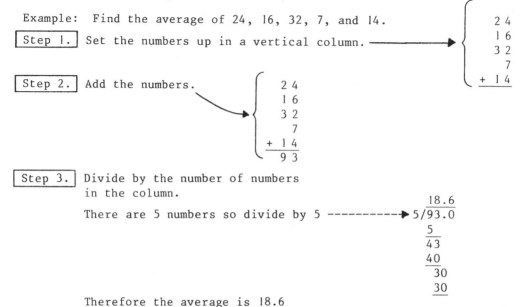

```
Example:  Find the average of 24, 16, 32, 7, and 14.              2 4
Step 1.  Set the numbers up in a vertical column. ———————→        1 6
                                                                  3 2
                                                                    7
                                                              +   1 4

Step 2.  Add the numbers.                          2 4
                                                    1 6
                                                    3 2
                                                      7
                                                +   1 4
                                                    9 3

Step 3.  Divide by the number of numbers
         in the column.                                    18.6
         There are 5 numbers so divide by 5 ————————→   5/93.0
                                                           5
                                                           43
                                                           40
                                                            30
                                                            30

         Therefore the average is 18.6
```

Change Fractions to Decimals and Change Decimals to Fractions:

3. **E6** How to change inches to fractions of a foot and to decimals of a foot. $12'' = 1'0''$ (1 foot). Therefore, inches over 12 will equal the fraction of a foot.

```
Example:  5" = 5/12 (fraction of a foot)     or            .416' (decimals of a foot)
                                                         12/5.000
[The denominator (lower number) of a                       48
fraction always divides into the numerator                 20        [If the decimal were carried 4
(top number) of a fraction]                                12        places .4166 it would be rounded
                                                           80        off to .417']
                                                           72
                                                            8
```

4. **E7** How to convert decimals of a foot to feet, inches, and 16ths.

[Rule: Multiply the decimal by the desired denominator.]

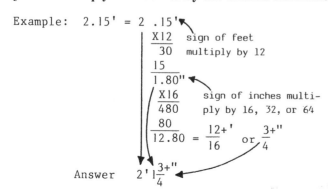

```
Example:  2.15' = 2 .15'
                     X12    sign of feet
                      30    multiply by 12
                      15
                    1.80"
                     X16    sign of inches multi-
                     480    ply by 16, 32, or 64
                      80      12+'      3+"
                   12.80  =  ————  or  ———
                              16         4

          Answer    2'1 3+"
                        ———
                         4
```

Info #1A – Convert Feet and Inches
to Decimals (Tape Measure in INCHES)

The reason for Multiplying "Decimals of Feet and Inches" by the Desire Denominator:

When finding decimals of a "Foot", always multiply by 12 because there are 12 inches in a foot. Therefore, the "Desired Denominator (lower number in the fraction)" is 12.

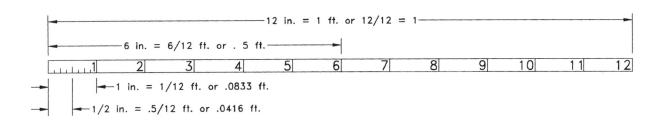

Review: 1 foot = $\frac{12"}{12"}$ or $12/12$ $\frac{1}{}$ full foot

Review: 6 inches = $\frac{6"}{12"}$ or $12/6.0$ $\frac{.5}{}$ of a ft. Therefore denominator 12 x .5' = 6"

Review: 1 inch = $\frac{1"}{12"}$ or $12/1.000$ $\frac{.083}{}$ of a ft. Therefore denomiator 12 x .083' = 1"
[12 x .083" = .996 or very close to 1"]

Review: 1/2 inch = $\frac{.5"}{12"}$ or $12/.5000$ $\frac{.0416}{}$ of a ft. Therefore denominator 12 x .0416' = 1/2"
[12 x .041 = .492 or very close to 1/2"]
[12 x .0416 = .4992 or closer to 1/2"]

[Note: In most cases, carry the decimal out 3 or 4 places to get the desire accuracy.]

When finding decimals of an "Inch", multiply by 8, 16, 32, or 64 because an inch can be divided into 8ths, 16ths, 32nds, or 64ths. Therefore the "Desired Denominator" in how accurate you want it to be. Examples; for 8ths multiply by 8, for 16ths multiply by 16, for 32nds multiply by 32, for 64ths multiply by 64, and so on.

Review: 1 inch = $\frac{8}{8}$ Or $\frac{16}{16}$ or $\frac{32}{32}$ Or $\frac{64}{64}$

Therefore: $\frac{3"}{8}$ = $\frac{.375"}{8/3.000}$ and 8 x .375" = 3/8"

$\frac{5"}{16}$ = $\frac{.3125"}{16/5.000}$ and 16 x .3125" = 5/16"

$\frac{3"}{32}$ = $\frac{.09375"}{32/3.0000}$ and 32 x .09375" = 3/32"

$\frac{17"}{64}$ = $\frac{.265625"}{64/17.0000}$ and 64 x .265625" = 17/64"

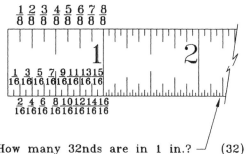

How many 32nds are in 1 in.? (32)
If there were increments of 64ths,
how many 64ths would be in 1 in.? (64)

Review: To multiply whole feet and decimals of an inch by 12, in most cases, multiply the decimal <u>only</u> times 12. Many of the longer tape measures are in feet and inches (See Info1B, in module #7, page 75, 76 for more information). Therefore, if you multiply the whole feet by 12, you would get inches and have to divide by 12 to get back into feet again. By practicing both ways, you will learn to distinguish between each type.

Example: 12.625' x 12 = 151.5". Most 100 ft. and 50 ft. tape measures are in both feet and inches. The needed answer would be 12 ft. 7 1/2 in. 12 x .625' = 7 1/2" plus 12 ft. = 12 ft. 7 1/2 in.

Trade Trick #1

<u>How to Make a Story Pole in all Inches and/or in Feet and Inches:</u>

Problem: You are given the piece of wood, metal, pipe, etc. on the right. Your job is to lay out 4 centerlines to ± 1/16 of an inch accuracy with a tape measure that has both feet and <u>total*</u> inches.

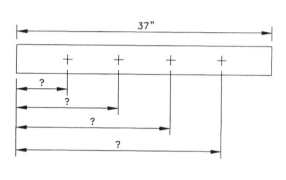

1. Calculate the dimension for the object. There are 4 centerlines, but 5 spaces. Therefore, divide 37" by 5.

$$
\begin{array}{r}
7.4" \\
5\overline{)37.0} \\
\underline{35} \\
20 \\
\underline{20}
\end{array}
$$

2. The 1st dimension is 7.4". 7.4" cannot be found on an American (English) tape measure. Therefore, it must be converted into feet, inches, and 16ths. An effective way of doing this is by making a "Story Pole" as shown below. <u>This method is more accurate than moving the tape measure 5 times for each dimension.</u>

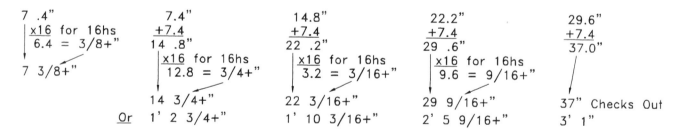

Or use a "Decimals of an Inch Equivalent Chart", inside the front cover, to convert.

1. 7.4" = 7 7/16−" or 7 3/8+"
   +7.4
2. 14.8" = 14 13/16−" or 14 3/4+"
   +7.4
3. 22.2" = 22 1/4−" or 22 3/16+"
    7.4
4. 29.6" = 29 9/16+" or 29 5/8−"
   +7.4
5. 37.0"   Answers Check Out

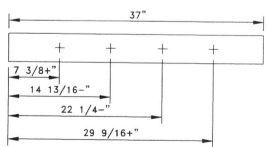

*Tape measures can be either <u>in all inches</u> or <u>in both feet and inches</u>. Therefore get in the habit of reducing to lowest terms, that is feet and inches.

Trade Trick #1 – Make a Story Pole
(Problem 1: 24 ¾″ Stick - 3 Centers)

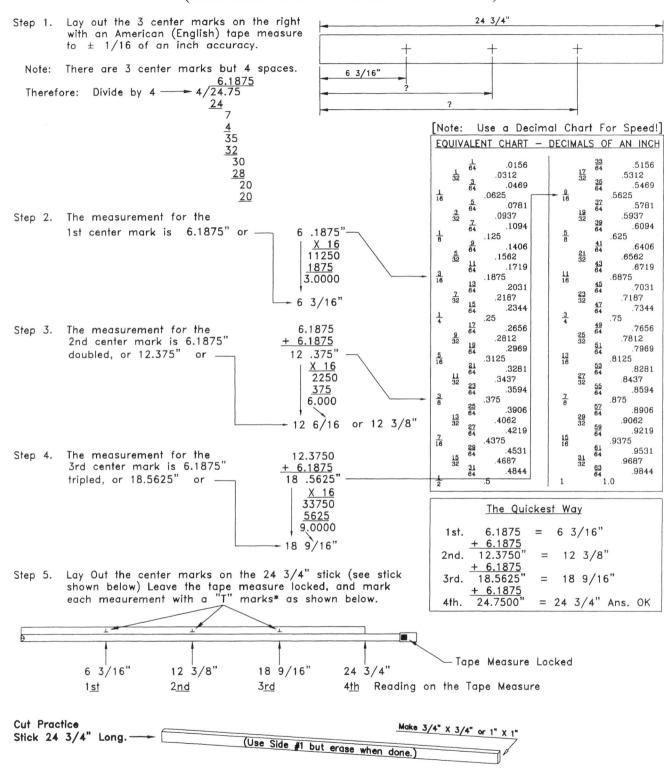

Step 1. Lay out the 3 center marks on the right with an American (English) tape measure to ± 1/16 of an inch accuracy.

Note: There are 3 center marks but 4 spaces.

Therefore: Divide by 4 ——▶

```
       6.1875
    4/24.75
      24
       7
       4
       35
       32
        30
        28
         20
         20
```

Step 2. The measurement for the 1st center mark is 6.1875" or

```
  6 .1875"
   X 16
  11250
  1875
  3.0000
```
▶ 6 3/16"

Step 3. The measurement for the 2nd center mark is 6.1875" doubled, or 12.375" or

```
   6.1875
 + 6.1875
 12 .375"
   X 16
   2250
   375
   6.000
```
▶ 12 6/16 or 12 3/8"

Step 4. The measurement for the 3rd center mark is 6.1875" tripled, or 18.5625" or

```
  12.3750
 + 6.1875
 18 .5625"
   X 16
   33750
   5625
   9.0000
```
▶ 18 9/16"

Step 5. Lay Out the center marks on the 24 3/4" stick (see stick shown below) Leave the tape measure locked, and mark each meaurement with a "T" marks* as shown below.

[Note: Use a Decimal Chart For Speed!]

EQUIVALENT CHART — DECIMALS OF AN INCH			
1/64	.0156	33/64	.5156
1/32 3/64	.0312 .0469	17/32 35/64	.5312 .5469
1/16 5/64	.0625 .0781	9/16 37/64	.5625 .5781
3/32 7/64	.0937 .1094	19/32 39/64	.5937 .6094
1/8 9/64	.125 .1406	5/8 41/64	.625 .6406
5/32 11/64	.1562 .1719	21/32 43/64	.6562 .6719
3/16 13/64	.1875 .2031	11/16 45/64	.6875 .7031
7/32 15/64	.2187 .2344	23/32 47/64	.7187 .7344
1/4 17/64	.25 .2656	3/4 49/64	.75 .7656
9/32 19/64	.2812 .2969	25/32 51/64	.7812 .7969
5/16 21/64	.3125 .3281	13/16 53/64	.8125 .8281
11/32 23/64	.3437 .3594	27/32 55/64	.8437 .8594
3/8 25/64	.375 .3906	7/8 57/64	.875 .8906
13/32 27/64	.4062 .4219	29/32 59/64	.9062 .9219
7/16 29/64	.4375 .4531	15/16 61/64	.9375 .9531
15/32 31/64	.4687 .4844	31/32 63/64	.9687 .9844
1/2	.5	1	1.0

The Quickest Way

1st.	6.1875	=	6 3/16"
	+ 6.1875		
2nd.	12.3750"	=	12 3/8"
	+ 6.1875		
3rd.	18.5625"	=	18 9/16"
	+ 6.1875		
4th.	24.7500"	=	24 3/4" Ans. OK

```
6 3/16"     12 3/8"     18 9/16"     24 3/4"
  1st         2nd         3rd          4th    Reading on the Tape Measure
```
Tape Measure Locked

Cut Practice Stick 24 3/4" Long. ——▶

(Use Side #1 but erase when done.)

Make 3/4" X 3/4" or 1" X 1"

Step 6. Check by measuring 6 3/16" between each "T" Mark.

*"T" marks insure greater accuracy. The exact point of measure is where the two lines meet at the "T".

Trade Trick #1 – Make a Story Pole
(Problem 2: 24 ¾" Stick - 4 Centers)

Practice Stick
24 3/4" Long. ——————→

Make 3/4" X 3/4" or 1" X 1"

(Mark Side #1, use "T" marks and draw square lines.)

Step 1. Lay out the 4 center marks on the right with an American (English) tape measure to ± 1/16 of an inch accuracy.

Note: There are 4 center marks but _____ spaces.

Therefore: Divide by _____)‾24.75‾

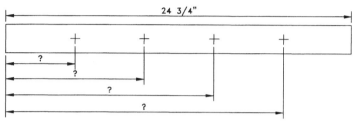

Step 2. The measurement for the 1st center mark is _____

Step 3. The measurement for the 2nd center mark is _____

Step 4. The measurement for the 3rd center mark is _____

Step 5. The measurement for the 4th center mark is _____

[Note: Use a Decimal Chart For Speed!]

EQUIVALENT CHART – DECIMALS OF AN INCH

	1/64	.0156		33/64	.5156
	1/32	.0312		17/32	.5312
	3/64	.0469		35/64	.5469
1/16		.0625	9/16		.5625
	5/64	.0781		37/64	.5781
	3/32	.0937		19/32	.5937
	7/64	.1094		39/64	.6094
1/8		.125	5/8		.625
	9/64	.1406		41/64	.6406
	5/32	.1562		21/32	.6562
	11/64	.1719		43/64	.6719
3/16		.1875	11/16		.6875
	13/64	.2031		45/64	.7031
	7/32	.2187		23/32	.7187
	15/64	.2344		47/64	.7344
1/4		.25	3/4		.75
	17/64	.2656		49/64	.7656
	9/32	.2812		25/32	.7812
	19/64	.2969		51/64	.7969
5/16		.3125	13/16		.8125
	21/64	.3281		53/64	.8281
	11/32	.3437		27/32	.8437
	23/64	.3594		55/64	.8594
3/8		.375	7/8		.875
	25/64	.3906		57/64	.8906
	13/32	.4062		29/32	.9062
	27/64	.4219		59/64	.9219
7/16		.4375	15/16		.9375
	29/64	.4531		61/64	.9531
	15/32	.4687		31/32	.9687
	31/64	.4844		63/64	.9844
1/2		.5	1		1.0

Step 6. Lay Out the center marks on the 24 3/4" stick. Leave the tape measure locked, and mark each meaurement with a "T" marks* as shown below.

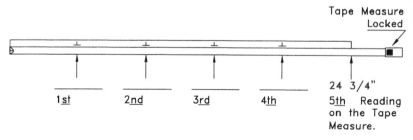

Tape Measure
Locked

1st ↑   2nd ↑   3rd ↑   4th ↑

24 3/4"
5th Reading on the Tape Measure.

The Quickest Way

1st.	_____	=	_____
	+		
2nd.	_____	=	_____
	+		
3rd.	_____	=	_____
	+		
4th.	_____	=	_____
	+		
5th.	24.7500"	=	24 3/4" Ans. OK

Step 7. Check by measuring _____ between each "T" Mark.

*"T" marks insure greater accuracy.

Objective Practice Problems for Module #2

B6 | Complex Fractions

1.
$$\dfrac{\dfrac{9}{16} + 2\dfrac{1}{4}}{\dfrac{11}{16} - \dfrac{5}{16}}$$

2.
$$\dfrac{\dfrac{7}{8} \times \dfrac{3}{4}}{9 \div 1\dfrac{1}{2}}$$

E8 | Find Averages

3. Find the Average of 21, 13, 44, 37, and 26 = _____.

4. Find the Average of 93, 75, 105, and 39 = _____.

E6 | Change Fractions to Decimals

5. Change 5/13 to a decimal _____.

6. Change 7/8 inches to decimals of an inch _____.

7. Change 4 1/2 inches to decimals of a foot _____.

E7 | Change Decimals to Fractions (change the decimals below to feet, inches, and ±1/16 inches).

8. 4.91 feet = _____.

9. 9.6 inches = _____.

10. 7.2 feet = _____.

"This page intentionally blank."

Math Training Module #3

Instructional Objectives: **Page No.**

Hands On:

Basic Math Study Notes for this Module – (These notes are for the 2nd half of page 2 of the Pretest)
(Powers, Square Roots, Cubic Roots, Direct Proportion, and Basic Percentage):

Powers: (The Scientific Calculator and Powers)

1. **H1** Use the Scientific Calculator to find the powers of numbers.

Examples: $9^2 =$ [9] and [x^2] = | DEG 81. |

$9^3 =$ [9] and [$\sqrt[x]{y}$] and [3] = | DEG 729. |

$9^4 =$ [9] and [$\sqrt[x]{y}$] and [4] = | DEG 6561. |

$9^5 =$ [9] and [$\sqrt[x]{y}$] and [5] = | DEG 59049. |

Square Roots: (The Scientific Calculator, Square Roots,
Cubed Roots, and so on.)

2. **H2** Use the Scientific Calculator to find the Roots of numbers.

Examples: $\sqrt{81}$ = [8][1] and [$\sqrt{x}$] = | DEG 9. |

$\sqrt[3]{729}$ = [7][2][9] and [2nd] and [$\sqrt[x]{y}$] and [3] = | DEG 9. |

$\sqrt[4]{6561}$ = [6][5][6][1] and [2nd] and [$\sqrt[x]{y}$] and [4] = | DEG 9. |

$\sqrt[5]{59049}$ = [5][9][0][4][9] and [2nd] and [$\sqrt[x]{y}$] and [5] = | DEG 9. |

Basic Math Study Notes (Continued)

Find Square Roots the Old Fashion Way - without a Calculator: (also see page 92 in the text book)

3. |H2| How to find the **Square Root** of a number the old fashion way.

|Step 1.| Separate the number into groups of twos from right to left of the whole number*.

|Step 2.| Find the largest root in the first group and subtract the square of that root from the first group.

|Step 3.| a) Bring down another group. b) Double the root. c) Find the root of the new group using the doubled root and another number. d) Subtract that product from the second group. Repeat Step 3 if the answer does not come out even.

|Step 4.| Check by squaring the answer (multiply the answer times itself).

Example
Problem: Find the square root of 1764 or $\sqrt{1764}$

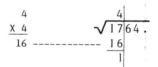

Right to left 2 spaces for each group.

The decimal point goes to the right of the whole number.

|Step 1.| Separate into groups of 2's (use light vertical lines as shown).

|Step 2.| Find the largest root in the first group (what whole number times itself is closest to 17?) 4 X 4 = 16. The largest root of the first group is 4. Place 4 above the 17 as shown. Write the square of the root (4 X 4 = 16) below 17 and subtract. 17 - 16 = 1.

```
  4
X 4
 16
```

```
      4
√ 17 64 .
   16
    1
```

|Step 3.| a) Bring down another group.

b) Double the root 4: 4 + 4 = 8.

c) Then ask yourself what number times itself and 8 will go into the new group 164. Try 3. Too big. Therefore, try 2 -- it works out. Place 2 above 64 and place the product 164 below 164 as shown.

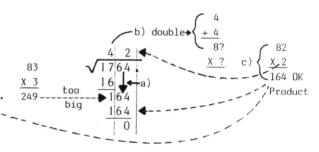

```
  83
X  3
 249
```
too big

d) subtract 164 - 164 = 0. Therefore, the answer is 42.

|Step 4.| Check by squaring the answer 42.

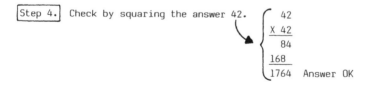

```
  42
X 42
  84
 168
1764   Answer OK
```

*When finding the square root of a number with an uneven number of digits such as $\sqrt{63971}$ separate from right to left as shown and calculate the same as above. If the number does not come out even, add zeros as shown.

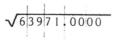

Basic Math Study Notes (Continued)

Practical Application of Finding the Cubed Root of a Number:

Example 1.   How big of a tank would be needed to hold a gallon of water?
One gallon of water holds 231 cubic inches of water.

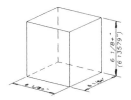

Step 1.   Find the cubed root of 231. Use a TI-36X scientific calculator*.

$\sqrt[3]{231}$ = [2] [3] [1] and [2nd] and [$\sqrt[x]{y}$] and [3] = | DEG 6.13579244 |

1 Gallon of Water
(231 cu. in.)

Step 2.   Change 6.13579244" so you can read the dimension on an American English tape measure.
Use a decimals of an inch equivalent chart to convert faster. 6.13579 = 6 1/8+"

Note each side of the cube is 6 1/8+".

Step 3.   Check by cubing 6.133579244.

6.13579244^3 = [6] [.] [1] [3] [5] [7] [9] [2] [4] [4] and [$\sqrt[x]{y}$] and [3] = | DEG 231. |

Example 2.   How big of a tank would be
needed to hold 25 gallons of gas?

Step 1.   Multiply 25 × 231 = 5775 cu. in.

Step 2.   Find the cubed root of 5775.

$\sqrt[3]{5775}$ = [5] [7] [7] [5] and [2nd]

and [$\sqrt[x]{y}$] and [3] = | DEG 17.94116593 |

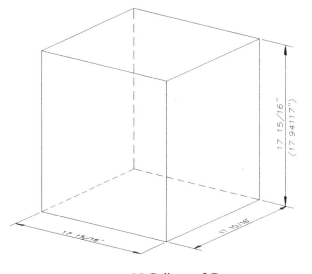

Step 3.   Change 17.94116" so you can read the dimension
on a tape measure. Use a decimal equivalent chart.

Note 17.94116" = 17 15/16"

25 Gallons of Gas
(5775 cu. in.)

Step 4.   Check by cubing 17.94116593.

17.94116593^3 = [1] [7] [.] [9] [4] [1] [1] [6] [5] [9] [3] and [$\sqrt[x]{y}$] and [3] = | DEG 5774.999998 |

*Most scientific calculators operate the same, if yours doesn't, refer to the calculator instructions manual.

Basic Math Study Notes (Continued)

Direct Proportion:

4. ☐I3☐ How to solve direct proportion problems.

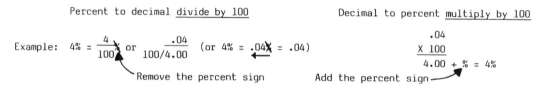

**[Rule: The Product of the Extremes is
Equal to the Product of the Means.]**

Extremes

3:12 :: 4:X   or

↑Means↑

$$\frac{3}{12} = \frac{4}{X}$$

$$\frac{3}{12} \diagdown \frac{4}{X}$$ Cross multiply (make an equivalent fraction)

3X = 12 X 4 Results are the same as the method on the left. Use the method that works best for you.

Step 1.	Multiply the extremes by the means and set up an equation.	3X = 12 X 4
Step 2.	Perform the operations indicated.	$\frac{3X}{3} = \frac{48}{3}$
Step 3.	Check by substituting 3(16) = 48	X = 16

48 = 48 Answer OK

Basic Percentage:

5. ☐G1☐ How to change a percent to a decimal. Divide the percent by 100 (or move the decimal point to the left two places) and remove the percent sign (%).

Percent to decimal <u>divide by 100</u>   Decimal to percent <u>multiply by 100</u>

Example: $4\% = \frac{4}{100}$ or $100/4.00$ (or 4% = .04 = .04)

Remove the percent sign

.04
X 100
4.00 + % = 4%

Add the percent sign

[If you divide by 100 to change a percent to a decimal, then to change a decimal to a percent, do the opposite and multiply by 100.]

6. ☐G2☐ How to change a decimal to a percent. Multiply the decimal by 100 – or simply move the decimal point two places to the right, and add the percent sign (%).

Example: Change .625 to a percent.

.625
X 100
62.500 or 62.5

| Step 1. | Multiply .625 X 100 ------------------- |

or

Move the point two places to right.   .625 = 62.5

| Step 2. | Add the percent sign (%). |

62.5% or $62\frac{1}{2}\%$

Therefore .625 = $62\frac{1}{2}\%$

[Remember when changing any decimal to a fraction, you multiply by the desired denominator. Since the denominator of a percent is always 100, multiply the decimal by 100 to change a decimal to a percent (fraction of 100.]

Basic Percentage: (Continued)

7. **G3** How to change a fraction to a percent. Change the fraction to a decimal, multiply by 100, and add the percent sign (%).

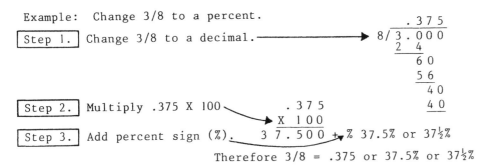

```
Example:   Change 3/8 to a percent.
                                                         . 3 7 5
 Step 1.   Change 3/8 to a decimal. ───────────▶  8/ 3 . 0 0 0
                                                     2  4
                                                       6 0
                                                       5 6
                                                         4 0
 Step 2.   Multiply .375 X 100 ──▼    . 3 7 5            4 0
                                     X  1 0 0
 Step 3.   Add percent sign (%).   3 7 . 5 0 0 ──▶% 37.5% or 37½%
                    Therefore 3/8 = .375 or 37.5% or 37½%
```

8. **G4** How to find the percentage of a number. Change the percent to a decimal, then multiply the decimal fraction times the number.

```
Example:   Find 4% of $20.00 = _____ .
                                                          .04  decimal
 Step 1.   Change 4% to a decimal.  Thus:  4% = 4/100  or 4 ÷ 100 or 100/4.00
                                                           4 00

 Step 2.   Multiply the number ─────────▶$20.00
           times the decimal fraction ────▶X.04
                                   .8000 = $.80  Answer or Percentage
```

A Unique Way to Look at Percentage:

The percent sign (%) means: The two zeros stand for 100 and the / (line of a fraction) means divide.
Therefore to change a percent to a <u>decimal</u> remove the percent sign (%) and divide by 100.

<u>EXAMPLES:</u>

```
100% = the Whole Pie          1% = 1 part of 100          1/2% = 1/2 of 1 part of 100

Or  100/100 = 1 Full Pie      Or  1/100 = .01 of the Full Pie    Or  (1/2)/100 = .005 of the Full Pie
```

Basic Percentage: (Continued)

25% = 25 parts of 100

Or $\frac{25}{100}$ = .25 of the Full Pie

250% = 250 parts of 100

Or $\frac{250}{100}$ = 2.5 Pies

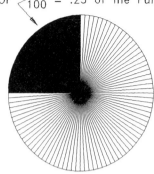

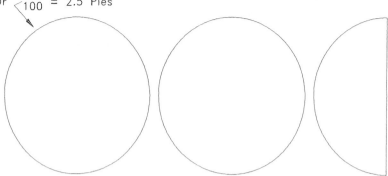

To change a fraction to a <u>Percent</u>, change the fraction to a decimal then multiply by 100 and add the % sign.

EXAMPLES:

Common Fractions:

1/2 = 2$\overline{)1.0}^{.5}$ 1/2 = .5 X 100 = 50.0 +% = 50%   [1/2 or 50% of the pie.]

7/8 = 8$\overline{)7.00}^{.875}$ 7/8 = .875 X 100 = 87.5 + % = 87.5% [7/8 or 87.5% of the pie.]

Mixed Numbers:

2 3/8 = 8$\overline{)3.000}^{.375}$ = 2.375 X 100 = 237.500 + % = 237.5% [2 3/8 or 237.5% pies.]

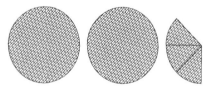

Decimal Fractions:

To Change a Decimal Fraction to a <u>Percent</u>, multiply the decimal or the whole number and decimal times 100 and add the % sign.

$\begin{array}{r} 2.75 \\ \times\ 100 \\ \hline \end{array}$

2.75 = 275.00 + % = 275%   [2.75 or 275% pies.]

Trade Trick #1 – Make a Story Pole
(Problem 3: 24 ¾″ Stick - 5 Centers)

Practice Stick
24 3/4" Long. ———→

Make 3/4" X 3/4" or 1" X 1"

(Mark Side #2, use "T" marks and draw square lines.)

Step 1. Lay out the 5 center marks on the right with an American (English) tape measure to ± 1/16 of an inch accuracy.

Note: There are 5 center marks but _____ spaces.

Therefore: Divide by _____ $\overline{)24.75}$

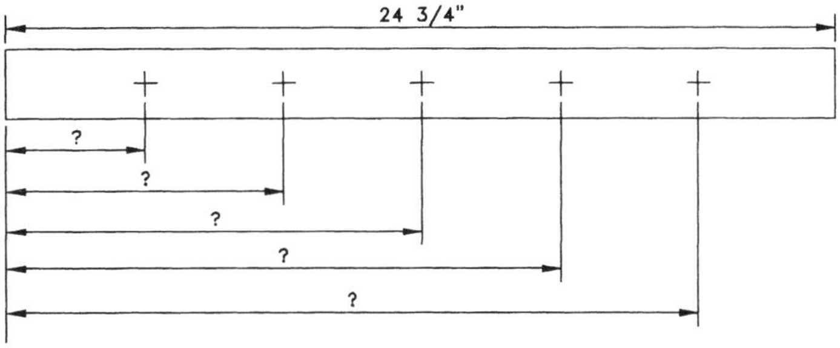

24 3/4"

?
?
?
?
?

Step 2. The measurement for the 1st center mark is _____

Step 3. The measurement for the 2nd center mark is _____

Step 4. The measurement for the 3rd center mark is _____

Step 5. The measurement for the 4th center mark is _____

Step 6. The measurement for the 5th center mark is _____

[Note: Use a Decimal Chart For Speed!]

EQUIVALENT CHART – DECIMALS OF AN INCH			
$\frac{1}{64}$	.0156	$\frac{33}{64}$	.5156
$\frac{1}{32}$	.0312	$\frac{17}{32}$	.5312
$\frac{3}{64}$	.0469	$\frac{35}{64}$	.5469
$\frac{1}{16}$	.0625	$\frac{9}{16}$	.5625
$\frac{5}{64}$	.0781	$\frac{37}{64}$	.5781
$\frac{3}{32}$	.0937	$\frac{19}{32}$	.5937
$\frac{7}{64}$	.1094	$\frac{39}{64}$	.6094
$\frac{1}{8}$	.125	$\frac{5}{8}$	.625
$\frac{9}{64}$	.1406	$\frac{41}{64}$	.6406
$\frac{5}{32}$	.1562	$\frac{21}{32}$	.6562
$\frac{11}{64}$	.1719	$\frac{43}{64}$	.6719
$\frac{3}{16}$	.1875	$\frac{11}{16}$	.6875
$\frac{13}{64}$	.2031	$\frac{45}{64}$	.7031
$\frac{7}{32}$	.2187	$\frac{23}{32}$	.7187
$\frac{15}{64}$	.2344	$\frac{47}{64}$	.7344
$\frac{1}{4}$	.25	$\frac{3}{4}$	.75
$\frac{17}{64}$	.2656	$\frac{49}{64}$	.7656
$\frac{9}{32}$	.2812	$\frac{25}{32}$	.7812
$\frac{19}{64}$	.2969	$\frac{51}{64}$	.7969
$\frac{5}{16}$	.3125	$\frac{13}{16}$	.8125
$\frac{21}{64}$	.3281	$\frac{53}{64}$	.8281
$\frac{11}{32}$	.3437	$\frac{27}{32}$	.8437
$\frac{23}{64}$	.3594	$\frac{55}{64}$	.8594
$\frac{3}{8}$	.375	$\frac{7}{8}$	.875
$\frac{25}{64}$	.3906	$\frac{57}{64}$	.8906
$\frac{13}{32}$	.4062	$\frac{29}{32}$	.9062
$\frac{27}{64}$	.4219	$\frac{59}{64}$	.9219
$\frac{7}{16}$	.4375	$\frac{15}{16}$	.9375
$\frac{29}{64}$	.4531	$\frac{61}{64}$	.9531
$\frac{15}{32}$	.4687	$\frac{31}{32}$	.9687
$\frac{31}{64}$	.4844	$\frac{63}{64}$	.9844
$\frac{1}{2}$	.5	1	1.0

Step 7. Lay Out the center marks on the 24 3/4" stick. Leave the tape measure locked, and mark each meaurement with a "T" marks* as shown below.

*"T" marks insure greater accuracy.

Tape Measure
Locked

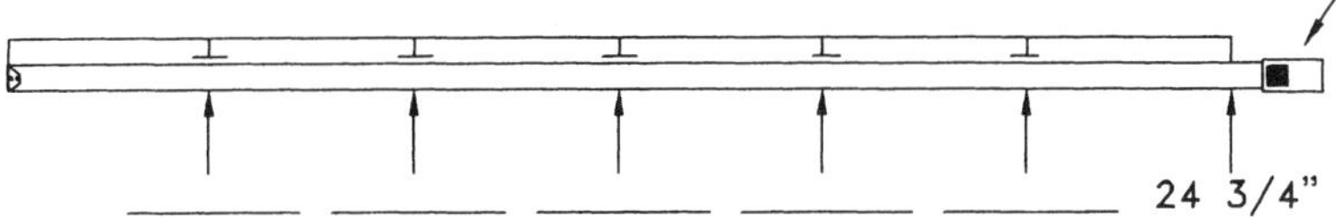

1st   2nd   3rd   4th   5th   6th Reading
on the Tape Measure

24 3/4"

The Quickest Way

1st.	_____	=	_____
	+ _____		
2nd.	_____	=	_____
	+ _____		
3rd.	_____	=	_____
	+ _____		
4th.	_____	=	_____
	+ _____		
5th.	_____	=	_____
	+ _____		
6th.	24.7500"	=	24 3/4" Ans. OK

Step 8. Check by measuring _____ between each "T" Mark.

Objective Practice Problems for Module #3

H1 — Powers

1. $3^3 =$ _____. $2^7 =$ _____.

H2 — Square Roots (do not use a calculator)

2. Find $\sqrt{20,449}$

H3 — Cubed Roots — Use a Scientific Calculator

3. What would be the dimensions of a tank (cube) that would hold 50 gallons of gas. Answer in feet, inches, and 16th. _____.

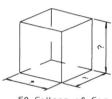

50 Gallons of Gas
1 gallon = 231 cu. in.

I3 — Direct Proportion

4. 9:12 :: X:16

X = _____.

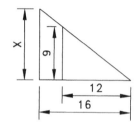

G1 — Change a Percent to a Decimal

5. Change 9 3/4% to a decimal fraction _____.

G2 — Change a Decimal to a Percent

6. Change .03125 to a percent _____.

G3 — Change a fraction to a Percent

7. Change 7/8 to a percent _____.

G4 — Find the Percent of a Number

8. Find 3 1/2% of $41.25 = _____.

Math Training Module #4

<u>**Instructional Objectives:**</u> <u>**Page No.**</u>

<u>**Hands On:**</u>

<u>**Basic Math Study Notes**</u> – **(These notes are for the last part of page 2 and page 3 of the Pretest)**
(<u>Basic Algebra - How to Manipulate Basic Formulas, Plane Geometry, Solid Geometry, Angles, and Tools for Transferring, Measuring, and Laying Out Angles</u>):

<u>**Basic Algebra:**</u> **(How to Manipulate Basic Formulas)**

1. Use basic algebra to solve problems involving basic formulas:

| J3 | Example 1. Find the width when the length and the area are known. | K7A | Example 2. Find the diameter when the circumference is known. |

Rule:	Area = length × width	Rule:	Circumference = π × the diameter
Formula:	A = lw	Formula:	C = πd
Substitute:	216' = 18'w	Substitute:	78.54" = 3.1416d
Calculate:	$\dfrac{216'}{18} = \dfrac{\cancel{18}'w}{\cancel{18}}$	Calculate:	$\dfrac{78.54"}{3.1416} = \dfrac{\cancel{3.1416}d}{\cancel{3.1416}}$
Answer:	12' = w	Answer:	25" = d

Plane Geometry: (Solve "Area" problems by using different types of number)

2. K2 Area problems can be solved and checked by using different types of numbers.

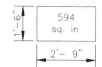

Example: The rectangle on the right has 594 sq. in. Note the different types of numbers that can be used to solve the same problem.

C4 Using Mixed Numbers   E4 Using Decimal Fractions   A4 Using Whole Numbers

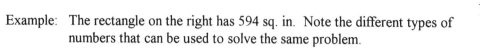

a) $2'\ 9'' \times 1'\ 6''$

$2\ 9/12'$ $1\ 6/12'$

$2\ 3/4'$ $1\ 1/2'$

$\dfrac{11}{4} \times \dfrac{3}{2} = \dfrac{33}{8}$ or 8/33.000

b)
$$2'\ 9'' = 2.75'$$
$$\times 1'\ 6'' = \times 1.5'$$
$$\underline{1375}$$
$$275$$
$$4.125\ \text{sq. ft.}$$

4.125 sq. ft. ◄—— [One method checks the other method] ——► 4.125 sq. ft.

c)
$$2'\ 9'' = 33''$$
$$\times 1'\ 6'' = \times 18''$$
$$\underline{264}$$
$$33$$
$$594\ \text{sq. in.}$$

144/594.000

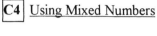

Note: 1 sq. ft. = 144 square inches   1 sq. yd. = 9 sq. ft.

D4 A review of the difference between <u>square measure</u> and <u>linear measure</u>.

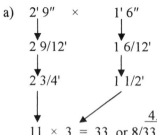

Examples:

Square Measure = Area

$$2'\ 8'' = 32''$$
$$\times 1'\ 5'' = \times 17''$$
$$\underline{224}$$
$$\underline{32}$$
544 sq. in. or 544 ÷ 144 = 3.77 sq. ft.

Linear Measure = Length

$$1'\ 2''$$
$$\times 5$$
$$\overline{5'10''}$$

Note: 1 linear yard = 36″

Solid Geometry: (Find the "Volume" of different geometric figures)

3. L2 How many <u>cubic feet</u> of material are needed to fill a rectangular solid 3 ft. × 9 ft. × 2 ft.? _____ .

How many <u>cubic yards</u> (remember a cubic yard is 3 ft. × 3 ft. × 3 ft.) are needed? _____ .

Step 1. The rule is: <u>V</u>olume equals the <u>l</u>ength × <u>w</u>idth × <u>h</u>eight. Therefore, the formula is ----------- V = lwh

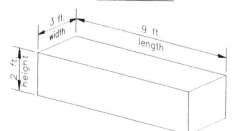

Step 2. Substitute the know values into the formula --------------------- V = 9 × 3 × 2

Solid Geometry (Continued)

Step 3.   Calculate the formula (do the
operations indicated) ------------

Note: 1 cubic
foot = 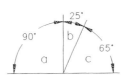 1728 cu. in.

$V = (9 \times 3) \times 2$
$V = 27 \times 2$

Thus the answer is --------------- $V = 54$ cu. ft.

Step 4.   Convert to cubic yards. $V = 2$ cu. yd.

Note: 1 cubic
yard =

27 cu. ft., therefore in 54 cu. ft.
there are ------------   2   cu. yd.
27/ 54
54

4.   **Review of Angles:** [See Task No. K11 page 151 and Task No. M1 page 170.]

The **complement of an angle** is the angle, which, when
added to another angle, equals 90°.

The complement of angle c (65°) is angle b (25°)
because 65° + 25° = 90°.

The **supplement of an angle** is the angle, which, when
added to another angle, equal 180°.

The supplement of angle b (120°) is angle a (60°)
because 120° + 60° = 180°.

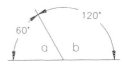

Types of Angles: Straight Angle =

   (straight line)

Right Angle =

Acute Angle =

      (any angle less than 90°)

Obtuse Angle =

   (any angle more than 90°)

Measure Angles with a Lay Out Square (continued)

Tools for Transferring, Measuring, and Laying Out Angles:

Transferring Exisiting Angles: [See Trade Trick #9, page 123 and 124. How to Transfer angles using a Lay Out Square.]

T–Bevel Closed

Wing Nut

T–Bevel Opened

STANLEY

Adjustable Blade

Transfer Angle to the Board (Steel) below.

Tongue

Blade

Unknown Angle ?°

Unknown Angle ?°

Transfer Angle with a T–Bevel

Transfer Angle with a Lay Out Square

Lay Out Square

Lay Out Given Angles: [See Trade Trick #11, page 133 and 134. Lay Out Angles using a Lay Square and a chart.] [See Info #10, page 131 and 132. Lay Out Angles with a Lay Out Square.]

Lay out a 63° (degree) angle on the board or steel shown above. Use a fixed protractor and a straight edge, an adjustable machinest protractor, or a Lay Out Square.

Machinist Protractor

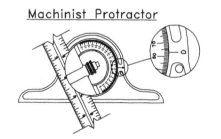

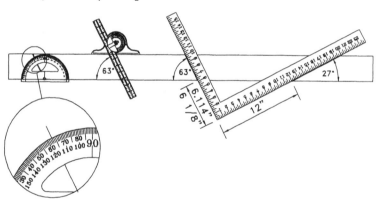

63°

63°

6 1/4"

6 1/8"

27°

12"

Measure Unknown Angles: [See Info #12, page 141 and 142. Measure Angles with a Lay Out Square (via the formula TOA). Page 142 is a review of of angles (degrees, minutes, and seconds).]

Transit

Set Horizontal circle to zero

Plumb Bob

Point A

Point B

10 feet

Vernier

33° 50'

Used to measure Degrees, Minutes, and Seconds.

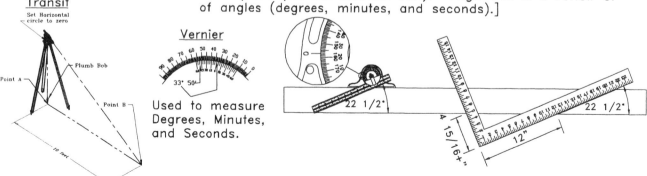

22 1/2°

22 1/2°

4 15/16+"

12"

[A transit can be used for measuring and laying out angles. See pages, 328–342 in the textbook.]

Info #2 - Formula C = πd
(Circumference = pi × diameter)

How to manipulate the formula " Circumference = pi times the diameter (C = πd)" to find the diameter when the circumference is known. To measure the diameter of a run of a large pipe would be impossible without cutting the pipe and/or by using a huge caliper (in most cases this is impractical). Therefore to find the diameter, this formula is especially helpful and fairly easy to use once the student has practiced it a few times.

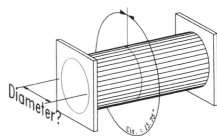

Example 1.   Measure the circumference of the pipe
shown on the right with a tape measure
to ±1/16 of an inch accuracy.

Note: Circumference = The distance around a circle.

Step 1.   Use the basic formula: C = πd
Also see Task $\boxed{\text{K7A}}$ in the textbook.

Step 2.   Substitute the known values   15.75" = 3.1416 × (d)
into the formula as shown.
[pi = 3.1416]

Step 3.   Get the unknown (d) by itself. $\dfrac{15.75"}{3.1416} = \dfrac{\cancel{3.1416} \times (d)}{\cancel{3.1416}}$
Therefore do the opposite as
indicated. Divide both sides by
3.1416. Note (d) will now be by
itself after canceling. Also, see
Task $\boxed{\text{J6}}$, page 125 in the textbook.

Step 4.   Now you have the formula to $\dfrac{15.75"}{3.1416} = d$
find the diameter when the
circumference is known.

Step 5.   Calculate. 15.75 ÷ 3.1416 =   5.013" = d
To divide decimal fractions,   5" = d
see Task $\boxed{\text{E5}}$ in the textbook.

Example 2.   Measure the circumference of the pipe
shown on the right with a tape measure
to ±1/16 of an inch accuracy.

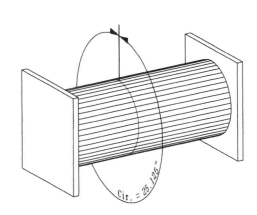

Step 1.   Use the basic formula: C = πd

How to use the Formula C = πd (continued)

Step 2. Substitute the known values into the formula as shown.

$$25.125" = 3.1416 \times (d)$$

Step 3. Get the unknown (d) by itself. Therefore do the opposite as indicated. Divide both sides by 3.1416. Note (d) will now be by itself after canceling. Also, see Task $\boxed{\text{J6}}$, page 125 in the textbook.

$$\frac{25.125"}{3.1416} = \frac{\cancel{3.1416} \times (d)}{\cancel{3.1416}}$$

Step 4. Now you have the formula to find the diameter when the circumference is known.

$$\frac{25.125"}{3.1416} = d$$

Step 5. Calculate. 25.125" ÷ 3.1416 = To divide decimal fractions, see Task $\boxed{\text{E5}}$ in the textbook.

$$7.9975" = d$$
$$8" = d$$

Example 3. Find the circumference of a circle that has a diameter of 12 inches.

Step 1. Use the formula:

$$C = \pi d$$

Step 2. Substitute the known values into the formula:

$$C = 3.1416 \times 12"$$

Step 3. Calculate:

$$C = 37.699"$$

Note the circumference around the 12 inch circle is 37 5/8[+]". This is pretty easy to calculate when the diameter can be measured. However there will be times (long runs of pipe, huge cylinders, big poles, etc.) when this cannot be done. This is a good example of why basic formulas have to be manipulated, at times, to solve basic problems.

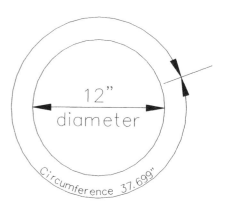

Trade Trick #2 – Squaring
[The 3-4-5 and 5-12-13 Squaring Techniques]

Make a 10" High Right Angle Using the 3-4-5 Squaring Technique:

Given: A 22" X 36" sheet of paper, a 18" straight edge, pencil, and ruler.

1. a) Tape a 22" X 36" sheet of paper* to your desk top, as shown below.

   b) Decide what combination of 3-4-5 can be used to make a 10" high right angle.

   e) Mark an approx. center mark and label it Point "a".

   f) Measure 12" to the the right of pt. "a". Mark pt. "b".

   Divide by 3 to get the largest combination if 3-4-5 that can be used to make the 10" high right angle. Use even numbers.

   Example:

   c) Multiply 3 time 3-4-5 as shown above. The largest combination is 9-12-15.

   d) Use your straight edge to draw a straight line, 1" or 2" off the bottom of the sheet as shown. The line does not have to be parallel to the bottom of the sheet.

2. a) Use a tape measure and swing a 15" arc (arc-1) from pt. b as shown.

   b) Use a tape measure and swing a 9" arc (arc-2) pt. a as shown.

   c) Where the two arcs cross is pt. c.

   [Helpful Hint – use the tape measure as you would use a compass to swing the circle arcs.]

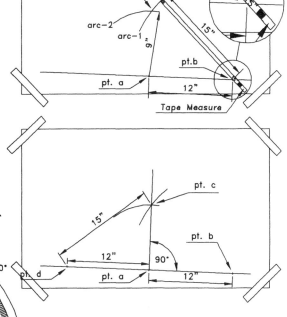

3. a) Use the straight edge and draw a line from pt. a through pt. c, as shown. You should now have a perfect 90° angle.

   b) Check the angle by measuring 12" from pt. a, and marking pt. d. The measurement from pt. c to point d should be 15".

   Or check by using the paper protractor provided in your workbook.

   [Note, if 3-4-5 was used instead of 9-12-15, and was off 1/16", the error would be increased 3 times, or would be 3/16".]

*Flip chart tablet paper works real good.

3-4-5 Squaring Technique (Continued)

Make a 10" X 14" Rectangle with the 3-4-5 Angle:

4. a) Measure vertically from pt. a
        through pt. c 10", label pt. d.

    b) Measure horizontally from pt. a through
        pt. b 14" and mark, label pt. e.

    c) Swing an arc from pt. e vertically 10"
        as shown, label arc-3.

5. Swing a 14" arc (arc-4) from pt. d, and cross
    arc-3 as shown. Label the crossing point, pt f.

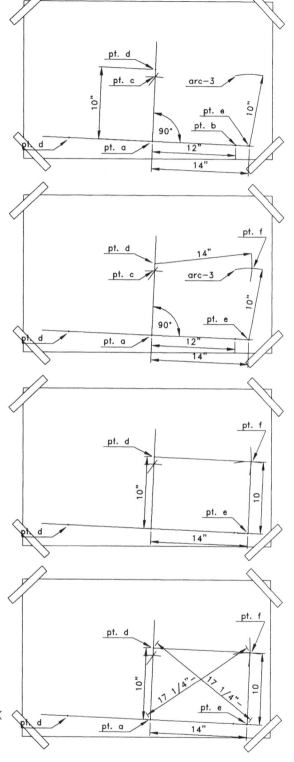

6. a) Use the straight edge and draw a line
        from pt. d through pt. f, as shown.

    b) Use the straight edge and draw a line
        from pt. e through pt. f, as shown.

    [You now should have a perfect rectangle.]

7. a) Check the diagonals from pt. d to pt. e
        and from pt. a through pt. f, as shown.
        The diagonals should be within ± 1/16 of
        an inch accuracy, if care was taken.

    b) Use the Formula:
$$a^2 + b^2 = c^2$$
$$10^2 + 14^2 = c^2$$
$$100 + 196 = c^2$$
$$296 = c$$
$$\sqrt{296} = c$$
$$17.20" = c \quad \text{Answer OK}$$

[This procedure is the same way a garage, a home, machines, etc. would be laid out. To
use the 5-12-13 squaring method -- do the same as above, but use 5-12-13, 10-24-26,
15-36-39, and so forth instead of a combination of 3-4-5.]

Info #3 - Formula $a^2 + b^2 = c^2$
(Rule of Pythagoras)

How to use the formula "$a^2 + b^2 = c^2$" (the Rule of Pythagoras) when any two sides of a <u>right</u> triangle are known can be extremely useful for squaring and laying out <u>right</u> triangles (90°) and rectangles. These triangles and rectangles are used to lay out and square up bolt holes (for pumps, motors, machines, etc.), structural metal, lines for buildings, etc..... the list goes on. Therefore it is very important that trades people know these concepts.

Formula: $a^2 + b^2 = c^2$

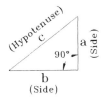

Example 1. Find the hypotenuse (side c) of a right triangle when side (a) equals 3 feet and side (b) equals 4 feet.

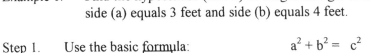

Step 1. Use the basic formula: Also see Task K5A in the textbook.

$$a^2 + b^2 = c^2$$

Step 2. Substitute the known values into the formula as shown.

$$3^2 + 4^2 = c^2$$

> **Note:**
> Side <u>a</u> could be found if sides b and c were known.
>
> **Example:**
> Formula: $a^2 + b^2 = c^2$
> Manipulate: $a^2 = c^2 - b^2$
> Subsitute: $a^2 = 5^2 - 4^2$
> Calculate: $a^2 = 25 - 16$
> $a^2 = 9$
> $a = \sqrt{9}$
> $a = 3$ ft.

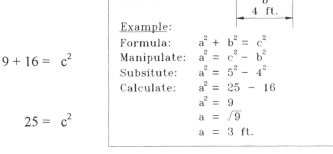

Step 3. Calculate the formula -- do the operations indicated.

$$9 + 16 = c^2$$

1st $\quad 3^2 = 3 \times 3 = 9$
2nd $\quad 4^2 = 4 \times 4 = 16$
3rd $\quad 9 + 16 = 25$

$$25 = c^2$$

Step 4. $c^2 = c \times c$ -- or what number times itself equals 25. Therefore, find the square root of 25.

$$25 = c$$

$$5 = c$$

Step 5. Check by making an equivalent triangle, make a rectangle and check the diagonals, or check mathematically.

$a^2 + b^2 = c^2$
$3^2 + 4^2 = 5^2$
$9 + 16 = 25$
$25 = 25$ Answer OK

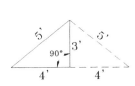

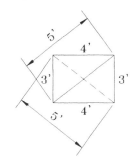

CALCULATE THE FORMULA a² + b² = c² (continued)

Example 2.   Find the hypotenuse (side c) of a right triangle when side (a) equals 12 inches and side (b) equals 16 inches..

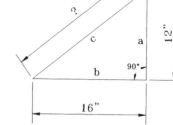

Step 1.   Use the basic formula:
Also see Task K5A in the book.

$$a^2 + b^2 = c^2$$

Step 2.   Substitute the known values into the formula as shown.

$$12^2 + 16^2 = c^2$$

Step 3.   Calculate the formula -- do the operations indicated.

$$144 + 256 = c^2$$

1st $12^2 = 12 \times 12 = 144$
2nd $16^2 = 16 \times 16 = 256$
3rd $144 + 256 = 400$

$$400 = c^2$$

Step 4. $c^2 = c \times c$ -- or what number times itself equals 400. Therefore, find the square root of 400.

$$\sqrt{400} = c$$

$$20 = c$$

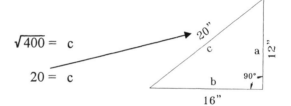

Step 5.   Check by making an equivalent triangle, make a rectangle and check the diagonals, or check mathematically.

$a^2 + b^2 = c^2$
$12^2 + 16^2 = 20^2$
$144 + 256 = 400$
$400 = 400$ Answer OK

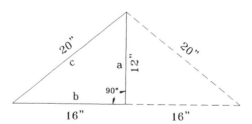

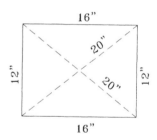

Note that Example 1. and Example 2. come out even. Therefore any combination of 3-4-5 will work to square any object or to find a 90° angle. However, the largest combination of 3-4-5 should be used for any given triangle or rectangle, see Task No. P1 for more information.

A few other examples:

	3 - 4 - 5	3 - 4 - 5	3 - 4 - 5	3 - 4 - 5	3 - 4 - 5	3 - 4 - 5
	×1 ×1 ×1	×2 ×2 ×2	×3 ×3 ×3	×4 ×4 ×4	×5 ×5 ×5	×6 ×6 ×6
	3 4 5	6 8 10	9 12 15	12 16 20	15 20 25	18 24 30

We can use the 3-4-5 squaring method to square any object by using the triangulation method alone, or by using the triangulation method and rectangular method together. For more information, see Task P1 or P1A .

CALCULATE THE FORMULA $a^2 + b^2 = c^2$ (continued)

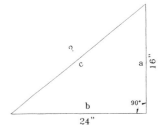

Example 3.   Find the hypotenuse (side c) of a right triangle when
side (a) equals 16 inches and side (b) equals 24 inches..

Step 1.   Use the basic formula: $a^2 + b^2 = c^2$
Also see Task K5A in the book.

Step 2.   Substitute the known values $16^2 + 24^2 = c^2$
into the formula as shown.

Step 3.   Calculate the formula -- do the
operations indicated. $256 + 576 = c^2$

1st $16^2 = 16 \times 16 = 256$
2nd $24^2 = 24 \times 24 = 576$
3rd $256 + 576 = 832$ $832 = c^2$

Step 4. $c^2 = c \times c$ -- or what number times
itself equals 832. Therefore, find the
square root of 832. Carry decimal $\sqrt{832} = c$
three places. $28.844" = c$

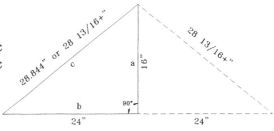

Step 5.   Check by making an equivalent
triangle, make a rectangle and check
the diagonals, or check mathematically.

Decimal 2 places: $a^2 + b^2 = c^2$
                     $16^2 + 24^2 = 28.84^2$
                     $256 + 576 = 831.746$
832.000 $832 = 831.745$ Answer close (within 1/4")
-831.746
 .254   *Error

Decimal 3 places: $a^2 + b^2 = c^2$
                     $16^2 + 24^2 = 28.844^2$
                     $256 + 576 = 831.976$
832.000 $832 = 831.976$ Answer close (within 1/32")
-832.976
 .034   *Error

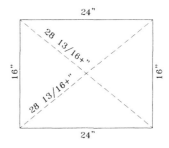

*Error Note: The error .034" is 1/32 of an inch off which is very close for most applications. The error
.255" is 1/4 of an inch off which is <u>not very accurate for most applications</u>. This is the very
reason a decimal should be carried out at least three places. However, there will be times the
decimal will have to be carried out to 4, 5, 6, etc. places for greater accuracy.

CALCULATE THE FORMULA $a^2 + b^2 = c^2$ (continued)

More Practical Application of the Rule of Pythagoras:

Example 4.   **Unequal roof pitches and the Rule of Pythagoras.** Illustrated below is an example of how to calculate the common rafters and the hip rafter for a roof that has unequal roof pitches. The common rafters have different runs but the same total rise. Unequal roof pitches are when the slopes of a roof are different but have the same total rise (meet at the same ridge).

Common Rafter #1:
[Also, see page 151]
12.65
× 6
75.90 = 6'- 3 7/8+"

$$a^2 + b^2 = c^2$$
$$4^2 + 12^2 = c^2$$
$$16 + 144 = c^2$$
$$160 = c^2$$
$$\sqrt{160} = c$$
$$12.65 = c$$

Common Rafters #2:
[Also, see page 151.]
13.42
× 4
53.68 = 4'- 5 5/8+"

$$a^2 + b^2 = c^2$$
$$6^2 + 12^2 = c^2$$
$$36 + 144 = c^2$$
$$180 = c^2$$
$$\sqrt{180} = c$$
$$13.42 = c$$

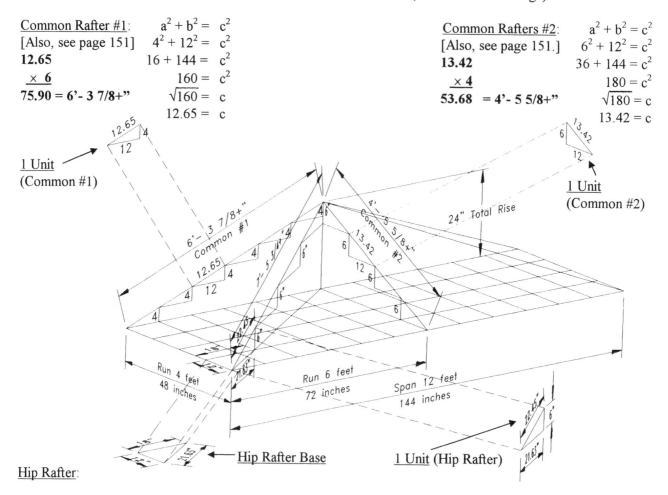

Hip Rafter:

Note the base of one unit of hip for an unequal roof <u>is not 17</u> because there are now two different runs. The run of an equal roof has a base of 12" and 12" with the diagonal being 16.97" or 17" rounded off. The runs of this particular roof is 4 ft. and 6 ft.. Therefore, in this case, the base of one unit of hip is 12" and 18". The diagonal of 12" and 18" is 21.633". The total rise is 24 inches and there are 4 units in the hip.

Find the Hip Base:

$$a^2 + b^2 = c^2$$
$$12^2 + 18^2 = c^2$$
$$144 + 324 = c^2$$
$$468 = c^2$$
$$\sqrt{468} = c$$
$$21.63 = c$$

Find One Unit of Hip Rafter:
[Also, see page 153.]
22.45
× 4
89.8   = 7'- 5 ¾+"

$$a^2 + b^2 = c^2$$
$$6^2 + 21.63^2 = c^2$$
$$36 + 467.86 = c^2$$
$$503,86 = c^2$$
$$\sqrt{503.86} = c$$
$$22.45 = c$$

[Note to find the side cuts (angles) of an unequal roof, see the formula SOH, CAH, & TOA on page 186]

Trade Trick #1 – Make a Story Pole
(Problem 4: 24 ¾″ Stick - 6 Centers)

**Practice Stick
24 3/4" Long.** ──→

Make 3/4" X 3/4" or 1" X 1"

(Mark Side #3, use "T" marks and draw square lines.)

Step 1.   Lay out the 6 center marks on the right with an American (English) tape measure to ± 1/16 of an inch accuracy.

Note: There are 6 center marks but _____ spaces.

Therefore: Divide by _____ $\overline{)24.75}$

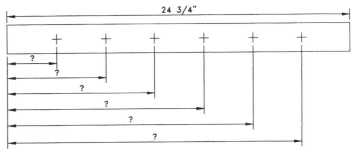

24 3/4"

Step 2.   Use the Quickest Way method below to Calculate the Story Pole Measurements.

The Quickest Way

1st.   _____   =   _____
        + _____

2nd.   _____   =   _____
        + _____

3rd.   _____   =   _____
        + _____

4th.   _____   =   _____
        + _____

5th.   _____   =   _____
        + _____

6th.   _____   =   _____
        + _____

7th.   **24.7500"**   =   **24 3/4" Ans. OK**

[Note: Use a Decimal Chart For Speed!]

EQUIVALENT CHART – DECIMALS OF AN INCH

	$\frac{1}{64}$	.0156	$\frac{33}{64}$	.5156
$\frac{1}{32}$		.0312	$\frac{17}{32}$	.5312
	$\frac{3}{64}$	.0469	$\frac{35}{64}$	.5469
$\frac{1}{16}$		.0625	$\frac{9}{16}$	.5625
	$\frac{5}{64}$	.0781	$\frac{37}{64}$	.5781
$\frac{3}{32}$		.0937	$\frac{19}{32}$	.5937
	$\frac{7}{64}$	.1094	$\frac{39}{64}$	.6094
$\frac{1}{8}$		.125	$\frac{5}{8}$	.625
	$\frac{9}{64}$	.1406	$\frac{41}{64}$	.6406
$\frac{5}{32}$		.1562	$\frac{21}{32}$	.6562
	$\frac{11}{64}$	.1719	$\frac{43}{64}$	.6719
$\frac{3}{16}$		.1875	$\frac{11}{16}$	.6875
	$\frac{13}{64}$	.2031	$\frac{45}{64}$	.7031
$\frac{7}{32}$		.2187	$\frac{23}{32}$	.7187
	$\frac{15}{64}$	.2344	$\frac{47}{64}$	.7344
$\frac{1}{4}$		.25	$\frac{3}{4}$	.75
	$\frac{17}{64}$	.2656	$\frac{49}{64}$	.7656
$\frac{9}{32}$		.2812	$\frac{25}{32}$	.7812
	$\frac{19}{64}$	.2969	$\frac{51}{64}$	.7969
$\frac{5}{16}$		.3125	$\frac{13}{16}$	.8125
	$\frac{21}{64}$	.3281	$\frac{53}{64}$	.8281
$\frac{11}{32}$		.3437	$\frac{27}{32}$	.8437
	$\frac{23}{64}$	.3594	$\frac{55}{64}$	.8594
$\frac{3}{8}$		.375	$\frac{7}{8}$	.875
	$\frac{25}{64}$	.3906	$\frac{57}{64}$	.8906
$\frac{13}{32}$		.4062	$\frac{29}{32}$	.9062
	$\frac{27}{64}$	.4219	$\frac{59}{64}$	.9219
$\frac{7}{16}$		.4375	$\frac{15}{16}$	.9375
	$\frac{29}{64}$	.4531	$\frac{61}{64}$	.9531
$\frac{15}{32}$		.4687	$\frac{31}{32}$	.9687
	$\frac{31}{64}$	.4844	$\frac{63}{64}$	.9844
$\frac{1}{2}$		.5	1	1.0

Step 3.   Lay Out the center marks on the 24 3/4" stick. Leave the tape measure locked, and mark each meaurement with a "T" marks* as shown below.

*"T" marks insure greater accuracy.

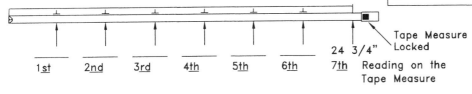

Tape Measure Locked

24 3/4"

1st   2nd   3rd   4th   5th   6th   7th   Reading on the Tape Measure

Step 4.   Check by measuring _____ between each "T" Mark.

Objective Practice Problems for Module #4

J2	Addition and Equations

1. X + 215 = 827

    X = _____ .

J3	Subtraction and Equations

2. X − 14 = 172

    X = _____ .

J4	Multiplication and Equations

3. 504 = 36w

    w = _____ .

J5	Division and Equations

4. $\frac{288}{B}$ = 16

    B = _____ .

K2	Surface Measure (Plane Geometry)

5. How many <u>square feet</u> of carpeting is needed to cover a rectangle 11'– 3" × 19'– 9"?
_____ .

6. How many <u>square yard</u>? _____ .

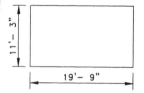

L2	Volume (Solid Geometry)

7. How many <u>cu. ft.</u> of sand is needed to fill a rectangular solid 2'– 9" × 9'– 0" × 12'– 6"?
_____ .

8. How many <u>cubic yards</u>? _____ .

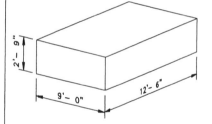

Rule: <u>Area</u> = <u>length</u> × <u>width</u>
Formula: A = lw

Rule: <u>Volume</u> = <u>length</u> × <u>width</u> × <u>Height</u>
Formula: V = lwh

K1	and	K11	page 151. Surface Measure in General (Angles)

9. A straight angle or a straight line is an angle that has _____ °.

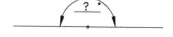

10. The complement of an angle is when one angle plus another angle equals 90°. What is the complement of angle A, 30°? Angle B = _____ °.

Math Training Module #5

[Note, square plates are welded on a piece of pipe to simulate long lengths of pipe
in industry where the circumference has to be measured to find the diameter. These
help demonstrate the application of basic algebra, and are easily made.]

Basic Math Study Notes – (Write Denominate Numbers, Indirect Proportion, Squaring Techniques, and Triangles):

Proper way to write Denominate Numbers:

1.   The proper way to write denominate numbers in <u>feet</u>, <u>inches</u>, and <u>fractions</u>.

Example: 7 feet 8 ¼ inches can be written as:

7 ft. 8 ¼ in. [abbreviations]

7' 8 ¼" [written in most text books and on most tests]

7' – 8 ¼" [written on most drawings and blueprints]
(7' – 8 ¼" does <u>not</u> mean 7 feet minus 8 ¼ inches)

Regardless of the method used, a separate
slot should be always used for each specific   feet   inch   fraction
denomination.   slot   slot   slot

Example: 7 feet is not just 7' ----------- but ----------- 7' 0" |or 7' - 0"

                   7 feet ¼ inch is not 7' ¼" --- but ----------- 7' 0 ¼" or 7' – 0 ¼"

                   7 feet 8 ¼ inches is ------------------------- 7' 8 ¼" or 7' – 8 ¼"

Indirect Proportion:

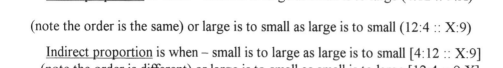

2. [I4] How to solve <u>indirect Proportion</u> problems. The only difference between direct and indirect proportion is the order. Example:

[For direct proportion, see Math Training Module #3, page 40 or Task Number **I3**, page 100.]

<u>Direct proportion</u> is when – small is to large as small is to large (4:12 :: 9:X)

(note the order is the same) or large is to small as large is to small (12:4 :: X:9)

<u>Indirect proportion</u> is when – small is to large as large is to small [4:12 :: X:9]
(note the order is different) or large is to small as small is to large [12:4 :: 9:X]

[Rule: **The Product of the Extremes is Equal to the Product of the Means.**]

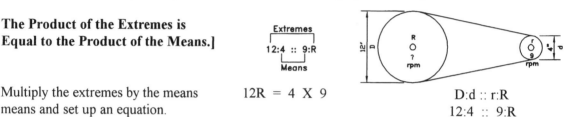

Step 1. Multiply the extremes by the means means and set up an equation.

$12R = 4 \times 9$

D:d :: r:R
12:4 :: 9:R

Step 2. Perform the operations indicated.

$$\frac{12R}{12} = \frac{36}{12}$$

[Indirect proportion is used mainly to solve pulley and gear problems. Objects that are indirectly proportional with each other.]

Step 3. Check by substituting --- $12(3) = 36$

$R = 3$ Answer

Answer Okay $36 = 36$

Note: rpm = rounds per minute
R = rpm of the large pulley
r = rpm of the little pulley
D = diameter of the large pulley
d = diameter of the little pulley

Squaring Techniques:

3. [P1] How to square up an object by using the largest combination of 3-4-5 technique. Example: Square up the object below without the use of a square.

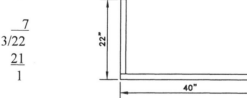

Step 1. Divide the small side by 3.

$$\begin{array}{r} 7 \\ 3\overline{)22} \\ \underline{21} \\ 1 \end{array}$$

Step 2. Take just the answer 7 and multiply it times each number in 3-4-5

$$\begin{array}{ccc} 3 & 4 & 5 \\ \times 7 & \times 7 & \times 7 \\ \hline 21 & 28 & 35 \end{array} = \text{Largest Combination}$$

Step 3. Lay out the object using the largest combination of 3-4-5 (21-28-35).

Step 4. If everything was done correctly, you would have a perfect 90° angle – check it with a big big square (lay out square). Review Trick #2.

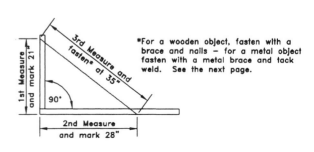

*For a wooden object, fasten with a brace and nails – for a metal object fasten with a metal brace and tack weld. See the next page.

[See the next page to check with the Rule of Pythagoras.]

Basic Math Study Notes (Continued)

Squaring Techniques (Continued):

4. **K5A** How to check the 3-4-5 Squaring Technique
   with the Rule of Pythagoras ($a^2 + b^2 = c^2$).

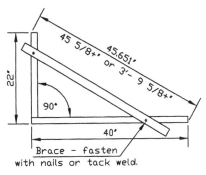

Step 1.   Use the formula: $a^2 + b^2 = c^2$

Step 2.   Substitute: $22^2 + 40^2 = c^2$

Step 3.   Calculate: $484 + 1600 = c^2$

$$2084 = c^2$$
$$\sqrt{2084} = c$$
$$45.651" = c$$

[See **Info #3** or Task No. **K5A** in the textbook,
if more information is needed and to review.]

Step 4.   Measure as shown. The dimension should be 45 5/8+". Use one method to check the other method.

The Triangle:

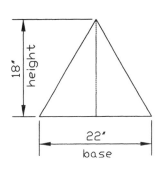

5. **K5** Calculate the area of a triangle.

     Rule: Area equal ½ the base times the height.

     Formula: A = ½ bh

     Substitute: A = ½ (22 ×18)

     Calculate: A = ½ × 396

                   A = 198 square inches

Types of Triangles:

6.   Review of triangles. For more information
on triangles, see Task No. **K1, K5, K5A,
K6A, K6B,** and **M1**.

```
a = vertical side, altitude
b = horizontal side, base
c = hypotenuse
A = Angle opposite vertical side
B = Angle opposite horizontal side
C = 90°
```

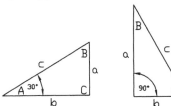

How to Label Triangles
(Also see, page 181 and 183)

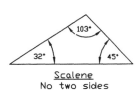

Scalene
No two sides
are equal.
(No angles are equal.)

Isosceles
Two sides are equal.
(Two angles are equal.)

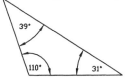

Obtuse Triangle
One angle is larger than 90°.

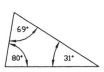

Acute Triangle
All angles less than 90°.

Equilateral
All sides are equal.
(All angles are equal.)

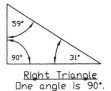

Right Triangle
One angle is 90°.

[Oblique Triangles are triangles
that have no 90° angles.]

How to Find Square Roots the Old Fashion Way

Problem 1.   Find the Square Root of 29413.   Set up and calculate as shown below:

[Note, the example below is an uneven number of digits. The number is split up into groups of two digits, left and right of the decimal. For an even number the same is true. However, the first group would then be a group of two. Example: $\sqrt{25|78|63|00}$ See Task No. [H2] in the textbook if more information is needed.]

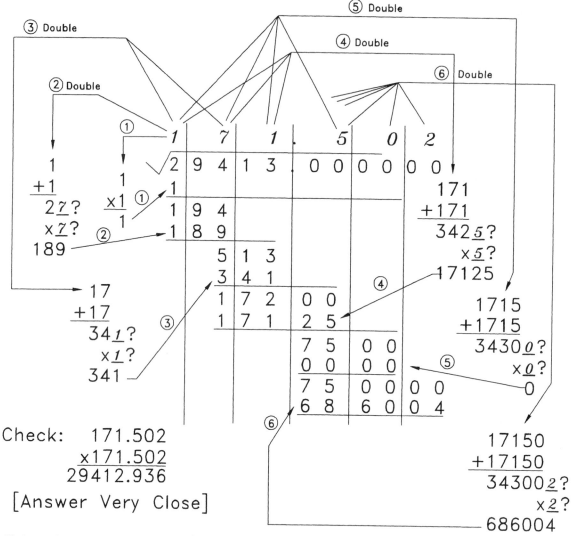

Check: 171.502
         ×171.502
         29412.936

[Answer Very Close]

[Note, when a calculator isn't used, this is the way Square Roots are solved.]

Problem 2.   Find the Square Root of $\sqrt{29413}$.

   Example: Find $\sqrt{29413}$

   Select: [2] [9] [4] [1] [3] [√x̄]   DEG
                                        171.5021866
   The display should show: Display

© Copyright 2005 Chenier Educational Enterprises, Inc.

Objective Practice Problems for Module #5

I4 Indirect Proportion

1. What size pulley would be needed
   to turn the small pulley (d) 720
   r.p.m.? _____.

2. How many teeth would be needed on
   the small sprocket (t) to turn it at the
   speed of 75 r.p.m.? _____.

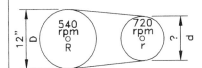

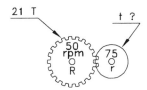

Rule: Pulley diameters are indirectly proportional to the r.p.m. of the pulleys.

Proportion: D:d :: r:R

Rule: The r.p.m. of gears are indirectly porpor-
tional to the number of their teeth.

Proportion: R:t :: r:T

P1 Squaring Techniques

3. Find the largest combination of 3–4–5 in <u>whole feet</u> that can
   be used to square up the object on the right. _____.

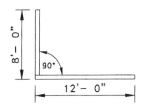

P1 Squaring Techniques

4. Find the largest combination of 3–4–5 in <u>whole feet</u> that can
   be used to square up the rectangle on the right. _____.

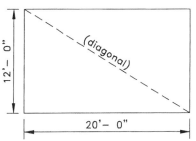

5. Find the largest combination of 5–12–13 in <u>whole feet</u> that can
   be used to square up the rectangle on the right. _____.

K5A

6. Use the formula $a^2 + b^2 = c^2$ to find the exact diagonal
   in feet, inches, and ±16th. = _____.

Objective Practice Problems for Module #5

K5   <u>Find the Area of Triangles</u>

7. How many <u>square feet</u> of material are contained in a triangle
   with a base of 17'– 0" and a height of 9'– 0"? _____ .

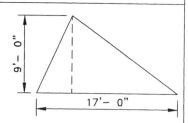

Rule: Area = 1/2 the base times the height.
Formula: A = 1/2 bh

H2   <u>Find the Square Root of a Number</u>

8. Find the square root of 7031
   manually (carry the decimal
   3 places).

   $$\sqrt{7031}$$

<u>Review Problems</u>

9. The circumference of a pipe is 7 1/2",
   What is the diameter of the pipe? _____ .

10. The diameter of a pipe is 1 5/16".
    What is the circumference of the pipe. _____ .

11. What is the proper way to write 10 feet 1/4",
    on a sketch or blueprint showing dimensions? _____ .

12. What is the proper way to write 10 feet 1/4",
    on a sketch or blueprint in a paragraph? _____ .

13. What is the proper way to write 21 feet,
    on a sketch or blueprint showing dimensions? _____ .

14. What is the proper way to write 21 feet,
    on a sketch or blueprint in a paragraph? _____ .

15. Change 113.45" to feet, inches, and ±16th. = _____ .

16. Change 24.03125" to feet, inches and   16th. = _____ .

17. Change 1/2% to a decimal = _____ .

18. Change 3/4 to a percent = _____ .

19. Change .07 to a percent = _____ .

20. Find 6% of $25.00 = _____ .

Math Training Module #6

Basic Math Study Notes – (Area of Circles, Circumference of Circles, Volume of Cylinders, Perimeters, and Parallelograms):

Areas of Circles:

1. $\boxed{\text{K7}}$ Find the Area of a circle.

Rule: Area equals <u>Pi</u> times the <u>radius squared</u>.

Formula:	$A = \pi r^2$	<u>Or</u>		$A = .7854 d^2$
Substitute:	$A = 3.1416\,(3^2)$			$A = .7854\,(6^2)$
Calculate:	$A = 3.1416 \times 9$			$A = .7854 \times 36$
Answer:	$A = 28.274$ sq. in.			$A = 28.274$ sq. in.

Circumference of a Circle:

2. $\boxed{\text{K7A}}$ Find the circumference (distance around) of a circle.

Rule: <u>Circumference</u> equals <u>pi</u> times the <u>diameter</u>.

Formula: $C = \pi d$

Substitute: $C = 3.1416\,(4)$

Calculate: $C = 12.5664'$ [Note the answer is in a decimal and has
                                   to be converted to read on a tape measure.]

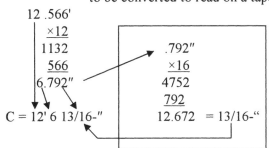

Answer: $C = 12'\ 6\ 13/16\text{-}''$

[Checked the answer by calculating in all inches. Example: $3.1416 \times 48'' = 150.7968''$ or $12'\ 6\ 13/16\text{-}''$.]

Find the diameter when the Circumference is Known:

3.   The preceding problem, demonstrated how to find the circumference of a circle by using the formula $C = \pi d$. By using the same formula, the diameter can be found if the circumference is known or measured. For example, assume you want to find the diameter of a tank with a circumference that measures 12'6 ¾". See the example below. [Note pi = 3.1416]

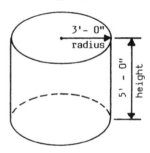

Step 1.	Use the formula -------------	$C = \pi d$

Step 2. Solve for d by dividing both sides by pi (π) -------- $\dfrac{C}{\pi} = \dfrac{\cancel{\pi} d}{\cancel{\pi}}$ $[\dfrac{C}{\pi} = d$ New Formula $]$

Step 3. Substitute the known values into the formula ----------------- $\dfrac{12.562}{3.1416} = d$

$[12'(6\ 3/4" = \dfrac{6.75}{12}$ or $\dfrac{.562}{12/6.75}) 12.562']$

Step 4. Calculate the formula (do the operations indicated) ----------- $3.998' = d$

$[12.562 \div 3.1416 = 3.998']$ $4'0" = d$

Volume of a Cylinder:

4. L7 Find the volume of a cylinder.

Rules: Volume equals pi times the <u>radius squared</u> times the <u>height</u>. Or, Volume equals ¼pi times the <u>diameter squared</u> times the <u>height</u>.

Formulas: $V = \pi r^2 h$ Or $V = .7854 d^2 h$

Substitute: $V = 3.14 \times 3^2 \times 5$

Calculate: $V = 3.14 \times (3 \times 3) \times 5$

$V = 3.14 \times (9 \times 5)$

$V = 3.14 \times 45$

$V = 141.3$ cu. ft.

Convert to cubic yards: $V = \dfrac{5.23}{27/141.30}$ cu. yd.

[1 cu. yd. = 27 cu. ft.]
$\begin{array}{r} 135 \\ \hline 6\ 3 \\ 5\ 4 \\ \hline 90 \\ 81 \\ \hline 9 \end{array}$

Convert to gallons: $V = \begin{array}{r} 141.3 \\ \times\ 7.48 \\ \hline 11304 \\ 5652 \\ 9891 \\ \hline 1056.924 \end{array}$ gal.

[1 cu. ft. = 7.48 gal.]

Finding the volume in terms of the diameter.

$V = .7854 d^2 h$

$V = .7854 \times 6^2 \times 5$

$V = .7854 \times (6 \times 6) \times 5$

$V = .7854 \times (36 \times 5)$

$V = .7854 \times 180$

$V = 141.372$ cu. ft.

<u>Use one method to check the other method.</u>

Basic Math Study Notes (Continued)

Perimeters:

5. K1 How to find the perimeter of geometric figures (polygons).

[Rule: To find the perimeter of a polygon, find the sum of all its sides.]

Example 1. Find the perimeter of the triangle shown below.

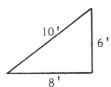

Add the 3 sides of the triangle $\left\{\begin{array}{r} 10' \\ 6' \\ + 8' \end{array}\right.$

Therefore, the perimeter is ----- 24'

Example 2. Find the perimeter of the hexagon shown below.

[A hexagon has 6 equal sides and 6 equal angles.]

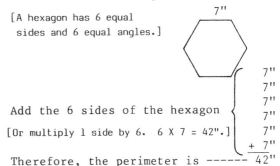

Add the 6 sides of the hexagon $\left\{\begin{array}{r} 7'' \\ 7'' \\ 7'' \\ 7'' \\ 7'' \\ + 7'' \end{array}\right.$

[Or multiply 1 side by 6. 6 X 7 = 42".]

Therefore, the perimeter is ------ 42"

The Parallelogram:

6. K3 How to find the area of a parallelogram by using two types of numbers.

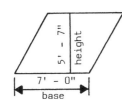

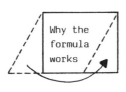

C4 Solve by Using Mixed Numbers

Rule: Area equals the base times the height.
Formula: A = bh

Substitute: A = 7 X $5\frac{7}{12}$

Calculate: A = $\frac{7}{1}$ X $\frac{67}{12}$ = $\frac{469}{12}$ = $12\overline{)469.00}$ $\xrightarrow{39.08}$

Answer: A = 39.08 sq. ft.

A4 Solve by Using Whole Numbers

A = bh

A = 84" X 67"

A = 5628 sq. in. $144\overline{)5628.00}$ $\xrightarrow{39.08}$

A = 39.08 sq. ft.

Note that both answers are the same.

[Try to get into the habit of checking all your problems by calculating at least two different ways. The pay-off for learning to check now will come on-the-job later.]

The example above demonstrates how to calculate the area of a parallelogram by using two different types of numbers.   The reason for this is so one type can be used to check the other type. Realistically, if you were on the job, you would have to do something like this to make sure the answer was correct.

"This page intentionally blank."

Info #4 – The Scientific Calculator and Basic Applied Math

Instructions How to Use the TI–36X Scientific Calculator:

1. Make sure you are in the DEG mode.
    The display should show:

    Display

    To get into this mode, either press [on/ac]

    or: Select [2nd] [DRG HYP] and the display will
    toggle from "DEG" to "RAD" to "GRAD".

    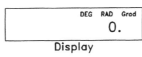
    Display

2. Calculate Fractions and Mixed Numbers.

    Example: Multiply 3/4 X 3 1/2 =

    Select: [3] [a%] [4] [×] [3] [a%] [1] [a%] [2] [=]

    The display should show:

    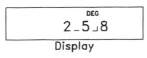
    Display

3. Calculate pi (∏) problems.

    Example: Find pi (∏).

    Select: [3rd] [÷]

    The display should show:

    3.141592654
    Display

4. Find the Square Root (√⁻) of a number.

    Example: Find √789

    Select: [7] [8] [9] [√x]

    The display should show:

5. Find the Square (9 X 9) of a number.

    Example: Find 9²

    Select: [9] [x²]

    The display should show:

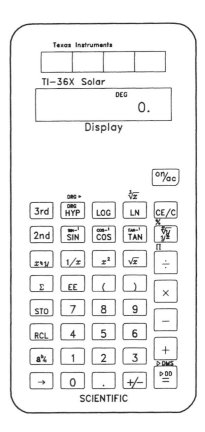

6. Find the Root (Exponent) of a
    a number. Example: Find $\sqrt[6]{64}$

    Select: [6] [4] [2nd] [ˣ√y] [6] [=]

    The display should show:

    Display

7. Change a Percent (%) to a decimal
    fraction. Example: Change 89%
    to a Decimal Fraction.

    Select: [8] [9] [3rd] [ˣ√y]

    The display should show:

    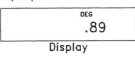
    Display

Trade Trick #1 – Make a Story Pole
(Problem 5: 24 ¾" Stick - 7 Centers)

Practice Stick 24 3/4" Long.

(Mark Side #4, use "T" marks and draw square lines.)

Make 3/4" X 3/4" or 1" X 1"

24 3/4"

Step 1. Lay out the 7 center marks on the right with an American (English) tape measure to ± 1/16 of an inch accuracy.

Note: There are 7 center marks but _____ spaces.

Therefore: Divide by _____ $\overline{)24.75}$

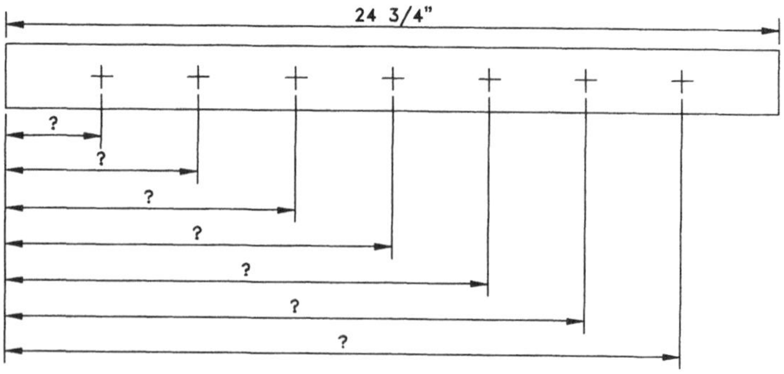

Step 2. Use the Quickest Way method below to Calculate the Story Pole Measurements.

The Quickest Way

1st.	_____	=	_____
	+ _____		
2nd.	_____	=	_____
	+ _____		
3rd.	_____	=	_____
	+ _____		
4th.	_____	=	_____
	+ _____		
5th.	_____	=	_____
	+ _____		
6th.	_____	=	_____
	+ _____		
7th.	_____	=	_____
	+ _____		
8th.	24.7500"	=	24 3/4" Ans. OK

Step 3. Lay Out the center marks on the 24 3/4" stick. Leave the tape measure locked, and mark each meaurement with a "T" marks* as shown below.

*"T" marks insure greater accuracy.

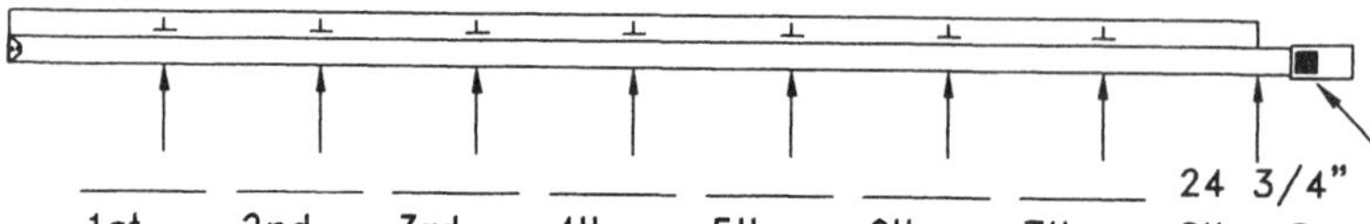

1st 2nd 3rd 4th 5th 6th 7th 8th
24 3/4"
Tape Measure Locked
Reading on the Tape Measure

Step 4. Check by measuring _____ between each "T" Mark.

[Note: Use a Decimal Chart For Speed!]

EQUIVALENT CHART – DECIMALS OF AN INCH

Fraction	Decimal		Fraction	Decimal
$\frac{1}{64}$	.0156		$\frac{33}{64}$	.5156
$\frac{1}{32}$	.0312		$\frac{17}{32}$	.5312
$\frac{3}{64}$	.0469		$\frac{35}{64}$	.5469
$\frac{1}{16}$	.0625		$\frac{9}{16}$	.5625
$\frac{5}{64}$	.0781		$\frac{37}{64}$	.5781
$\frac{3}{32}$	.0937		$\frac{19}{32}$	.5937
$\frac{7}{64}$	.1094		$\frac{39}{64}$	.6094
$\frac{1}{8}$	.125		$\frac{5}{8}$	.625
$\frac{9}{64}$	.1406		$\frac{41}{64}$	.6406
$\frac{5}{32}$	.1562		$\frac{21}{32}$	.6562
$\frac{11}{64}$	.1719		$\frac{43}{64}$	.6719
$\frac{3}{16}$	.1875		$\frac{11}{16}$	.6875
$\frac{13}{64}$	.2031		$\frac{45}{64}$	.7031
$\frac{7}{32}$	.2187		$\frac{23}{32}$	.7187
$\frac{15}{64}$	.2344		$\frac{47}{64}$	.7344
$\frac{1}{4}$	.25		$\frac{3}{4}$	.75
$\frac{17}{64}$	.2656		$\frac{49}{64}$	.7656
$\frac{9}{32}$	.2812		$\frac{25}{32}$	.7812
$\frac{19}{64}$	.2969		$\frac{51}{64}$	.7969
$\frac{5}{16}$	.3125		$\frac{13}{16}$	.8125
$\frac{21}{64}$	.3281		$\frac{53}{64}$	.8281
$\frac{11}{32}$	.3437		$\frac{27}{32}$	.8437
$\frac{23}{64}$	.3594		$\frac{55}{64}$	.8594
$\frac{3}{8}$	.375		$\frac{7}{8}$	.875
$\frac{25}{64}$	.3906		$\frac{57}{64}$	.8906
$\frac{13}{32}$	.4062		$\frac{29}{32}$	.9062
$\frac{27}{64}$	.4219		$\frac{59}{64}$	.9219
$\frac{7}{16}$	.4375		$\frac{15}{16}$	.9375
$\frac{29}{64}$	.4531		$\frac{61}{64}$	.9531
$\frac{15}{32}$	.4687		$\frac{31}{32}$	.9687
$\frac{31}{64}$	.4844		$\frac{63}{64}$	.9844
$\frac{1}{2}$	.5		1	1.0

Objective Practice Problems for Module #6

K7 | Area of a Circle (carry decimals 3 places):

1. How many <u>square feet</u> of material are contained in a circle with a radius of 7' 0" _____.

7'– 0"
radius

2. How many <u>square yards</u>? _____.

Rule: Area = <u>pi</u> times the <u>radius squared</u>.
Formula: $A = \pi r^2$

K7A | Circumference of a Circle (carry decimals 3 places):

3. What is the circumference of a circle that has a diameter of of 9' 9"? _____

9'– 9"
diameter
Circumference

Rule: Circumference equals <u>pi</u> times the <u>diameter</u>.
Formula: $C = \pi d$

K7A | Find the diameter when the circumference is known (carry decimals 3 places):

4. What is the diameter of a pipe that has a circumference of 11"? _____.

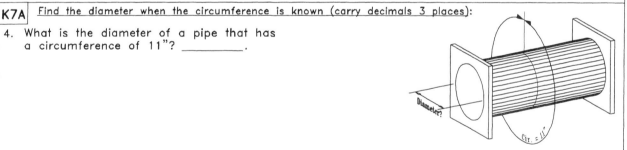
Diameter?
Cir. = 11"

L7 | Volume of a Cylinder (carry decimals 3 places):

5. What is the volume, in gallons, of a cylinder tank that has a diameter of 3' 0" and a height of 3'– 9 3/8"? _____.

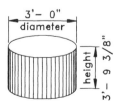
3'– 0"
diameter
height
3'– 9 3/8"

Objective Practice Problems for Module #6

K1 Perimeter (carry decimals 3 places):

6. What is the perimeter of the octagon shown below? _____.

7. What is the perimeter of the geometric figure shown below, in inches? _____.

in ft. and in.? _____.

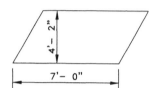

K3   Area of a Parallelogram (carry decimals 3 places):

8. What is the area of the parallelogram shown on the right? _____.

Rule: Area equals base times the height.
Formula: A = bh

P1   Review Problems

9. Find the largest combination of 3−4−5 in whole feet that can be used to square up the rectangle on the right. _____.

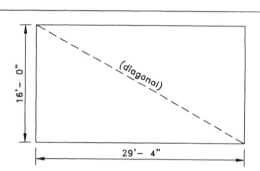

P1

10. Find the largest combination of 5−12−13 in whole feet that can be used to square up the rectangle on the right. _____.

K5A

11. Use the formula $a^2 + b^2 = c^2$ to find the exact diagonal of the rectangle in feet, inches, and ±16th. = _____.

Math Training Module #7

Instructional Objectives:

Hands On:

☐ *Application Problem* - Practice Centering and spacing via a piece of paper and a ruler or a tape measure. Use scrape paper, scrape boards, or poster board.

Basic Math Study Notes – (Conversion using all Feet, How to find ½ of a Denominate Number, and Trapezoids):

Conversion using all Feet:

1. [E7] How to convert decimals of feet into feet, inches, and 16^{ths}. Below is an example of a conversion problem. The problem is a simple problem that could pop up on practically any job. Can you lay out each dimension with an American (English) tape measure? Hopefully this problem will show you why conversion is so important and why these problems are on all the practice modules.

Example: Lay out the object below to ± 1/16 of an inch.

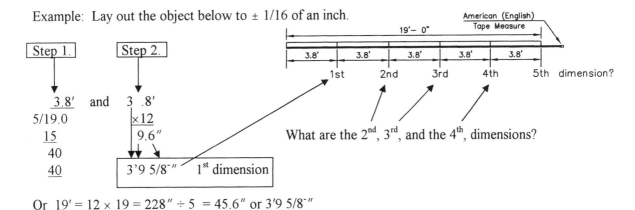

Or 19' = 12 × 19 = 228" ÷ 5 = 45.6" or 3'9 5/8⁻"

[Note: Whether you use feet or inches to calculate – you still must convert. Many tape measures are in both feet and inches, not all inches. Therefore, converting both ways is very important.]

<u>**Find ½ of a Denominate Number:**</u>

2. ☐D6 How to find ½ of a denominate number.

Example: Find ½ of 5' 2 1/2".

<u>Method 1</u>

$$\frac{31.25''}{2/62.5''} = 2'\ 7\ 1/4''$$

5' 2 1/2" = 62.5"

[5 × 12 = 60", and 60 + 2 ½ = 62.5"]

<u>Method 2</u>

```
  2'    7.25"
2/5'    2.5"
  4
 1=+12
  14
  14
   5
   4
  10
  10
```

<u>Method 3</u>
(Do mentally – take ½ of each
number as shown, and add.)

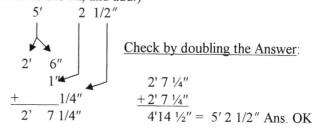

<u>Check by doubling the Answer</u>:

```
    2' 7 ¼"
  +2' 7 ¼"
   4'14 ½" = 5' 2 1/2" Ans. OK
```

<u>**Trapezoids:**</u>

3. ☐K4 How to find the area of a Trapezoid.

Rule: Area = ½ the sum of the bases times the height.

Formula: A = ½ (b + b')

Substitute: A = ½ (6 + 9) 7

Calculate: A = ½ (15) × 7

A = ½ × 105

A = 52 ½ square feet

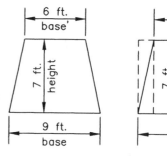

Another way to look at a trapezoid:
Note, the center rectangle is 6 X 7
or 42 sq. ft. One of the two other
rectangles 1.5 X 7 = 10.5 sq. ft.
plus the 42 sq. ft. = 52.5 sq. ft.
Or 1/2bh of each triangle yields the
same answer.

How many square inches in 52 ½ square feet? Hint, 1 square foot equals 144 square inches.
Substitute inches in place of feet and calculate. This is another way to check the answer.

Info #1B – Convert Feet and Inches
to Decimals (Tape Measure in FEET and INCHES)

Conversion using all "Feet" for Special Tape Measures".

    Many American English tape measures (especially 50 ft. and 100 ft. tapes) are in just "Feet" and "Inches", verses <u>all inches*</u>. Therefore, when converting, it is best to convert in "Feet" and "Decimals of Feet" to make it easier to measure later. The example below will illustrate how and why.

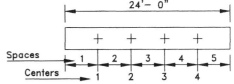

Problem: You are given the piece of wood, metal, pipe, etc. on the right. Your job is to lay out 4 centerlines to ± 1/16 of an inch accuracy with a tape in feet and inches.

1.   Looking at the sketch (top right), you will see that there are 4 center lines, but <u>5 spaces</u>. Therefore, the first step in solving the problem is to divide by 5. (a common error is to divide by 4 centerlines, but there are actually 5 spaces. Drawing a sketch of the problem will help eliminate this type of error.)

Therefore, each space is 4.8 feet from center to center.

$$5\overline{)24.0} = 4.8'$$

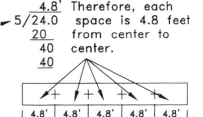

[Note: You cannot find 4.8 feet on an American tape measure. Therefore, you must convert.]

2.   Convert 4.8' so you can read the dimension on an American (English) tape measure to ± 1/16 of an inch accuracy.

    1st   Pull 4' out because that is already whole feet.

    2nd   Multiply the <u>decimal only</u> by 12, the desired denominator –– this changes the decimal to inches. Indicate with the inch sign (").

    3rd   Pull 9" out because you now have 9 whole inches.

    4th   Multiply the <u>decimal only</u> by 16 for 16ths, the desired denominator.

    5th   Pull out 9 because you now have 9 whole 16ths of an inch.

    [Note 9/16+" and 5/8–" are the same. Use the decimals of an inch equivalent chart to verify this.]

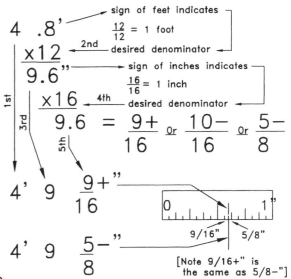

*Changing 24 feet to <u>all inches</u> equals 288 inches, and 288 divided by 5 equals 57.6 inches. The tape measure would be in feet and inches. Therefore, you would have to divide by 12 (whole inches only) to get the dimension back in feet again.

Conversion using all Feet (continued)

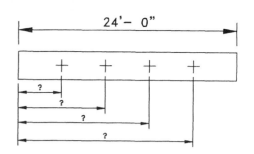

24'– 0"

3. List in order (make a story pole) the 4 dimensions so you can read them on the tape measure without having to move the tape*.

Making a Story Pole:

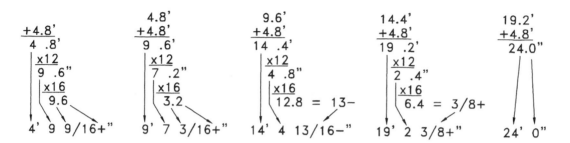

1st dimension	2nd dimension	3rd dimension	4th dimension	5th dimension [Check]

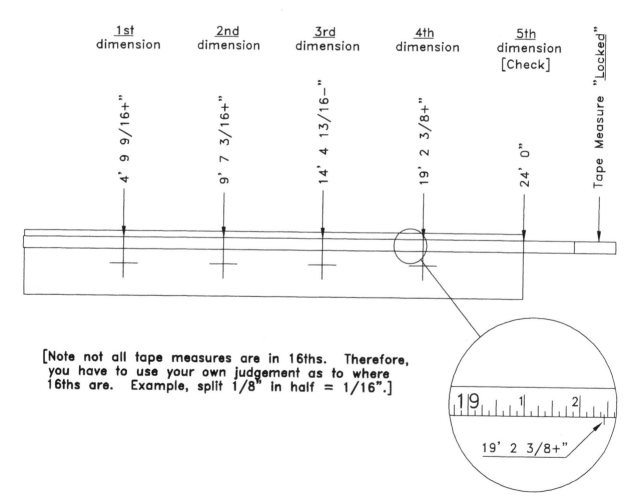

[Note not all tape measures are in 16ths. Therefore, you have to use your own judgement as to where 16ths are. Example, split 1/8" in half = 1/16".]

19' 2 3/8+"

*Note if the tape measure was moved for each dimension, the changes for error would increase 4 times. The very purpose for a story pole.

[See page 57 and 166 for other examples of story poles.]

Trade Trick #3 – Centering and Spacing
[Find ½ of a Denominate Number, Centering, & Spacing]

How to Find 1/2 of a Denominate Number, Centering, and Spacing Tricks:

Find the Center of the Object (Denominate Number) shown below, MENTALLY:

Example 1. Find the center (lengthwise) of the object on the right.

[Also, see Task No. D6 and D7 in the textbook.]

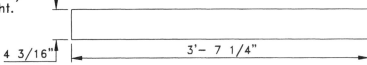

4 3/16"   3'– 7 1/4"

3'– 7 1/4"

a) What is 1/2 of 3 feet? [Think!] ⟶ 1'– 6"

b) What is 1/2 of 7 inches? [Think!] ⟶ 3 1/2"

c) What is 1/2 of 1/4"? [Think!] ⟶ +   1/8"

d) Add. ⟶ 1'– 9 5/8"

e) Check by doubling. ⟶ { 1'– 9 5/8"
    Or better yet, check by measuring.   + 1'– 9 5/8"
                                            2'–18 10/8"

   (2'–18 10/8" = 2'–19 2/8") or = 3'– 7 1/4" Answer OK

Find the Center of the Object shown below, by using a Trade Trick:

Example 2. Find the center (widthwise) of the object on the right by using a ruler or a tape measure.

a) Angle ruler to the nearest whole number, 5. As shown.

b) Mark 1/2 of 5" or 2 1/2".

4 3/16"

c) Turn the ruler parallel to the Center Line to check. The dimension reads 2 3/32".

[There is no need to read the dimension, mark the ruler and go to the next step.]

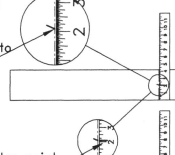

ANOTHER TRICK: a) Mark the ruler at the center point.

b) Slide the ruler up to where the center mark and outside edge meet. Center mark is OK.

Find 1/2 of a Denominate Number, Centering, & Spacing (Continued)

Space (divide) the Object shown below into Four Equal pieces:

Example 3. Divide the object on the right into four equal pieces, vertically, by using a ruler or a tape measure.

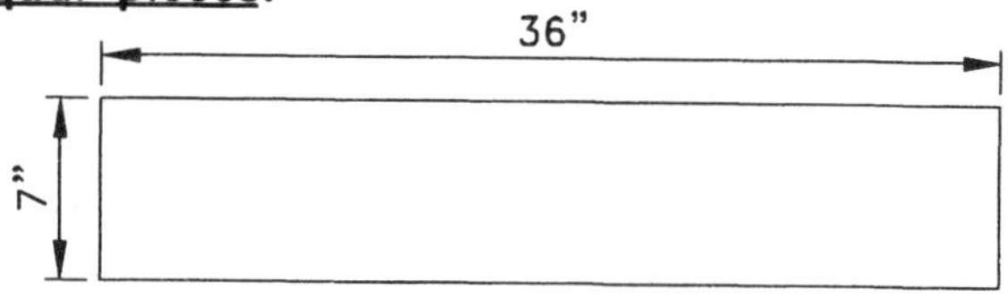

36"

7"

a) Angle ruler to the nearest whole number divisible by 4 (example: 8 ÷ 4 = 2). In this case the whole number is 8.

b) Mark; 2", 4", and 6". [Always mark with "T" marks to locate the exact point.]

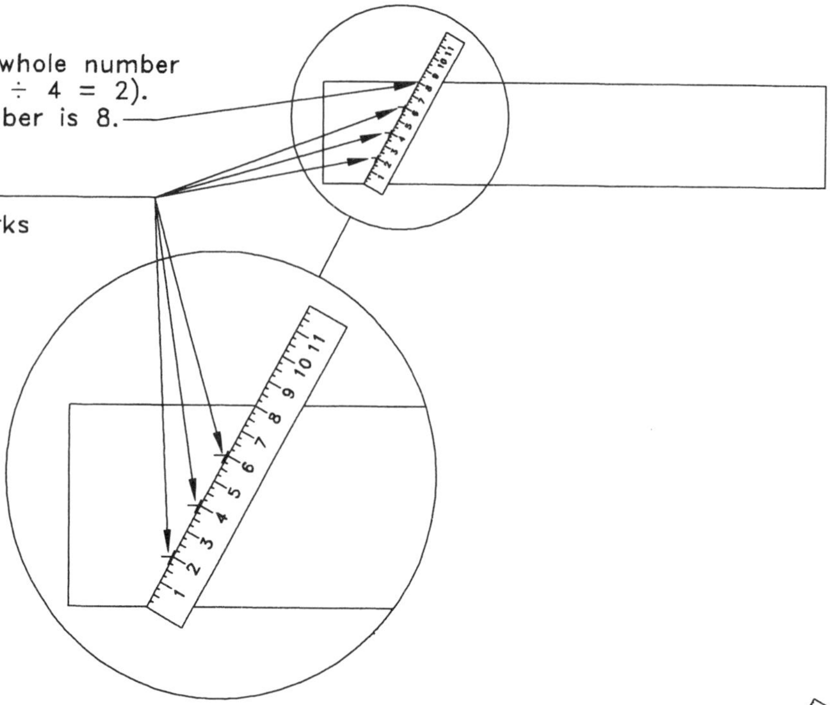

c) Mark the opposite end of the object the same way. Use "T" marks.

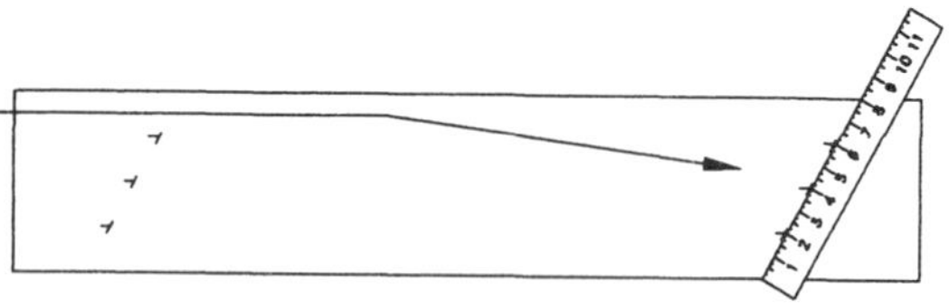

d) Use a straight edge or a combination square to extend the lines, as shown.

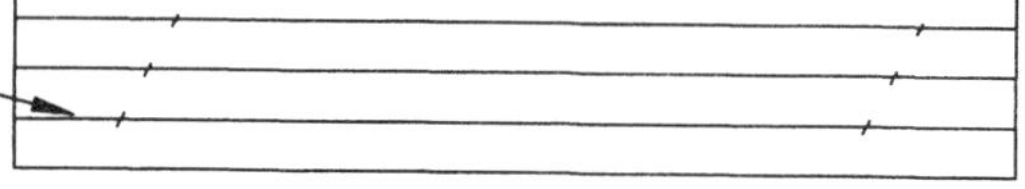

e) Check by measuring each space for for accuracy. Or 7 ÷ 4 = 1 3/4". Checks out OK.

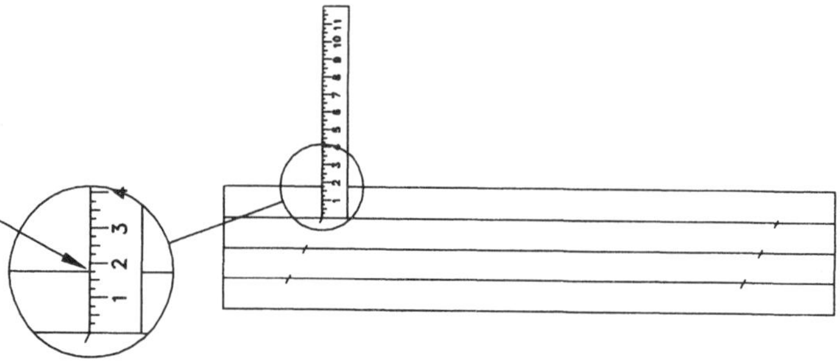

Trade Trick #1 – Make a Story Pole
(Problem 6: 8'- 0″ Stick - 4 Centers)

Cut Practice
Stick 8'– 0" Long. ⟶

Make 3/4' X 3/4' or 1' X 1'

(Mark Side #1, use 'T' marks and draw square lines.)

Step 1.   Lay out the 4 center marks on the right with an American (English) tape measure to ±1/16 of an inch accuracy.

Note: There are 4 center marks but 5 spaces.

Therefore: Divide by 5

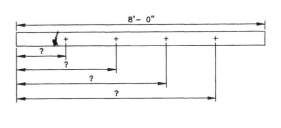

$$5 \overline{)8.0} = 1.6$$
$$\underline{5}$$
$$30$$
$$\underline{30}$$

Step 2.   List in order (make a story pole) the 4 dimensions so you can read them on the tape measure without having to move it.

Making a Story Pole:

1 .6'
|x12
7 .2"
|x16
3.2
1' 7 3/16+"

1.6'
+1.6'
3 .2'
|x12
2 .4"
|x16
6.4
3' 2 6/16+"

3.2'
+1.6'
4 .8'

4.8'
+1.6'
6 .4'

6.4'
+1.6'
8.0"

1st dimension	2nd dimension	3rd dimension	4th dimension	5th dimension [Check]

1' 7 3/16+"   3' 2 3/8+"   8' 0"   Tape Measure "Locked"

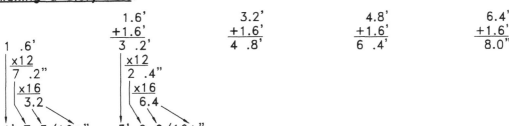

Step 3.   Lay out the center marks (use "T" marks) on the 8'– 0" stick. Do not move the tape measure. Leave in the locked positon as shown above.

Step 4.   Check by measuring 1' 7 3/16+" between each "T" mark.

[Note not all tape measures are in 16ths. Therefore, you have to use your own judgement as to where 16ths are. Example, split 1/8" in half = 1/16". See the example on page 76.]

Objective Practice Problems for Module #7

E7 | Conversion using Feet and Inches (Tape Measure in FEET and INCHES) – Info #1B

1. Change 5.271' to feet, inches, and 16ths. = _____.

2. Change 77.875" to ft., in., and 16ths. = _____.

3. Change 57 3/4" to ft., in., and 16ths. = _____.

4. Change 108.125' to ft., in., and 16ths. = _____.

5. Change 225 1/2" to ft., in., and 16ths. = _____.

D6 | Find 1/2 of a Denominate Number, Centering, and Spacing – Trade Trick #3

6. Find 1/2 of 9' 4 1/4" = _____.

7. Find 1/2 of 17' 9 3/8" = _____.

8. Find 1/2 of 10' 0 7/8" = _____.

D6 | Find 1/2 of a Denominate Number, Centering, and Spacing – Trade Trick #3

9. Center the objects below with a ruler or tape measure and a straight edge, or name the tool that would be needed to center the object.

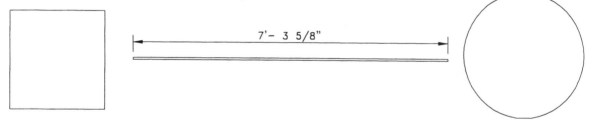

7'– 3 5/8"

D7

10. Divide the object below horizontally 3 spaces, and vertically 4 spaces with a ruler or a tape measure and a straight edge.

K4 | Area of a Trapezoid

11. What is the area of the trapezoid on the right, in square feet? _____.

12. What is the area of the trapezoid on the right, in square inches? _____.

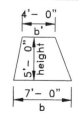

4'– 0"
b'
5'– 0" height
7'– 0"
b

Rule: Area = 1/2 the sum of the bases times the height.
Formula: A = 1/2 (b + b')h

Math Training Module #8

Instructional Objectives:

Hands On:

☐ *Application Problem* - Practice Leveling with a Plumb Bob, use **Trade Trick #4** as a guide.

☐ *Application Problem* - Practice Leveling with a Water Level, use **Trade Trick #5** as a guide.

☐ *Application Problem* - Practice laying out braces on a large sheet of paper with a Lay Out Square. Use **Trade Trick #6** and the **Basic Math Study Notes** below as a guide.

☐ *Application Problem* - Practice the 3-4-5 and the Rule of Pythagoras ($a^2 + b^2 = c^2$) squaring methods on a sheet of paper. Use a Lay Out Square and **Info #3** as a guide.

Basic Math Study Notes – (Brace Measure and Calculate the Length of a Brace):

Brace Measure: [Also see Task No. R1 and R1A in the textbook, if more information is needed.]

1. $\boxed{R1}$ How braced measure is determined.

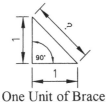

One Unit of Brace

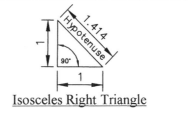

Isosceles Right Triangle

One unit of brace is determined by using the Rule of Pythagoras Task No. $\boxed{K5A}$.

Formula:	$a^2 + b^2 =$	c^2
Substitute:	$1^2 + 1^2 =$	c^2
Calculate:	$1 + 1 =$	c^2
	$2 =$	c^2
	$\sqrt{2} =$	c
$1.414213562 =$		c

A brace is an isosceles right triangle (has two equal sides and one angle is 90°). A true brace will <u>always</u> be an isosceles right triangle. And one unit of brace will always have a hypotenuse of 1.414. However, 1.414 could be inches, feet, meters, and so on. For more information on Brace Measure, see Task No. $\boxed{R1}$

[Note, for most brace jobs carry the decimal 3-5 places. However, 1.414 is the most common number.]

Basic Math Study Notes (Continued)

<u>**How to Calculate the Length of a Brace:**</u>

2.   Find the length of the brace on the right. Carry the decimal 3 places.

Rule: To find the length of a Brace multiply the length of the Side times 1.414.
Formula: B = S(1.414)

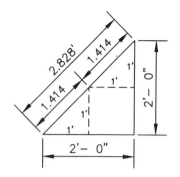

Step 1.   Multiply the diagonal of one
unit of brace (1.414) times (×)   1.414
the length of a side --- thus ---   × 2
                                    2.828'

Step 2.   Convert the decimal so you
can read the dimension on
an American English tape
measure.

2 .828'   .936"
  ×12   for inches   ×16   for 16th
  1656   5616
  828   936
  9.936"   14.976 = 15/16" (very close)

2' 9 15/16"

[Note how conversion problems are always popping up!]

Step 3.   Check by calculating in all inches. 24" × 1.414 = 33.936" or 2' 9 15/16". Answer Okay.]

3.   Find the length of the brace on the right. Carry the decimal
3 places.

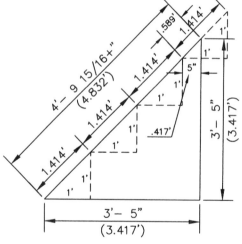

Step 1.   Convert 5" to decimals of a foot.

5" = 5/12' or .416667'   <u>Or</u>   3.417' (decimal 3 places)

Step 2.   Multiply the diagonal of one
unit of brace (1.414) times (×)   3.417
the length of a side --- thus ---   × 1.414
                                     4.831638'

Step 3.   Convert the decimal so you
can read the dimension on
an American English tape
measure.

4 .832'   .984"
  ×12   for inches   ×16   for 16th
  1664   5904
  832   984
  9.984"   15.744 = 15/16[+]"

4' 9 15/16[+]"

[Check the above brace by calculating it in all inches. One method will check the other method.]

[Also see, the <u>Lay Out Square</u> and <u>Brace Measure</u>, page 229.]

Trade Trick #4 – Level with a Plumb Bob
[Level Vertically: Level (Plumb) Pipe, Tubing, Walls, etc.]

How to Level with a Plumb Bob - Level Vertically:

[Level Pipe, Tubing, Fence Post, Telephone Poles, etc.]

Step 1.   Hold the Plumb Bob in your hand and eyeball
the object being leveled. The string holding the
Plumb Bob should be center of the object being
leveled. Note this object is perpendicular (90°)
to the wall.

Step 2.   Make the necessary adjustments to the object
in this position.

Step 3.   Reposition the Plumb Bob at a 90° angle from
the first position and eyeball the object. The
string holding the Plumb Bob should be center
of the object. Note the Plumb Bob is now parallel
to the wall.

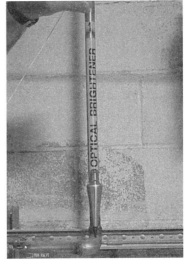

Step 4.   Make the necessary adjustments to the object
in this position.

Step 5.   Check the object by returning to the first position,
90° from the wall. Then switch to the next position,
parallel to the wall.

Step 6.   Double check the object with a Spirit Level .
Many times it is difficult to have a Spirit Level
that is long enough and/or is in a difficult position
to use. This is where a Plumb Bob is very easy
to use. A Plumb Bob can also be used to level
very tall objects, such as telephone poles with
ease. This is the tool that most linemen use.

[Note for more information on Spirit Levels, see Task No. Q3, pages
344 through 347 in the textbook. This section of the textbook will
illustrate different types of spirit levels, how to check them for accuracy,
and tricks how to use them.]

Level with a Plumb Bob (Continued)

How to Level with a Plumb Bob – Level Vertically:

[Level walls with a Plumb in oil.]

Step 1.   Secure the plumb line equal distances from
the two walls being leveled as shown.
Make sure this spacer block will enable the
plumb line to be in the center of the oil can
for freedom of movement.

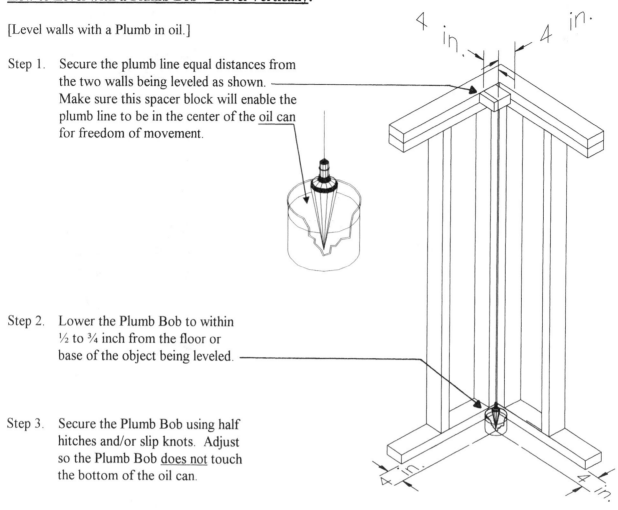

Step 2.   Lower the Plumb Bob to within
½ to ¾ inch from the floor or
base of the object being leveled.

Step 3.   Secure the Plumb Bob using half
hitches and/or slip knots. Adjust
so the Plumb Bob <u>does not</u> touch
the bottom of the oil can.

Step 4.   Set the Plumb Bob into a can of heavy oil*
(20-30 weight). Fill can ½ to ¾ full.

Step 5.   Take measurements – adjust the top two walls until the measurements at the bottom match the
measurements at the spacer positions on the top. In this case the measurements should be 4″.

[Note for more information on Plumb Bobs, see Task No. Q4, pages 348 through 351 in the textbook. This
section will illustrate how to plumb (level) poles, Christmas trees, and a motor.]

*The oil will help stop the Plumb Bob from swinging, especially if there is a little breeze. Do not use a Plumb
  Bob if it is too windy.

Trade Trick #5 – Level with a Water Level
[Level Horizontally: Level a Patio (Footings, Blocks, Beams, etc.)]

How to Level with a Water Level (Lay Out and Level a Patio via 3–4–5 and the Water Level):

Example 1.   The largest combination of 3–4–5 (6–8–10, in this case) and the water
level* are used to square and level the cement patio pads shown below.

[Also, refer to Task No. P1, P1A, P2, Q1, Q2, Q3, and Q4 in the textbook. These tasks demonstrate the
3–4–5 and 5–12–13 squaring techniques, the water level in more detail, spirit levels, the transit and
builders level, and the plumb bob. The intent of this module is to give you insight on how to square
and level. As there are many different ways to build patios and decks, but most important they must
be square (true in dimension) and plumb (level).]

1. Make a story pole of all the needed elevations.
2. Use the largest combination of 3–4–5, in this
    case, 6–8–10 to square the patio.
3. Place grade stakes 16" – 24" above the
    ground (grade).
4. Establish level lines with a water level
    or other leveling instruments.
5. Transfer level lines to the top
    of the footings.
6. Set the footing forms and
    pour the concrete.

Patio Story Pole:
[Design the patio
for elevations.]

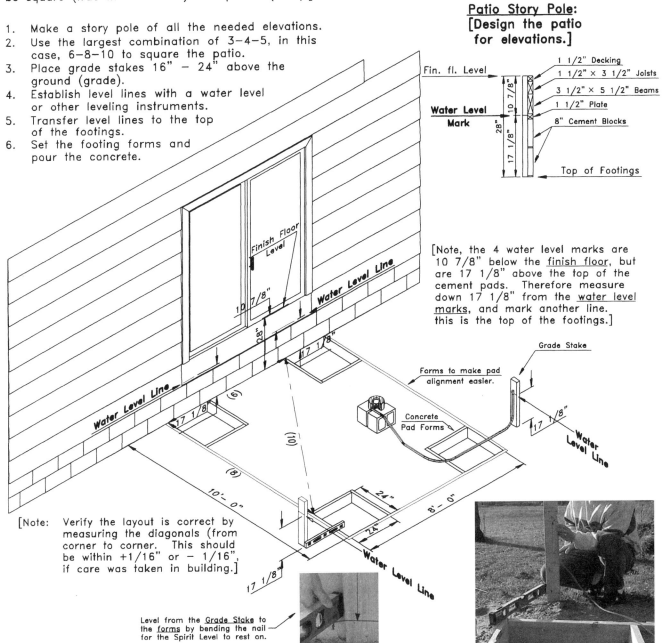

[Note, the 4 water level marks are
10 7/8" below the finish floor, but
are 17 1/8" above the top of the
cement pads. Therefore measure
down 17 1/8" from the water level
marks, and mark another line.
this is the top of the footings.]

[Note: Verify the layout is correct by
measuring the diagonals (from
corner to corner. This should
be within +1/16" or − 1/16",
if care was taken in building.]

Level from the Grade Stake to
the forms by bending the nail
for the Spirit Level to rest on.

*A transit, builders level, spirit levels, laser levels, etc. can be used   to find elevations.
However, the water level is the most economical and accurate (water seeks it's own level).

Lay Out a Patio with the 3-4-5 Squaring Technique and the Water Level (Continued)

How to Check Elevations via the Water Level as the Patio is Built:

Example 2. Note how the story pole reference dimensions Ⓐ and Ⓑ relate to the actual building of the patio. This is a self checking technique.

Patio Story Pole:

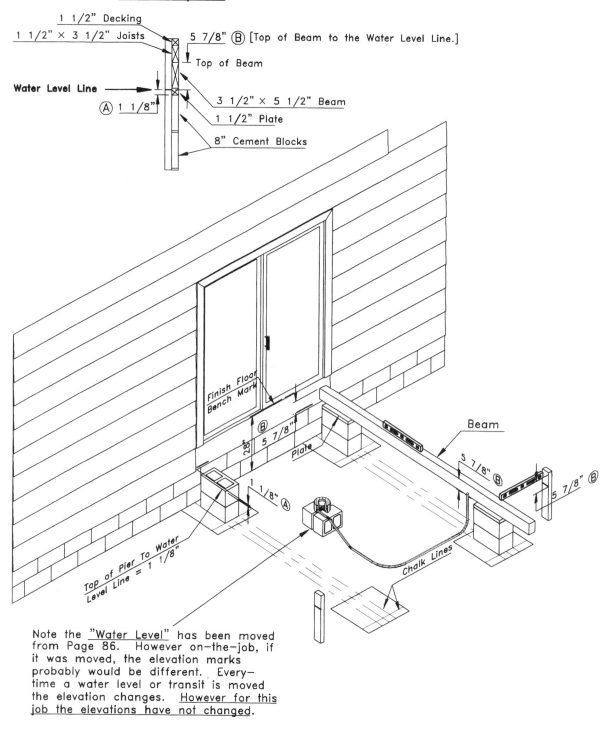

1 1/2" Decking

1 1/2" × 3 1/2" Joists

5 7/8" Ⓑ [Top of Beam to the Water Level Line.]

Top of Beam

Water Level Line

Ⓐ 1 1/8"

3 1/2" × 5 1/2" Beam

1 1/2" Plate

8" Cement Blocks

Finish Floor Bench Mark

Ⓑ 5 7/8"

28"

Plate

1 1/8" Ⓐ

Beam

5 7/8" Ⓑ

5 7/8" Ⓑ

Top of Pier To Water Level Line = 1 1/8"

Chalk Lines

Note the "Water Level" has been moved from Page 86. However on-the-job, if it was moved, the elevation marks probably would be different. Every-time a water level or transit is moved the elevation changes. However for this job the elevations have not changed.

Lay Out a Patio with the 3−4−5 Squaring Technique and the Water Level (Continued):

How to Check Elevations via the Water Level Mark as the Patio is Built:

Example 3.   Note how the story pole reference dimension Ⓒ relates to the patio floor
Joist.   It is the dimension from the Water Level Line to the top of the Joists.

Patio Story Pole:

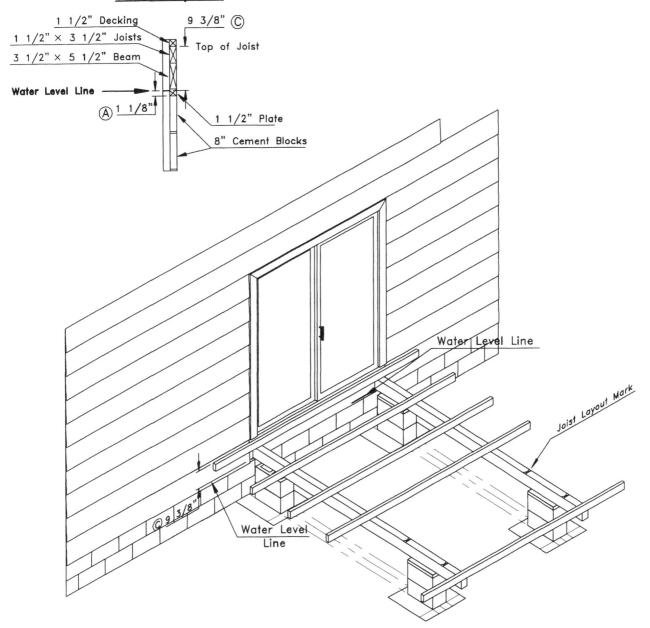

Lay Out a Patio with the 3-4-5 Squaring Technique and the Water Level (Continued)

How to Check Elevations via the Water Level Mark until the Patio is Finished:

Example 4.   Note how the top of the deck is even with the finish floor.   Therefore, all elevations marks and calculations are correct.

Patio Story Pole:

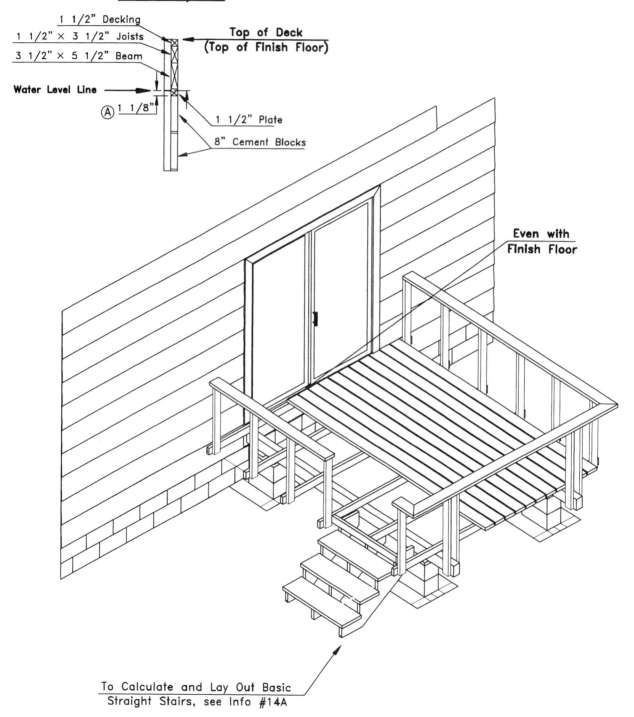

1 1/2" Decking
1 1/2" × 3 1/2" Joists
3 1/2" × 5 1/2" Beam

Top of Deck
(Top of Finish Floor)

Water Level Line →

Ⓐ 1 1/8"

1 1/2" Plate

8" Cement Blocks

Even with Finish Floor

To Calculate and Lay Out Basic Straight Stairs, see Info #14A

Trade Trick #6 – Brace Measure
[Calculate the Brace when the Side is Known]

Calculate the Brace: [Also, see Task No. R1 & R1A in the textbook for more info.]

Example 1.   Note how the brace can be used to both <u>support (brace)</u> and <u>level (plumb)</u> the wall shown below. This will work, <u>only if the base (floor) which the brace is nailed to is level (horizontally)</u>. If in doubt, check for level with a spirit level.

1) The brace below was determined to have a side of 6 feet (72"). Therefore to find the brace, **use the Formula: B = S(1.414)**, multiply: $6 \times 1.414 = 8.484'$.

2) Convert 8.484' to feet, inches, & 16ths.

3) Check by calculating in inches. $72 \times 1.414 = 101.808$" or

$$\begin{array}{r} 8\ .484' \\ \times 12" \\ \hline 5\ .808" \\ \times 16 \\ \hline 12.928 \end{array}$$

8' 5 13/16–"

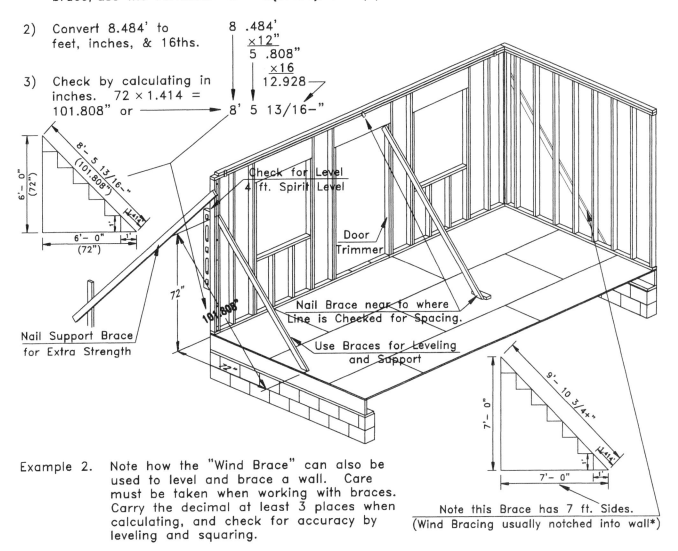

Check for Level
4 ft. Spirit Level

Door Trimmer

Nail Brace near to where Line is Checked for Spacing.

Use Braces for Leveling and Support

Nail Support Brace for Extra Strength

6' – 0" (72")

6' – 0" (72")

72"

101.808"

72"

8' – 5 13/16" (101.808")

9' – 10 3/4+"

7' – 0"

7' – 0"

Note this Brace has 7 ft. Sides.
(Wind Bracing usually notched into wall*)

Example 2.   Note how the "Wind Brace" can also be used to level and brace a wall. Care must be taken when working with braces. Carry the decimal at least 3 places when calculating, and check for accuracy by leveling and squaring.

1) In example 2 above, the brace has a side of 7 feet (84"). Therefore to find the brace, **use the Formula: B = S(1.414)**, multiply: $7 \times 1.414 = 9.898'$

2) Convert 9.898' to feet, inches, and 16ths.

3) Check by calculating in inches. $84" \times 1.414 = 118.776"$ and $118.776" = 9'- 10\ 3/4+"$. The answer is correct.

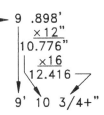

$$\begin{array}{r} 9\ .898' \\ \times 12" \\ \hline 10.776" \\ \times 16 \\ \hline 12.416 \end{array}$$

9' 10 3/4+"

*Wind braces are, sometimes, used to plumb walls before the sheathing is applied. Plywood sheathing can also be applied before raising the wall(s). <u>Or</u>, a 4 x 8 foot sheath of plywood can be used to square the corner and the sheathing can be applied later.

Practical Application of Brace Measure (Continued)

Example 3.   Use braces to align beams, angle iron, pipe, etc.

a) <u>Find the Brace in all "FEET":</u>

10 feet = 10 × 1.414 = 14. 14 feet ⎯⎯⎯⎯⎯⎯⎯⎯⎯⎯⎯⎯➤

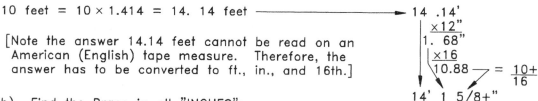

[Note the answer 14.14 feet cannot be read on an
American (English) tape measure. Therefore, the
answer has to be converted to ft., in., and 16th.]

b) <u>Find the Brace in all "INCHES":</u>

120 inches = 120 × 1.414 = 169.68 inches <u>Or</u> 14' 1 5/8+"

[Note the answer 169.68" must be converted to ft., in., and
16th., too. The answer is the same − 14' 1 5/8+". There−
fore, one method can be used to check the other method.]

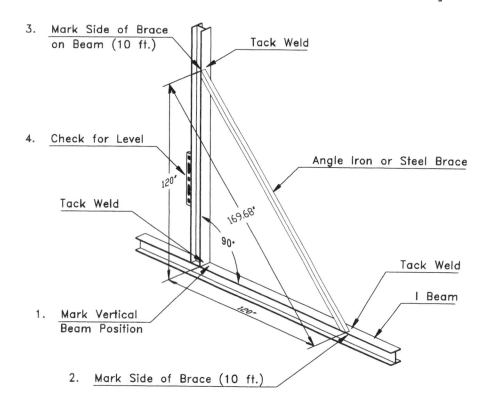

[Note: Refer to the textbook, Task No. R1 and R1A, for more information on brace
measure. Go to the next page for another unique way to use brace measure.]

[Also see, the <u>Lay Out Square</u> and <u>Brace Measure</u>, page 229.]

Practical Application of Brace Measure (Continued)

<u>**Another Unique Way to use Brace Measure:**</u>

Example 4. Run a pipe, tubing, conduit, etc. from the hole in the floor so that it will be perpendicular (90°) to the wall. In the center there could be any kind of object.

1. Measure the distance from the center of the hole (pipe stub, tubing, object, etc.) in the floor, perpendicular to the wall as shown below. The measurement is 3'–9 1/4".

2. Convert 3'– 9 1/4" to all inches and all feet.

Example: 3'– 9 1/4" = 45.25"

$$3' \quad \frac{9\ 1/4}{12} = 3.\underline{7708}'$$

3. Multiply: 45.25"
                  X 1.414
                  63.9835" or 5'– 3 15/16+"

        3 .7708'
        X 1.414
        5 .3319'
          X 12
          6638
          3319
          3.9828"

        5'– 3 15/16+"

[Note one method checks the other method — this builds confidence.]

4. Measure from the center of the object 5'– 3 15/16+" and mark the wall as shown.

5. Measure back 3'– 9 1/4", the side of the brace as shown. brace as shown.

6. Check by measuring left of the center-line on the wall as shown. This will work only if the wall is long enough.

7. Install pipe, tubing, conduit, etc.

[Note: Refer to the textbook, Task No. R1 and R1A, for more information on brace measure.]

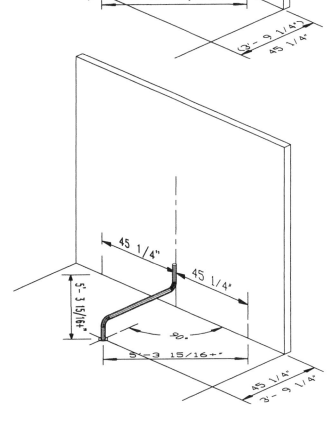

Objective Practice Problems for Module #8

R1 | Brace Measure – Trade Trick #6:

1. Find the length of the brace on the right.
   Give the answer in inches and 16ths. = _____.

   Give the answer in ft., in., and 16ths. = _____.

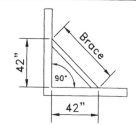

2. Find the length of the brace on the right.
   Give the answer in inches and 16ths. = _____.

   Give the answer in ft., in., and 16ths. = _____.

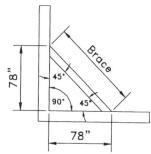

D6 | Review Problems

3. Find the center of the object on the right = _____.

4. Find 1/2 of 11' 3 3/8" = _____.

5. Find 1/2 of 23' 1 1/2" = _____.

6. Divide the object below horizontally 4 spaces, and vertically 5 spaces with a ruler or a tape measure and a straight edge.

N1A

7-10.   Calculate all the dimensions missing below to ±1/16th of an inch.

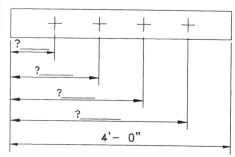

The 3-4-5 Squaring Method
(Chalk Line Problem #1)

Given: Two persons, two tape measures, sharp pencils or markers, a chalkline, and a clean concrete floor or equivalent. Also use Trade Trick #2 on page 51, for reference as how to chalk the lines.

Directions: Lay out the rectangle shown below with a chalkline and a tape measure(s). The dimensions should be ±1/16th of an inch accurate. Use the largest combination of 3-4-5 in all feet, and check the diagonals for equality when finished. The diagonals should be within +1/16 or −1/16 inch accurate.

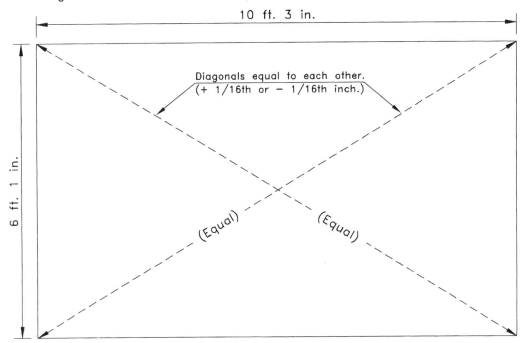

10 ft. 3 in.

6 ft. 1 in.

Diagonals equal to each other.
(+ 1/16th or − 1/16th inch.)

(Equal)   (Equal)

Evaluation:

1. Dimensions accurate to ±1/16th of an inch. _____.

2. Diagonals accurate to +1/16th or −1/16th of an inch. _____.

3. The proper combination of 3-4-5 was used. _____.

4. The diagonal calculates (use the formula $a^2 + b^2 = c^2$) to _____.

Chalk Lines

Tips:

- For <u>greater accuracy*</u> hold "1 inch" or "1 foot" on the tape measure, <u>but</u> make sure it is added to the measurement before marking. Measure again, but do not hold an inch or a foot to check the dimension. A common mistake is to forget to add what is held. Get into the habit of measuring twice (measure, then check the measurement again).

- Hold the chalkline fairly tight, and snap in the air above the measurement points. Then proceed to chalk the line or lines. This will help prevent smearing of the chalkline.

- Practice makes perfect. Alternate partners and practice laying out the rectangle a couple of times. In no time you will be doing it like a pro.

*Many times the tape measure ends are damaged or hard to hold accurately because of the flexible end pieces used for hooks. This is the main reason for holding an inch or foot.

The 5-12-13 Squaring Method
(Chalk Line Problem #2)

Given: Two persons, two tape measures, sharp pencils or markers, a chalkline, and a clean cement floor or equivalent. Also use Trade Trick #2 on page 51, for reference as how to chalk the lines.

Directions: Lay out the rectangle shown below with a chalkline and two tape measures. The dimensions should be ±1/16th of an inch accurate. Use the largest combination of 5-12-13 in all <u>inches</u>, and check the diagonals for equality when finished. The diagonals should be within +1/16 or -1/16 inch accurate.

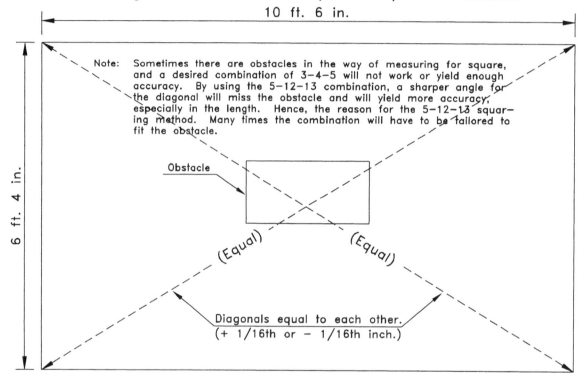

10 ft. 6 in.

6 ft. 4 in.

Note: Sometimes there are obstacles in the way of measuring for square, and a desired combination of 3-4-5 will not work or yield enough accuracy. By using the 5-12-13 combination, a sharper angle for the diagonal will miss the obstacle and will yield more accuracy, especially in the length. Hence, the reason for the 5-12-13 squaring method. Many times the combination will have to be tailored to fit the obstacle.

Obstacle

(Equal)   (Equal)

Diagonals equal to each other.
(+ 1/16th or - 1/16th inch.)

<u>**Evaluation:**</u>

1. Dimensions accurate to ±1/16th of an inch. _____.

2. Diagonals accurate to +1/16th or -1/16th of an inch. _____

3. The diagonal calculates (use the formula $a^2 + b^2 = c^2$) to _____.

Chalk Lines

Tips:

- For <u>greater accuracy</u>* hold "1 inch" or "1 foot" on the tape measure, <u>but</u> make sure it is added to the measurement before marking. Measure again, but do not hold an inch or a foot to check the dimension. A common mistake is to forget to add what is held. Get into the habit of measuring twice (measure, then check the measurement again).

- Hold the chalkline fairly tight, and snap in the air above the measurement points. Then proceed to chalk the line or lines. This will help prevent smearing of the chalkline.

- Practice makes perfect. Alternate partners and practice laying out the rectangle a couple of times. In no time you will be doing it like a pro.

*Many times the tape measure ends are damaged or hard to hold accurately because of the flexable end pieces used for hooks. This is the main reason for holding an inch or foot.

Math Training Module #9

Hands On:

☐   *Application Problem* - Lay out and prove brace measure on a sheet of paper.

☐   *Application Problem* - Lay out and prove how to find the side when the brace is known.

☐   *Application Problem* - Make a Story Pole, Problem 7: 8'- 0" Stick (6 Centers) 98

Objective Practice Problems: Calculate the Practice Problems for Math Training Module #9............ 99, 100

Basic Math Study Notes – (Find the Side when the Brace is Known and Brace Measure Review):

Find the Side when the Brace is Known: [Also see Task No. R2 and R2A in the textbook.]

1. R2 How to find the length of the side when the brace is known.

   **Rule: Length of the Side equals .707 times the Brace.
   Formula: S = .707B**

[Note: .707106781 is the reciprocal of 1.414 (1/1.414213562) and
    also the sine of a 45° angle.]

Step 1. Use the formula: -------------------- $S = .707B$

Step 2. Substitute the known values
    into the formula -------------------- $S = .707 \times 13.4375''$

Step 3. Calculate the formula (do the   13.4375
    operations indicated) --------------- $S =$ × .707
                                              9.5003125''

Step 4. Convert the decimal so you   9 .500"
    can read the dimension on | ×16
    an American tape measure.   8.000 = 8/16 or ½"

                                         9 ½"

[Check: 9.5 × 1.414 = 13.433"
    The more decimals used
    ---- the more accuracy.]

Basic Math Study Notes (Continued)

2. [R2A] Another type of problem where the .707 formula can be used is shown below.

    Example: Find the length of the side of the square inscribed within the circle on the object below. Note in this example, a millwright or machinist would probably be measuring this item. Therefore, there should be more accuracy. Carry out to as many decimal points as needed.

Step 1. Use the formula: -------------------- $S = .707106781B$

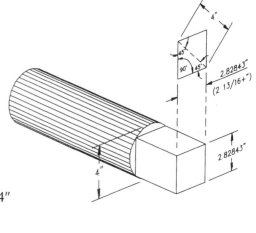

Step 2. Substitute the known values into the formula -------------------- $S = .707106781 \times 4''$

Step 3. Calculate the formula (do the operations indicated) --------------

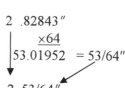

$$S = \begin{array}{r} .707106781 \\ \times\ 4 \\ \hline 2.828427124'' \end{array}$$

Step 4. Convert the decimal so you can read the dimension on an American English scale.

$$\begin{array}{r} 2\ .82843'' \\ \times 64 \\ \hline 53.01952\ = 53/64'' \end{array}$$

$$2\ 53/64''$$

[Note: The above formula is <u>one of the tricks of the trades</u>. Many standard parts, such as pipe elbows, metal braces, wood braces, etc., are made up of 45° angles. In reality the formula is the inverse of 1.414 or the sine of a 45° angle.]

Brace Measure (Review):

1. [R1] How braced measure is determined.

One Unit of Brace

One unit of brace is determined by using the Rule of Pythagoras Task No. [K5A].

Formula: $a^2 + b^2 = c^2$
Substitute: $1^2 + 1^2 = c^2$
Calculate: $1 + 1\ = c^2$
               $2 = c^2$
            $\sqrt{2} = c$
    $1.414213562 = c$

Isosceles Right Triangle

A brace is an isosceles right triangle (has two equal sides and one angle is 90°). A true brace will <u>always</u> be an isosceles right triangle. And one unit of brace will always have a hypotenuse of 1.414. However, 1.414 could be inches, feet, meters, and so on. For more information on Brace Measure, see Task No [R1]

[Note, for most brace jobs carry the decimal 3-5 places. However, 1.414 is the most common number.]

Trade Trick #7 – Find Side of Brace
[Calculate the Side when the Brace is known]

Calculate the Side when the Brace is Known: [Also see Task No. R2 & R2A in the textbook.]

Example 1.   A pre–cut brace can be used to brace and plumb walls. However, the length of the side will have to be determined. The brace measures 10'– 7 1/4". as shown in the illustration below.

1) Measure the brace that is already cut. The brace measures 10'– 7 1/4". Therefore to find the side, **use the Formula: S = .707B**, multiply 7'– 7 1/4" in decimals of feet or in decimals of inches times .707*.

2) Convert 10'– 7 1/4" to decimals of a feet = $10'– 7\frac{\frac{1}{4}''}{12}$ = 10.60416 × .707 = 7.49714' Or 7'– 6"

3) Check by calculating in inches. Convert 10'– 7 1/4" to decimals of inches = 127 1/4" = 127.25" .707 ×= 89.96575 (90)", Or 7'– 6"

4) Check: Side 7'– 6" = 7.5'
$$\begin{array}{r} 7.5' \\ \times\ 1.414 \\ \hline 10.605' \end{array}$$
$$\begin{array}{r} 10\ .605' \\ \times\ 12 \\ \hline 7.26'' \end{array}$$

Answer OK ──────► 10' 7 1/4"

*Use .70711 for greater accuracy. The reciprocal of 1.414 is .707 and the reciprocal of 1.41421 is .70711. Three decimal places is accurate enough for this application. [.70711 is also the sine of a 45° angle, see page 264 in the textbook.]

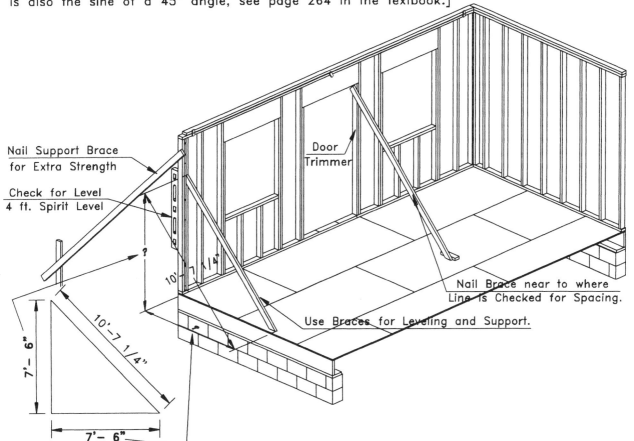

Nail Support Brace for Extra Strength

Check for Level 4 ft. Spirit Level

Door Trimmer

Nail Brace near to where Line is Checked for Spacing.

Use Braces for Leveling and Support.

10'– 7 1/4"

7'– 6"

7'– 6"

Trade Trick #1 – Make a Story Pole
(Problem 7: 8'- 0" Stick - 6 Centers)

Practice Stick 8'- 0" Long. ——————→

Make 3/4" X 3/4" or 1" X 1'

‹Mark Side #2, use 'T' marks and draw square lines.›

Step 1.   Lay out the 6 center marks on the right with an American (English) tape measure to ±1/16 of an inch accuracy.

Note: There are 6 center marks but ____ spaces.

Therefore: Divide by _____   ‾‾‾‾/8.0

8'- 0"

+   +   +   +   +   +

?
?
?
?
?
?

Step 2.   List in order (make a story pole) the dimensions so you can read them on the tape measure without having to move it.

Making a Story Pole (refer to Problem 6, page 79, if more information is needed):

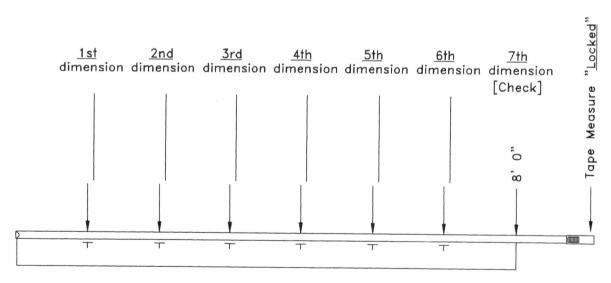

1st dimension 2nd dimension 3rd dimension 4th dimension 5th dimension 6th dimension 7th dimension [Check]

8' 0"

Tape Measure "Locked"

T   T   T   T   T   T

Step 3.   Lay out the center marks (use "T" marks) on the 8'- 0" stick. Do not move the tape measure. Leave in the locked positon as shown above.

Step 4.   Check by measuring _____ between each "T" mark.

[Note not all tape measures are in 16ths. Therefore, you have to use your own judgement as to where 16ths are. Example, split 1/8" in half = 1/16". See the example on page 76.]

Objective Practice Problems for Module #9

R2 <u>Find the Side when the Brace is Known – Trade Trick #7:</u>

1. Find the length of the sides of the brace on the right.
   Give the answer in inches and ±16ths. = _____.

   Give the answer in ft., in., and ±16ths. = _____.

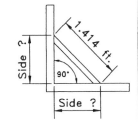

2. Find the length of the sides of the brace on the right.
   Give the answer in inches and ±16ths. = _____.

   Give the answer in ft., in., and ±16ths. = _____.

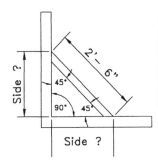

R1 <u>Review Problems – Brace Measure:</u>

3. Find the length of the brace on the right.
   Give the answer in inches and ±16ths. = _____.

   Give the answer in ft., in., and ±16ths. = _____.

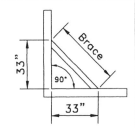

4. Find the length of the brace on the right.
   Give the answer in inches and ±16ths. = _____.

   Give the answer in ft., in., and ±16ths. = _____.

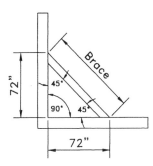

<u>Review Problems</u>

5. Change 2 1/2" to decimals of a foot = _____.

6. Change 9/16" to decimals of a foot = _____.

7. Change 7.0625' to feet, inches, and ±16ths. = _____.

8. Change 107.8125" to feet, inches, and ±16ths. = _____.

9. Change 1/4% to a decimal = _____.

10. Change 125% to a decimal = _____.

11. Change 2.125 to a percent = _____.

Objective Practice Problems for Module #9

N1B   <u>Review Problems (Continued)</u>

12–18.   Calculate all the dimensions on the right
to ft., in., and ±1/16th of an inch accuracy.

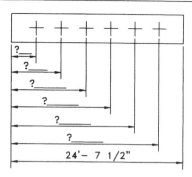

24'– 7 1/2"

P1   <u>Review Problems – Squaring Techniques</u>:

19. Find the largest combination of
3–4–5 in <u>whole feet</u> that can
used to square up the rectangle
on the right. _____.

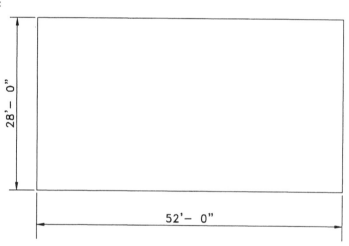

28' – 0"

52' – 0"

P1

20. Find the largest combination of 5–12–13 in
<u>whole feet</u> that can be used to square up the
rectangle on the right. _____.

K5A

21. Use the formula $a^2 + b^2 = c^2$ to find the exact diagonal
of the rectangle above in feet, inches, and ±16th. = _____.

Math Training Module #10

Hands On:

☐   *Application Problem* - Practice how to calculate Hero's formula. Prove with the Rule of Pythagoras, and the basic area if a triangle formula (A = ½bh).

☐   *Application Problem* - Practice with the Scientific Calculator to find the Sine, Cosine, and Tangent of Angles. Compare these calculations with the textbook Trig Tables. Find the Angles from the Sine, Cosine, and Tangent of Angles.

☐   *Application Problem* - Practice Brace Measure and Find the Side when the Brace is Known on a sheet of paper.

Basic Math Study Notes - (Hero's Formula and 1/2bh, and Another Way to Prove Hero's Formula):

Hero's Formula and ½ bh:

1.   How to calculate Hero's formula.

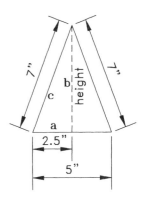

      Formula: A = √s(s-a)(s-b)(s-c)
            s = ½ (a + b + c)

Calculate: $s = \frac{1}{2} (5 + 7 + 7)$ $A = \sqrt{9.5(9.5 - 5)(9.5 - 7)(9.5 - 7)}$

          $s = \frac{1}{2} (19)$ $A = \sqrt{9.5(4.5)(2.5)(2.5)}$

          $s = 9.5$ $A = \sqrt{9.5(28.125)}$

                                 $A = \sqrt{267.1875}$

                                 $A = 16.346$ sq. in. Answer

Another Way to Prove Hero's Formula, and to Find the Height:

2.   Listed below is another way to prove Hero's formula. Find the height and the area of an isosceles triangle* by using the formula A = ½ bh in conjunction with the Rule of Pythagoras (Task No. K5A) when certain factors are known.

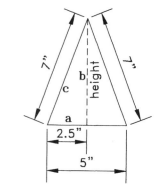

Example: Refer to the isosceles triangle on the right to
                solve for each specific unknown listed below.

Find the <u>height</u> by using the Rule of Pythagoras.

Formula: $a^2 + b^2 = c^2$

Substitute: $a^2 + 2.5^2 = 7^2$

Calculate: $a^2 + 6.25 = 49$

                $a^2 = 49 - 6.25$

                $a^2 = 42.75$

                $a = \sqrt{42.75}$

                $a = 6.538"$ (height)

Find the <u>area</u> by using the formula A = ½bh now that the height is known.

Formula: A = ½bh

Substitute: A = ½ X 5 X 6.538

Calculate: A = ½ X (5 X 6.538)

              A = ½ X 32.69

              A = 16.345 sq. in.

Find the <u>height</u> by using the formula A = ½bh when the area is known.

Formula: A = ½bh

Substitute: 16.345 = ½ X 5 X h

Calculate: 16.345 = (½ X 5) X h

$$\frac{16.345}{2.5} = \frac{2.5 \text{ X } h}{2.5}$$

         6.538 = h

[By using the above example, it is clear to see how the parts of triangles can be found by using different formulas to solve for specific unknowns. To find out more about triangles and different polygons encompassed within circles, see Task Number K6A through K6G .]

*An isosceles triangle is a triangle that has two equal sides and two equal angles.

Info #5 – Hero's Formula
$[A = \sqrt{s(s-a)(s-b)(s-c)}$ and $s = \frac{1}{2}(a + b + c)]$

Review: Find the Area of a Triangle when the Height is Known.

Formula: Area = 1/2bh

   Area = 1/2(4)(3)

   Area = .5 (12)

   Area = 6 sq. ft.

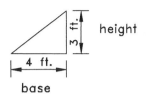

How to Find the Area of a Triangle when the Height is not Known:

Problem 1.   Find the Area of the Oblique Triangle on the right.

Hero's Forumla: $A = \sqrt{s(s-a)(s-b)(s-c)}$
   $s = 1/2(a + b + c)$

$s = 1/2(5 + 5 + 8)$ $A = \sqrt{9(9 - 5)(9 - 5)(9 - 8)}$

$s = 1/2(18)$ $A = \sqrt{9(4)(4)(1)}$

$s = 9$ $A = \sqrt{9 \times 16}$

   $A = \sqrt{144}$

   $A = 12$ sq. ft.

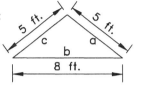

[Note, the example shows that the formula works because this triangle is double the right triangle shown above.]

Problem 2.   Find the Area of the Oblique Triangle on the right.

Hero's Forumla: $A = \sqrt{s(s-a)(s-b)(s-c)}$
   $s = 1/2(a + b + c)$

$s = 1/2(41 + 69 + 48)$

$s = 1/2(158)$

$s = 79$

$A = \sqrt{79(79 - 41)(79 - 69)(79 - 48)}$

$A = \sqrt{79(38)(10)(31)}$

$A = \sqrt{79 \times 11780}$

$A = \sqrt{930620}$

$A = 964.69$ sq. in.

$A = 6.70$ sq. ft.

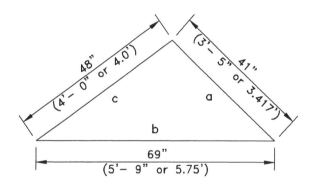

Calculate and Check by using "Feet".

$s = 1/2(3.417 + 5.75 + 4.0)$

$s = 1/2(13.166')$

$s = 6.583$

$A = \sqrt{6.583(6.583 - 3.417)(6.583 - 5.75)(6.583 - 4)}$

$A = \sqrt{6.583(3.166)(.833)(2.583)}$

$A = \sqrt{6.583 \times 6.812}$

$A = \sqrt{44.84}$

$A = 6.69$ sq. ft.   or   6.70 sq. ft.

Info #6 – The Scientific Calculator
and Trig Functions (Sin., Cos., and Tan.)

Note: Make sure the Calculator is in the DEG mode. If you are not in the DEG mode, see INFO #4, page 69. The display should show:

How to Calculate the Functions of Angles:

1. Calculate the Sine, Cosine, and Tangent of angles.

   Example 1. Find the SIN of 45° angle.

   Select: [4] [5] [SIN]

   The display should show: | DEG |
   | 0.707106781 |
   Display

   Example 2. Find the COS of 52° angle.

   Select: [5] [2] [COS]

   The display should show: | DEG |
   | 0.615661475 |
   Display

   Example 3. Find the TAN of 15° angle.

   Select: [1] [5] [TAN]

   The display should show: | DEG |
   | 0.267949192 |
   Display

Calculate the Angles from the Functions of Angles:

2. Calculate the Angle from the Sine, Cosine, and Tangent angle functions.

   Example 1. Find the Angle from the SIN. 0.707106781 (Carry Decimal 3–5 Places).

   Select: [.] [7] [0] [7] [1] [2nd] [SIN]

   The display should show: 45° | DEG |
   | 44.99945053 |
   Display

   Example 2. Find the Angle from the COS. 0.615661475 (Carry Decimal 3–5 Places).

   Select: [.] [6] [1] [5] [6] [2nd] [COS]

   The display should show: 52° | DEG |
   | 52.0044697 |
   Display

   Example 3. Find the Angle from the TAN. 0.267949192 (Carry Decimal 3–5 Places).

   Select: [.] [2] [6] [7] [9] [2nd] [TAN]

   The display should show: 15° | DEG |
   | 14.99737025 |
   Display

   [Note how the Functions of Angles and the Angles themselves relate to each other. This can also be verified in the Text Book Trig Tables.]

Objective Practice Problems for Module #10

<u>Hero's Formula – Info #5 (carry decimal 3 places)</u>:

1. Find the area of the oblique triangle shown on the right.

    Area in square inches = _____.

    Area in square feet = _____.

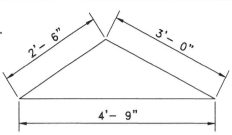

Formula: A = √s(s−a)(s−b)(s−c)
           s = 1/2 (a + b + c)

<u>Hero's Formula – Info #5 (carry decimal 3 places)</u>:

2. Find the area of the oblique triangle shown on the right.

    Area in square inches = _____.

    Area in square feet = _____.

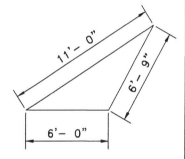

Formula: A = √s(s−a)(s−b)(s−c)
           s = 1/2 (a + b + c)

<u>The Scientific Calculator and Trig Functions – Info #6</u>:

Use a scientific calculator to find the sine, cosine, and tangent of the angles listed below.

3. Sin. 45° = _____   4. Cos. 17° = _____   5. Tan. 15° = _____

6. Sin. 25° = _____   7. Tan. 85° = _____   8. Cos. 33° = _____

9. Sin. 10° = _____   10. Cos. 40° = _____

Objective Practice Problems for Module #10

<u>The Scientific Calculator and Trig Functions</u> – (Continued)

Use a scientific calculator and/or the textbook trig tables to find the angles of the angle functions listed below (carry the decimals 3 places).

11. Cos. .8910 = _____ .   12. Tan. 1.2799 = _____ .   13. Sin. .4226 = _____ .

14. Cos. .7431 = _____ .   15. Sin. .37461 = _____ .   16. Cos. .92718 = _____ .

17. Tan. .40403 = _____ .   18. Sin. .06976 = _____ .

R2   <u>Review – Find the Side when the Brace is Known – Trade Trick #7</u>:

19. Find the length of the sides of the brace on the right.
Give the answer in inches and   16ths. = _____ .

Give the answer in ft., in., and   16ths. = _____ .

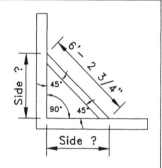

R1   <u>Review – Brace Measure – Trade Trick #6</u>:

20. Find the length of the brace on the right.
Give the answer in inches and   16ths. = _____ .

Give the answer in ft., in., and   16ths. = _____ .

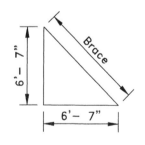

Math Training Module #11

Hands On:

☐   *Application Problem* - Practice how to read micrometers and calipers by using machined blocks.

☐   *Application Problem* - Practice basic sketching by using machined blocks, bushings, braces, etc. (or pick any desired object to sketch).

☐   *Application Problem* - The Scientific Calculator and Trig Functions. Use in conjunction with the Text Book Trig Tables.

Basic Math Study Notes:
(Types of micrometers and verniers, and basic sketching).

Types of Micrometers and Reading Tips:

Has a Vernier Scale on the Thimble

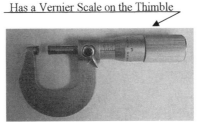
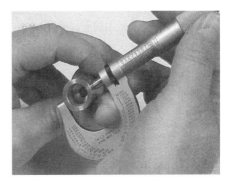

Task No. N2 Micrometer
[Marked in Thousandths (.001″) inch]

Task No. N2A Vernier Micrometer
[Marked in Ten-Thousandths (.0001″) inch]

Micrometer Holding Technique
[Hold with little finger - adjust with Thumb]

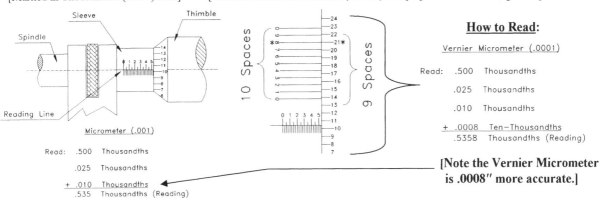

How to Read:

Vernier Micrometer (.0001)

Read: .500   Thousandths
         .025   Thousandths
         .010   Thousandths
     + .0008   Ten-Thousandths
        .5358   Thousandths (Reading)

[Note the Vernier Micrometer
is .0008″ more accurate.]

Micrometer (.001)

Read: .500   Thousandths
         .025   Thousandths
     + .010   Thousandths
        .535   Thousandths (Reading)

Math Study Notes (Continued)

Types of Vernier Calipers and Reading Tips:

How to read the Vernier Caliper.

Every inch on the bar is divided into 20 equal spaces. Each line is spaced 1/20 or .050 inches. Every second mark between the inch lines is numbered and equals one-tenth of an inch or .100".

The vernier plate is divided into 50 equal spaces, each line representing .001". Every fifth line is numbered-5, 10, 15, 20, ... 45, 50-for easy counting.

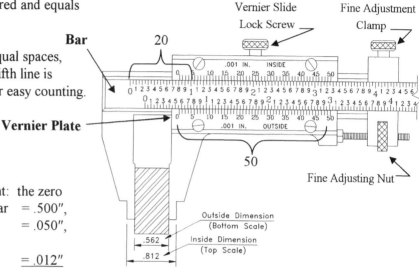

Task No. N3 Vernier Caliper

To read the vernier caliper on the right: the zero on the vernier plate in past 5 on the bar = .500",
the zero is also past the next mark = .050",
and the line on the vernier plate that lines up with the line on the bar = .012"
Add all the values up = .562" Read five hundred sixty two thousandths.

How to read the Dial Caliper.

Every inch on the bar is divided into 10 equal spaces, each line represents .100". The dial is divided into 100 equal spaces which each space representing .001".

Dial Caliper

To read the dial caliper on the right: the 5 on the bar is shown (6 is not full) which = .500",
and the dial reads 62 thousandths = .062"
Add the values up = .562"
Read five hundred sixty two thousandths.

Note the "Outside" and the "Inside" dimensions are the same for this Caliper.

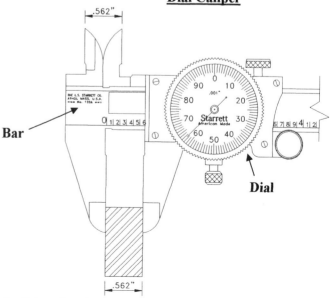

Basic Math Study Notes (Continued)

Types of Vernier Calipers and Reading Tips:

How to read the Electronic Digital Caliper.

Note what you see is what you get. This instrument is a good example of how technology has advanced. The instrument reads .783″ or if toggled will read 19.8882 mm (.783″ × 25.4 mm = 19.8882mm).

Digital Caliper

Note complete instructions on how to zero, how to change from metrics to English, and how to change from metrics to English are included with the Digital Caliper.

Basic Sketching (One and Two Point Perspectives):

One Point Perspectives: Draw the object on the right.

Two Point Perspective: Draw the same object shown above.

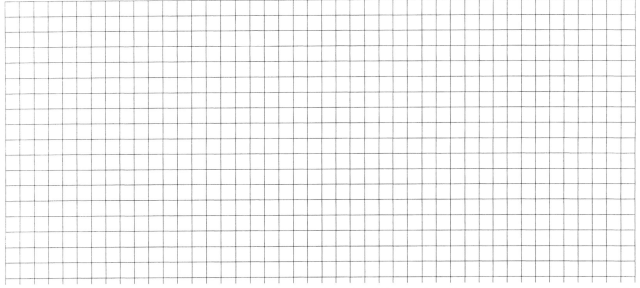

Basic Math Study Notes (Continued)

Basic Sketching (One and Two Point Perspectives):

Draw a One Point Perspective of the object on the right in the space provided below. Use Info #8, page 113 as a reference, if needed. The large diameter is 1.25″, the small diameter is .7854″, and the drill hole is .5″ diameter × .816″ deep.

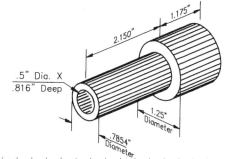

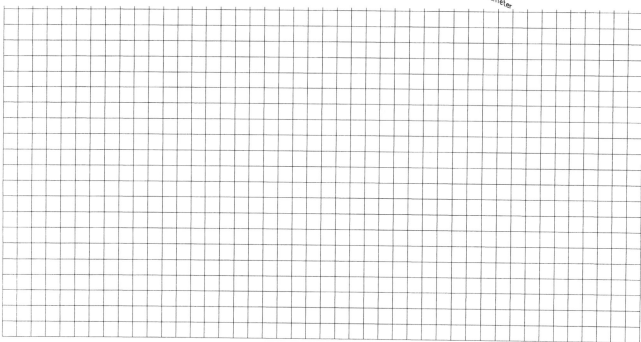

Draw a Two Point Perspective of the object shown above in the space provided below. More engineer paper is available in Appendix C in the back of the book.

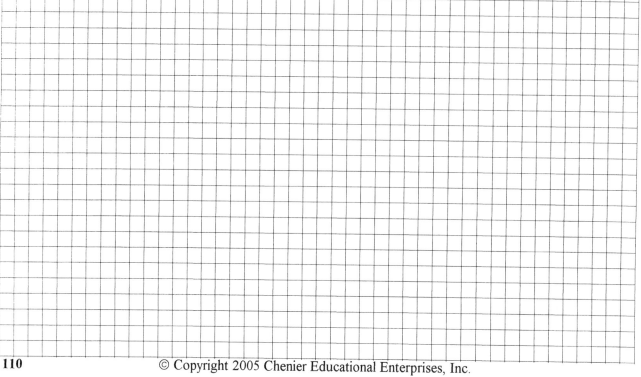

Info #7 – Read Micrometers, Verniers, and Calipers

How the Micrometer is Made-Up:

Each line = 1 (one) 40th of an inch.

Or $\frac{1}{40}$ = .025 or 25 Thousandths.

Therefore, each revolution of the "Thimble" = 25 Thousandths.

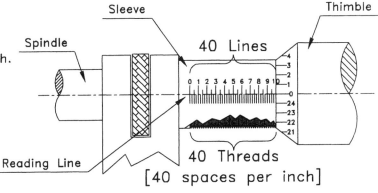

[Also see page 107 for the proper micrometer holding technique.]

The Micrometer [Marked in Thousandths (.001") inch]:

Micrometer (.001)

Read: .500   Thousandths

        .025   Thousandths

   + .010   Thousandths

        .535   Thousandths (Reading)

The Vernier Micrometer [Marked in Ten-Thousandths (.0001") inch]:

Vernier Micrometer (.0001)

Read: .500   Thousandths

        .025   Thousandths

        .010   Thousandths

   + .0008 Ten-Thousandths

        .5358 Ten-Thousandths (Reading)

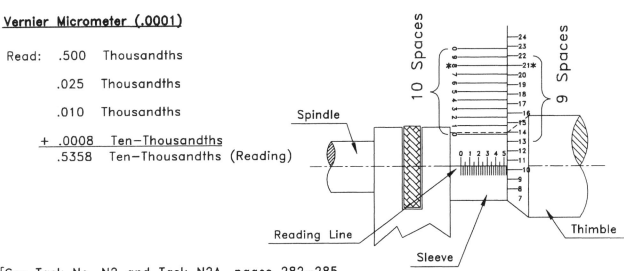

[See Task No. N2 and Task N2A, pages 282-285 in the text book, if more information is needed.]

[Calipers (Vernier, Dial, and Digital) on the next page].

Micrometers and Calipers (Continued)

Types of Vernier Calipers and Reading Tips (Also see page 108 and 109):

How to read the Vernier Caliper.

Every inch on <u>the bar</u> is divided into 20 equal spaces. Each line is spaced 1/20 or .050 inches. Every second mark between the inch lines is numbered and equals one-tenth of an inch or .100".

<u>The vernier plate</u> is divided into 50 equal spaces, each line representing .001". Every fifth line is numbered-5, 10, 15, 20, ... 45, 50-for easy counting.

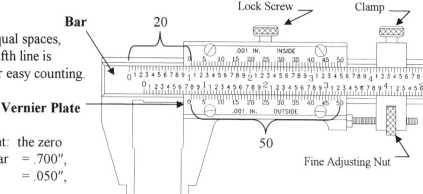

To read the vernier caliper on the right: the zero
on the vernier plate in past 7 on the bar = .700",
the zero is also past the next mark = .050",
and the line on the vernier plate that
lines up with the line on the bar = .033"
Add all the values up = .783" Read seven hundred eighty three thousandths.

How to read the Dial Caliper.

Every inch on <u>the bar</u> is divided into 10 equal spaces, each line represents .100". The <u>dial</u> is divided into 100 equal spaces which each space representing .001".

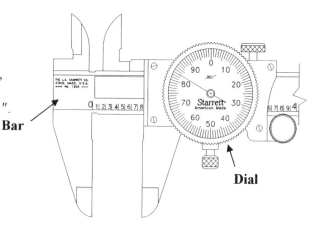

To read the dial caliper on the right: the 7 on the
bar is shown (8 is not full) which = .700",
and the dial reads 83 thousandths = .083"
Add the values up = .783"
Read seven hundred eighty three thousandths.

How to read the Electronic Digital Caliper.

Note what you see is what you get. This instrument is a good example of how technology has advanced. The instrument reads .783" or if toggled will read 19.8882 mm (.783" × 25.4 mm = 19.8882 mm).

Digital Caliper

Note complete instructions on how to zero, how to change from metrics to English, and how to change from metrics to English are included with the Digital Caliper.

Info #8 – Basic Sketching
(One and Two Point Perspectives)

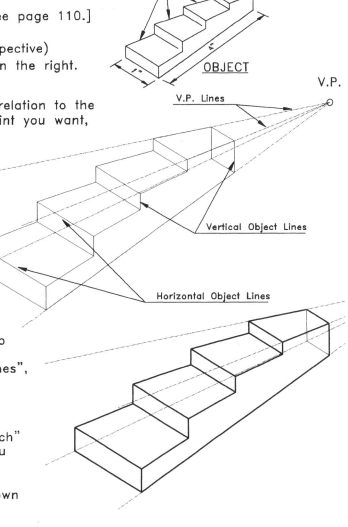

Equal Distance

OBJECT

V.P.

V.P. Lines

Vertical Object Lines

Horizontal Object Lines

One Point Perspective (Sketches): [Also see page 110.]

Problem 1. Draw a One Point Sketch (Perspective) of the Machined Block shown on the right.

1. Establish a V.P. (Vanishing Point) in relation to the size paper you have and the view point you want, as shown on the far right.

2. Rough out the sketch, as shown on the right.

1st Use a <u>Straight Edge</u> and a <u>Sharp Pencil</u> to draw "Very Light Object Lines", as shown on the right.

2nd Use a "Straight Edge" and a "Sharp Pencil" and draw "<u>Very Lightly</u>" the "Vertical" and "Horizontal Object Lines", as shown on the right.

3. Once you are satisfied that the "Sketch" matches the "Object" (as good as you as you can get it):

1st Darken all the "Object Lines" as shown on the right.

2nd Erase all the "Lightly Drawn Object Lines", as shown.

4. Once you are satisfied with the sketch, dimension your "Micrometer Readings", as shown on the right.

    Dimension the Width, the Length, and the Steps, if desired.

    Write the number of the "Machine Block" on the Sketch, as shown.

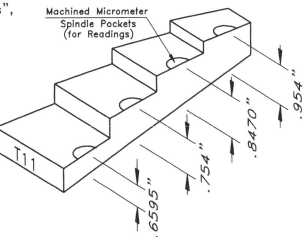

Machined Micrometer Spindle Pockets (for Readings)

T11

.6595"   .754"   .8470"   .954"

[Note: The One Point Perspectives is not a true Perspective –– for a truer Perspective, use the Two Point Perspective on the next page.]

Basic Sketching — One and Two Point Perspectives (continued)

Two Point Perspective (Sketches):

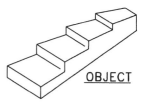

Probem 1. Draw a Two Point Sketch (Perspective)
of the Machined Block shown on the right.

1. Establish two (2) V.P. (Vanishing Point) in relation to the size paper you have and the view point you want, as shown below.

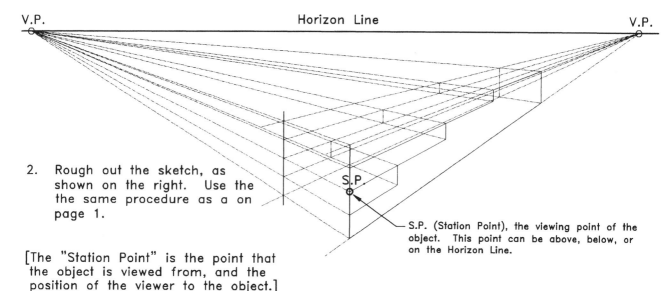

V.P.   Horizon Line   V.P.

2. Rough out the sketch, as shown on the right. Use the the same procedure as a on page 1.

S.P.

S.P. (Station Point), the viewing point of the object. This point can be above, below, or on the Horizon Line.

[The "Station Point" is the point that the object is viewed from, and the position of the viewer to the object.]

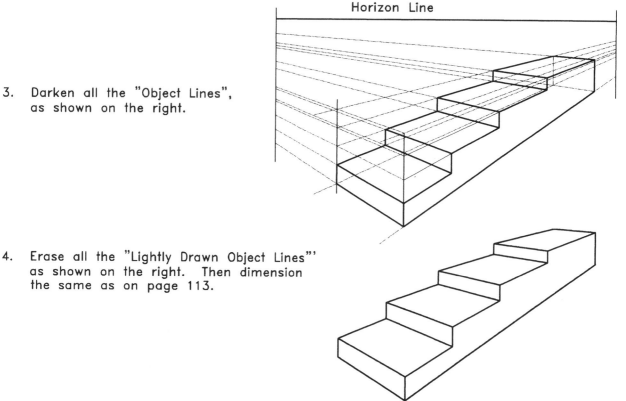

Horizon Line

3. Darken all the "Object Lines", as shown on the right.

4. Erase all the "Lightly Drawn Object Lines"' as shown on the right. Then dimension the same as on page 113.

[Note: The "Two Point Perspective" is a more accurate Perspective. It is more similar to a real picture. All lines taper to the V.P. as like looking down a railroad track.]

Objective Practice Problems for Module #11

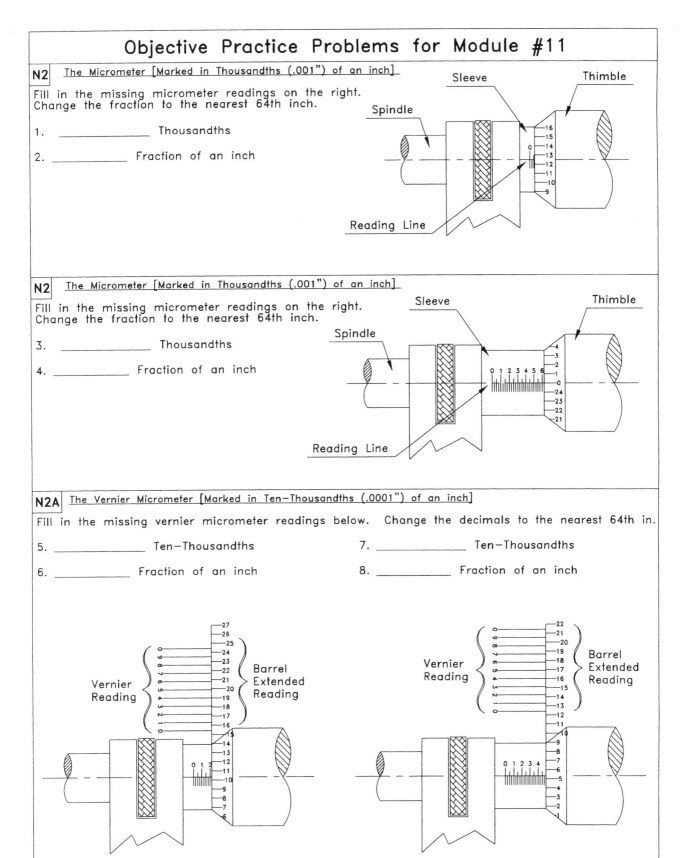

N2 The Micrometer [Marked in Thousandths (.001") of an inch]

Fill in the missing micrometer readings on the right.
Change the fraction to the nearest 64th inch.

1. _____ Thousandths

2. _____ Fraction of an inch

Spindle   Sleeve   Thimble

Reading Line

N2 The Micrometer [Marked in Thousandths (.001") of an inch]

Fill in the missing micrometer readings on the right.
Change the fraction to the nearest 64th inch.

3. _____ Thousandths

4. _____ Fraction of an inch

Spindle   Sleeve   Thimble

Reading Line

N2A The Vernier Micrometer [Marked in Ten–Thousandths (.0001") of an inch]

Fill in the missing vernier micrometer readings below.   Change the decimals to the nearest 64th in.

5. _____ Ten–Thousandths

6. _____ Fraction of an inch

7. _____ Ten–Thousandths

8. _____ Fraction of an inch

Vernier Reading   Barrel Extended Reading

Vernier Reading   Barrel Extended Reading

Objective Practice Problems for Module #11

The Dial Caliper [Marked in Thousandths (.001") of an inch]

Fill in the missing dial caliper readings below.   Change the decimal to the nearest 64th of an inch.

9. _____ Thousandths   11. _____ Thousandths

10. _____ Fraction of an inch   12. _____ Fraction of an inch

13. _____ Thousandths   15. _____ Thousandths

14. _____ Fraction of an inch   16. _____ Fraction of an inch

N3 The Vernier Caliper [Marked in Thousandths (.001") of an inch]

Fill in the missing vernier caliper reading below.   Change the decimal to the nearest 64th inch.

17. _____ Thousandths   18. _____ Fraction of an inch

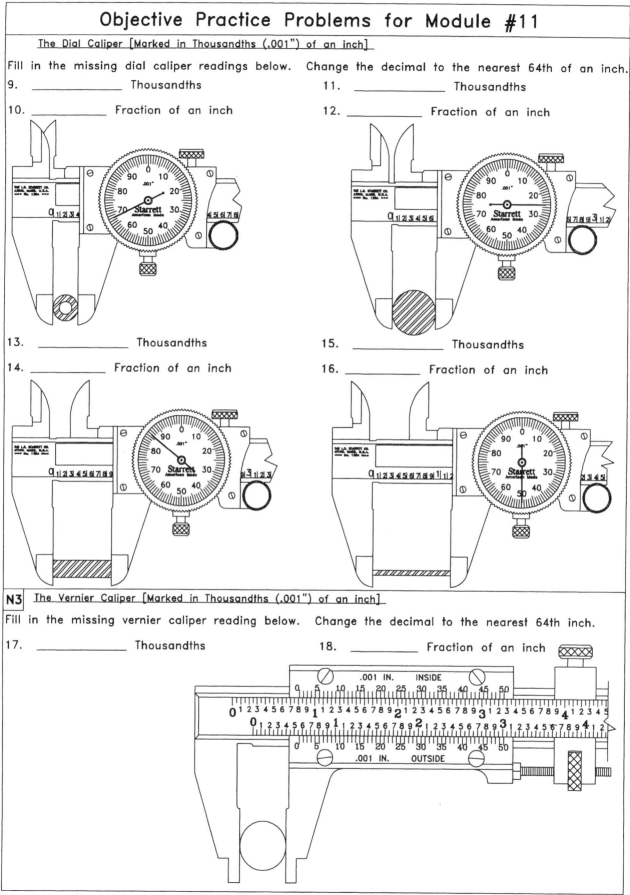

Math Training Module #12

Instructional Objectives:

Hands On:

☐ *Application Problem* - Practice Setting up a Dowel Jig for different size Drill Bits.

☐ *Application Problem* - Practice how to Draw Circles with a Lay Out Square.

☐ *Application Problem* - Practice Copying and Transferring Angles using a Lay Out Square.

☐ *Application Problem* - Practice Shimming for level using Tar Paper.

Basic Math Study Notes (The Dowelling Jig and Drilling Tips):

The Dowel Jig:

The dowel jig is included in this book because it is a very useful and economical tool that helps prevents the drill bit from wandering. This wandering can happen even with an expensive drill press. It also improves accuracy. It is not only a dowel jig, but can be used for a guide for drilling and/or centering precision holes in metal, wood, plastic, etc. Once you experience this unique tool, you probably will make a home for it in your tool box, too.

Note:

The Dowel Jig shown is a GENERAL
Model No. 840: UPC No. 24120

Manufactured by:
GENERAL TOOLS mfg. Co., LLC
New York, NY 10013

GENERAL TOOLS mfg. Co., LLC
Montreal, Canada H9R 1E1

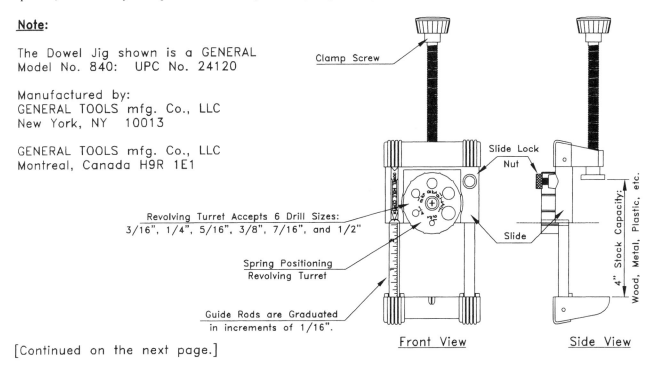

Clamp Screw

Slide Lock Nut

Slide

Revolving Turret Accepts 6 Drill Sizes:
3/16", 1/4", 5/16", 3/8", 7/16", and 1/2"

Spring Positioning
Revolving Turret

Guide Rods are Graduated
in increments of 1/16".

4" Stock Capacity: Wood, Metal, Plastic, etc.

Front View   Side View

[Continued on the next page.]

Basic Math Study Notes (Continued)

More About the Dowel Jig:

The dowel jig can also be used to drill through the center of small shafts or dowels. To do this small, tapered blocks would have to be made. See the example shown below.

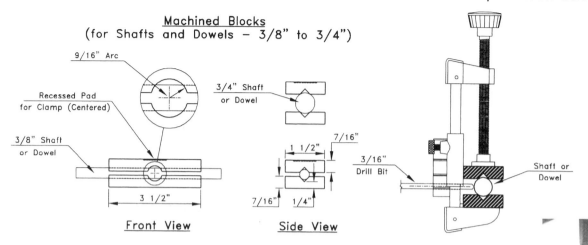

Drilling Tips:

1. Use a center punch, when possible, to mark drill holes in metal, plastic, or soft metals.

2. For larger holes, <u>drill a pilot hole</u>. This hole should be approximately 3/16″ to 1/4″, this will depend on the size of the hole and the end of the drill bit. Make the pilot hole a little larger than the tip of the drill bit.

3. For larger holes that need to be very accurate, scribe the diameter of the hole with a wing divider as shown.

   Then use a center punch to make a series of punch marks around the circle. This will give you visual aid how the hole is progressing as you drill the hole.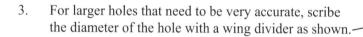

   Another tip is to gradually increase the size of the hole after the pilot hole is drilled. This way you will not drift off all at once.

   [For holes above ½″ and beyond the reach of the dowel jig, use a portable magnetic drill motor and/or a drill press, if possible.]

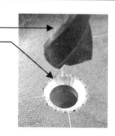

Finished Hole

4. The dowel jig can be used as a pilot for some holes above 1/2″. Drill a pilot hole, then drill a 1/2″ hole with the dowel jig. Then drill the larger hole with a larger drill motor (1/2″ heavy duty), being careful, as these type drills have a lot of torque and can be dangerous. Consult the owner's manual, if in doubt.

To draw circles with a Lay Out Square, see Trade Trick #8, page 121 and 122.
To transfer angles with a Lay Out Square, see Trade Trick #9, page 123 and 124.
To shim for level horizontally and vertically, see Trade Trick #10, page 125 and 126.

Info #9 – The Dowel Jig
[as a Drill Guide and Drilling Tips]

How to Set-Up The Dowel Jig to Drill Holes (For Drilling Tips, see page 117 and 118):

Example 1.   Set-up the dowel jig for the piece of material on the right.

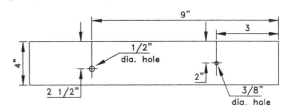

Step 1.   Mark the exact center of the drill holes on the material to be drilled. Use a square to mark the exact location.

[Optional – if metal, center punch the hole and drill a pilot hole before going to Step 2.]

Step 2.   a) Open the CLAMP-SCREW wider than work piece. Place the FIXED-JAW against the side of the work piece aligned with the INDEX MARK at the 3/8" hole center mark.

   b) Gently tighten the CLAMP SCREW.

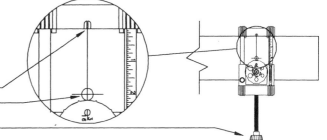

Step 3.   a) Loosen SLIDE LOCK and move SLIDE along SCALE ROD to the 2" mark as shown.

   b) Tighten SLIDE LOCK SCREW.

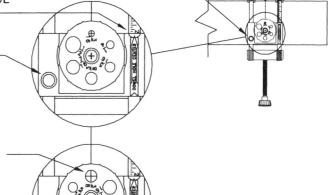

Step 4.   a) Lift TURRET and turn so that the correct size hole (3/8") is in line with the INDEX MARK.

   b) Drill dowel hole to correct depth, or all the way through, for bolt, pin, shaft, etc. holes.

Step 5.   a) Loosen CLAMP SCREW and move the dowel jig sideways to the next hole (1/2") as shown. Make sure the FIXED-JAW is against the side of the work piece and aligned with the INDEX MARK as in Step 2.

   b) Tighten SLIDE LOCK SCREW.

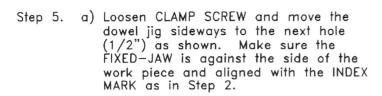
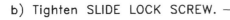
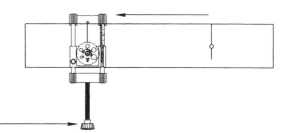

119

Step 6. a) Loosen SLIDE LOCK and move SLIDE along SCALE ROD to the 2 1/2" mark as shown.

   b) Tighten SLIDE LOCK SCREW.

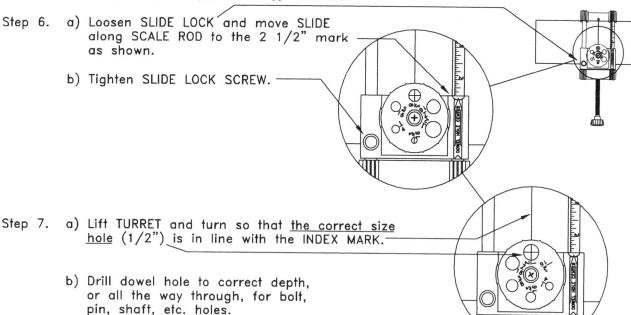

Step 7. a) Lift TURRET and turn so that <u>the correct size hole (1/2")</u> is in line with the INDEX MARK.

   b) Drill dowel hole to correct depth, or all the way through, for bolt, pin, shaft, etc. holes.

[Note the above example represents a drill press more than a dowel jig because the holes are drilled through and are off center. The example below depicts a dowel situation.]

How to Set-Up The Dowel Jig for Dowel Holes:

Example 2. Set-up the dowel jig for the board on the right.

Step 1. Mark the hole centers on the material for the INDEX MARK.

Step 2. Open CLAMP-SCREW and align the hole center mark with the INDEX MARK Retighten CLAMP-SCREW.

Step 3. Loosen SLIDE-LOCK and adjust SLIDE to 3/4" mark as shown.

Step 4. Adjust TURRET for a 1/2" hole.

Step 5. Drill 1/2" hole to 1 1/2" deep. Note Collar for a a depth gauge.

Step 6. Repeat the process for the next hole.

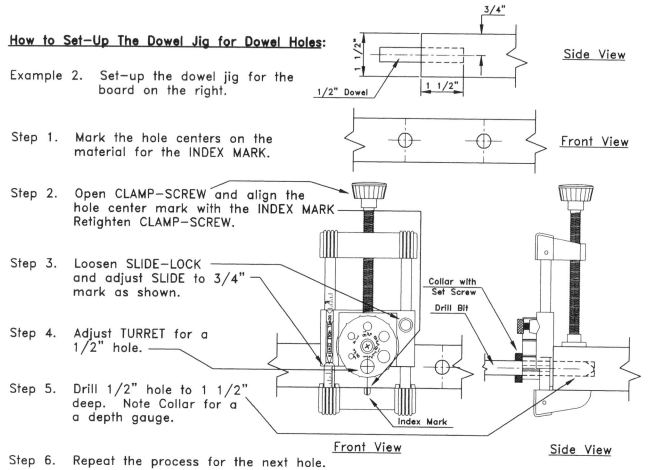

3/4"

1 1/2"

1 1/2"

1/2" Dowel

Side View

Front View

Collar with Set Screw

Drill Bit

Index Mark

Front View

Side View

© Copyright 2005 Chenier Educational Enterprises, Inc.

Trade Trick #8 – Draw Circles with a Square
[How to use the Lay Out Square to Draw Circles]

<u>How to use the Lay Out Square to Draw Circles</u>: [Aso see Task No. 09, page 310 in the textbook.]

<u>Why circles can be drawn with a Lay Out Square:</u>

Draw any angle inside the semi−circle of a circle and it becomes a right angle. Or a right triangle with the base of the semi−circle. See the drawing below.

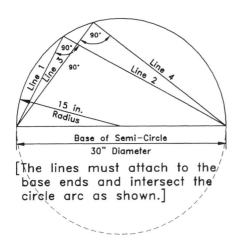

[The lines must attach to the base ends and intersect the circle arc as shown.]

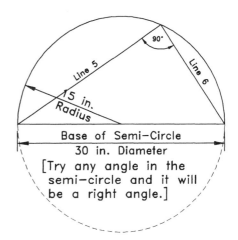

[Try any angle in the semi−circle and it will be a right angle.]

Using the principle shown above, set−up the Lay Out Square to draw an eight inch circle as shown below.

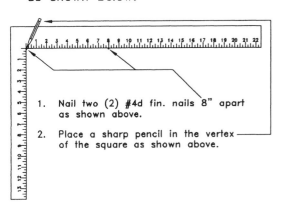

1. Nail two (2) #4d fin. nails 8" apart as shown above.

2. Place a sharp pencil in the vertex of the square as shown above.

3. Rotate the square on the two nails, and mark with the pencil as you go.

[The square <u>must stay tight to the nails</u> as you mark with the pencil as the square moves.]

Note the Circle Arc Forming.

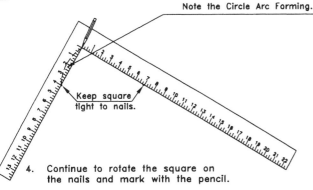

4. Continue to rotate the square on the nails and mark with the pencil.

4. Continue to rotate the square on the nails and mark with the pencil.

[Continue on the next page.]

How to use the Lay Out Square to Draw Circles (Continued)

<u>Why circles can be drawn with a Lay Out Square</u>:

The drawing below shows the preceeding page in prespective.

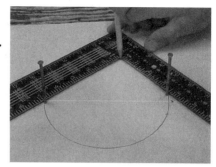

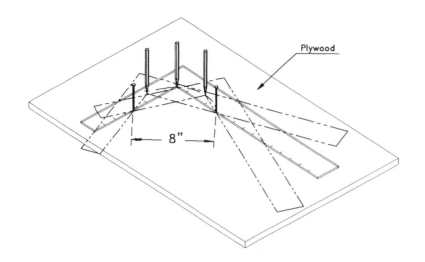

Continue to rotate the square on the nails and mark with the pencil, until the circle is is complete. Practice this concept on a piece of plywood. In no time you will be an expert.

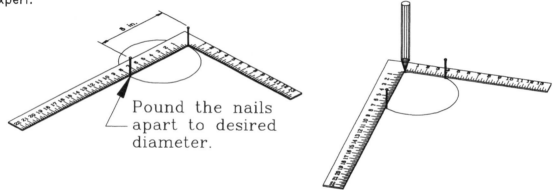

Pound the nails apart to desired diameter.

Another unique method to draw circles is to use a stick of wood and drill (nail) a pivot point in one end. Use the other end to fasten or hold the pencil as you swing the arc to make the circle. This is a good method to use to make large circles. Use the method(s) that work best for you.

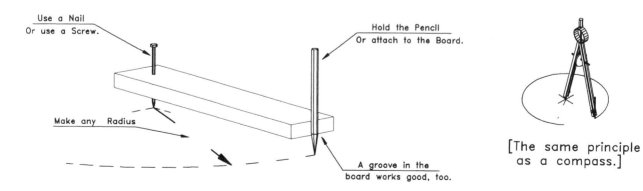

[The same principle as a compass.]

Trade Trick #9 – Copy Angles
[How to Copy and Transfer an Angle using a Lay out Square or T-Bevel]

How to Copy and Transfer Angles using the Lay Out Square: [See Task No. 01, page 292 in the textbook.]

Example 1.   Copy and transfer the angle shown on the object shown below.

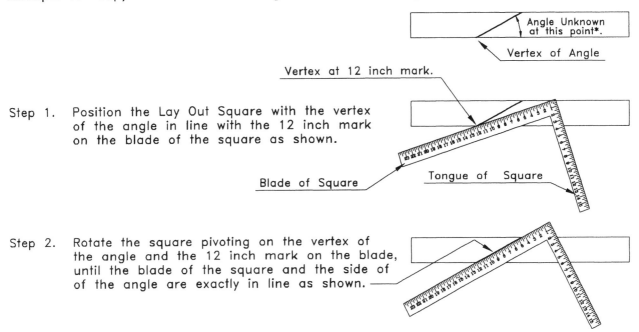

Vertex at 12 inch mark.

Angle Unknown at this point*.

Vertex of Angle

Step 1.   Position the Lay Out Square with the vertex of the angle in line with the 12 inch mark on the blade of the square as shown.

Blade of Square   Tongue of Square

Step 2.   Rotate the square pivoting on the vertex of the angle and the 12 inch mark on the blade, until the blade of the square and the side of of the angle are exactly in line as shown.

Step 3.   Place a mark on the tongue of the square (with a pencil or marker) at the exact point where the line and the square meet.   In this case, mark 6 3/8" (the best that you can see with the naked eye).

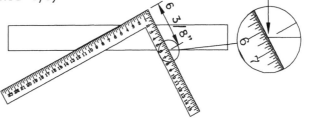

Step 4.   Position the copied angle on the square (12" and 6 3/8") over the object being transferred to, and mark the tonque side of the square with a pencil or marker. Use a straight edge to extend the line as shown.

Transferred Angle

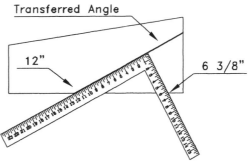

12"   6 3/8"

[*How to determine angle – continued on the next page.]

How to Copy and Transfer Angles using the Lay Out Square (Continued)

Step 5. To determine the angle in degrees, if needed, use the formula TOA. The angle that needs to be solved for is 12" on the adjacent side and 6 3/8" on the opposite side. Change the fractions to decimals and calculate the angle.

Formula: (TOA) Tangent = Opposite/Adjacent

Tan. = $\dfrac{\text{Opp.}}{\text{Adj.}}$

Substitute: Tan. = $\dfrac{6.375"}{12"}$

Calculate: Tan. = .53125

Tan.⁻¹ = 27.97947°

Answer: 28° (degrees)

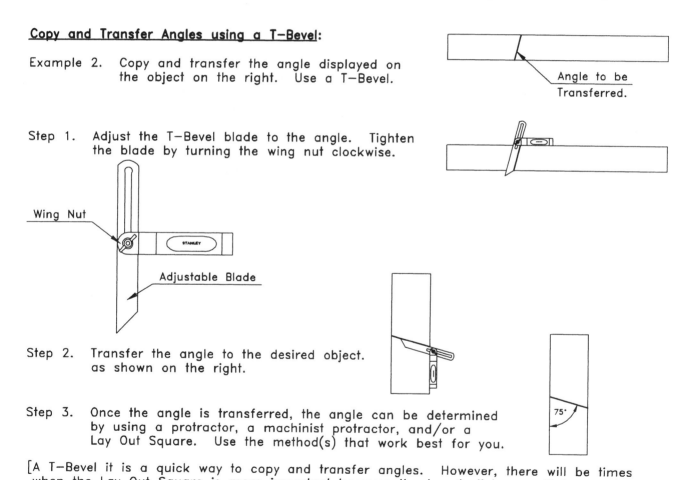

[The more care taken in the measurement the more accurate the angle. This angle would be close enough for this application. For closer angles use a more accurate measuring instrument. See page 48. For more information on TOA, see page 140 and 141.]

Copy and Transfer Angles using a T-Bevel:

Example 2. Copy and transfer the angle displayed on the object on the right. Use a T-Bevel.

Angle to be Transferred.

Step 1. Adjust the T-Bevel blade to the angle. Tighten the blade by turning the wing nut clockwise.

Wing Nut

STANLEY

Adjustable Blade

Step 2. Transfer the angle to the desired object. as shown on the right.

Step 3. Once the angle is transferred, the angle can be determined by using a protractor, a machinist protractor, and/or a Lay Out Square. Use the method(s) that work best for you.

75°

[A T-Bevel it is a quick way to copy and transfer angles. However, there will be times when the Lay Out Square is more important because the base* distance will be greater (especially if the object is warped). By practicing different methods, it will be easier to select the proper method for each specific job.]

*The base of a Lay Out Square is 12 inches plus, and the base of a T-Bevel is 5 1/2".

Trade Trick #10 - Shimming Tricks
[How to Shim for Level Horizontally or Vertically]

How to Shim for Level Horizontally:

Example 1. Shim a door jamb for level. This could be a small exterior door or a large sliding glass door which has a built in sill (door bottom). The principle is the same for both.

Step 1. Determine the approximate measurement that the floor is off-level. use a spirit level and a straight edge as shown on the right. See Front Views page 126, if this illustration is not clear.

Step 2. Install shim 1. Staple if needed. —

[Shim, in this case, is 30 lb. felt that measures approximately 1/16 inch. Cut the felt with a utility knife and use your own judgement for the shim width and length.

Step 3. Install Shim 2. Staple if needed. —

Step 4. Install shim 3. Staple if needed. —

Step 5. Install shim 4 and 5. Staple if needed. Check for level and make adjustments if necessary. You are now ready for installation.

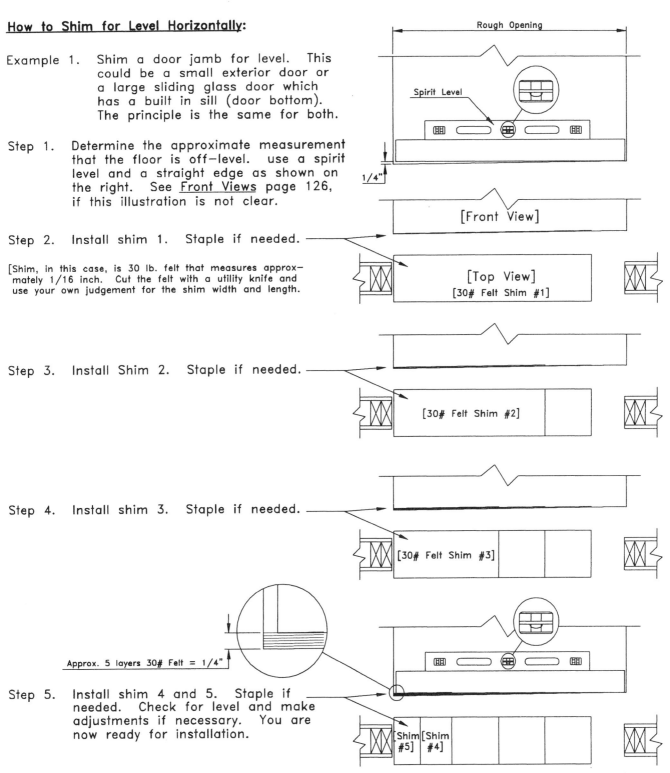

Rough Opening

Spirit Level

1/4"

[Front View]

[Top View]
[30# Felt Shim #1]

[30# Felt Shim #2]

[30# Felt Shim #3]

Approx. 5 layers 30# Felt = 1/4"

[Shim #5] [Shim #4]

[Note this same principle can work for leveling floors at entry ways, where two floors meet, window sills, etc. This is an excellent method to use for moderate leveling jobs. Use your own discretion and common sense when leveling with felt paper, card board, paper, etc.]

Shimming Tricks (Continued)

How to Shim for Level Vertically:

Example 2. Level a door jamb (frame). Now that the base (sill) is level the frame can be leveled (plumbed). A door frame has to be level vertically and horizontally (every which way).

Step 1. This door has a sill, therefore there is no need for a spreader (see note below). Insert the frame in the opening as shown. Tack the sill in place and verify for level.

Step 2. Level side jambs. Use a long level, or a level and a straight edge as shown on both Vertical jambs — simultantiousy; level and place shims, tacking them as you go. DO NOT DRIVE NAILS IN ALL THE WAY IN UNTIL ALL THE JAMBS ARE LEVEL (PLUMB) AND STRAIGHT.

[Place shims where they are needed; top and bottom of the frame, by hinges, where the frame is bowed, by door knob, etc.]

Step 3. Cut shims off after you are sure the jamb is level and plumb. <u>Or</u> wait until the door is hung. This way the door can be fine tuned to the frame.

Step 4. Hang the door.

[Note the main purpose of this module is to illustrate how to shim, not to hang doors. There are too many different types of doors and scenarios to list. <u>The point is that they must all be level (plumb) and true in dimension. That is basic practical math.</u>]

Shims:

Most manufactured shims are 1/4" × 1 1/2"× 8"

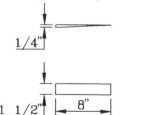

1/4"

1 1/2"   8"

[Shims can be used to level windows, cabinets, framing components, beams, etc.]

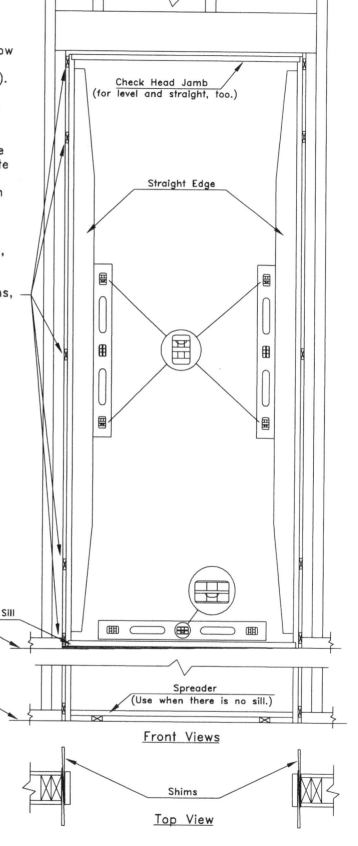

Check Head Jamb (for level and straight, too.)

Straight Edge

Sill

Sub Floor

Finish Floor

Spreader (Use when there is no sill.)

__Front Views__

Shims

__Top View__

© Copyright 2005 Chenier Educational Enterprises, Inc.

Objective Practice Problems for Module #12

Below are a few typical drill jobs. Explain how each job should be done and the tools that could be used to best obtain the accuracy needed.

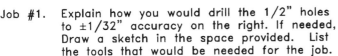

Job #1. Explain how you would drill the 1/2" holes to ±1/32" accuracy on the right. If needed, Draw a sketch in the space provided. List the tools that would be needed for the job.

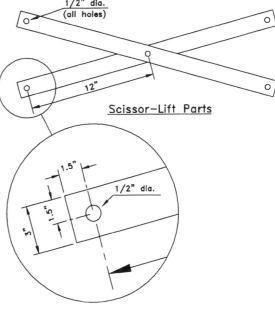

Step 1.

Step 2.

Step 3.

Step 4.

Step 5.

Step 6.

Job #2. Explain how you would drill the 1" holes for the motor base on the right. Drill holes to ±1/16" accuracy. List the tools that would be needed for the job.

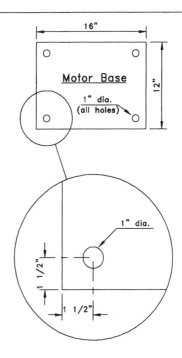

Step 1.

Step 2.

Step 3.

Step 4.

Step 5.

Step 6.

Objective Practice Problems for Module #12

<u>Draw Circles with a Square — Trade Trick #8:</u>

Draw a sketch and explain how to draw a 7 1/2" circle with a Lay Out Square in the space provided below.

<u>Copy Angles [How to Copy and Transfer Angles using a Lay Out Square] — Trade Trick #9:</u>

Draw a sketch and explain how to transfer an angle with a Lay Out Square in the space provided below.

<u>Shimming Tricks — Trade Trick #10:</u>

The floor where a sliding glass door is to be installed is 3/8" off level. In the space provided below, explain what you would do to level the door sill, and draw a sketch illustrating each step. The shim material is 30# felt which is approximately 1/16" thick.

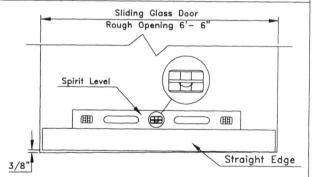

Step 1.

Step 2.

Step 3.

Step 4.

Step 5.

Step 6.

Math Training Module #13

Instructional Objectives:

Hands On:

☐ *Application Problem* - Practice Drawing Angles with the Lay Out Square and Angle Tangents.
☐ *Application Problem* - Practice Drawing Angles with a Lay Out Square and a Chart.

Basic Math Study Notes (Use the Tangent of Angles and a Lay Out Square to Lay Out Angles, use a Lay Out Square and Chart to Lay Out Angles, and use the 100th Scale and 12th Side of a Square):

Use the Tangent of any angle to Lay Out Any Angle with the Lay Out Square.

Example 1. A 30° angle has a tangent of .57735 to the 5th decimal place. This can be found in the textbook, page 250 or by using a scientific calculator.

What this means is a right triangle with a unit of one (1) that has a 30° angle is made up of one side as 1 and the other side as .57735. See below.

1 Unit of tan at 30° = .57735

Or =

Therefore 12 Units (in inches) =

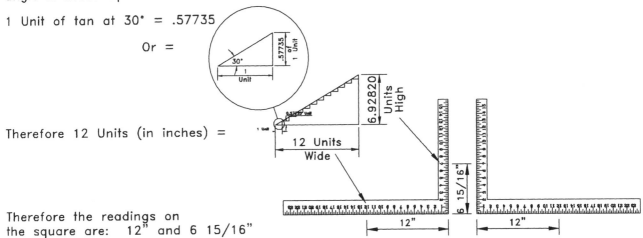

Therefore the readings on the square are: 12" and 6 15/16"

[See Info #10 on page 131 to set up the Lay Out Square for a 30° angle, and page 132 for a 15° angle. The same procedure can be used to lay out any angle. It also would be helpful to study Info #15, page 183, or study Task No. M1, pages 170–265 in the textbook.]

Use the Tangent of any angle to Lay Out Any Angle with the Lay Out Square (Continued).

Example 2.   A 12° angle has a tangent of .21256 to the 5th decimal place.   This can be found in the textbook, page 232 or by using a scientific calculator.

What this means is a right triangle with a unit of one (1) that has a 12° angle is made up of one side as 1 and the other side as .21256.   See below.

1 Unit of tan at 12° = .21256.

                    Or =

Therefore 12 Units (in inches) equals 2.55072" = 2 9/16"

Therefore the readings on the square are: 12" and 2 9/16"

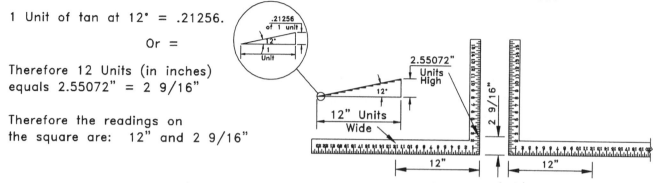

The Lay Out Square and a Chart:

Given the information in the preceeding examples, a chart can be made to lay out any desired angle with a Lay Out Square.   Refer to the charts on page 133 and 134.   The examples listed below demonstate how the charts were made up.

Examples for Even Degrees to Inch Chart on page 133:

1° = Tan. .01745 × 12 = .209"* — Hold 12" and 1/4—" on the Lay Out Square.
2° = Tan. .03492 × 12 = .419" — Hold 12" and 7/16—" on the Lay Out Square.
3° = Tan. .05241 × 12 = .629" — Hole 12" and 5/8" on the Lay Out Square.
And so on ....

*Carrying the decimal 3 places for this application is close enough.

Examples for Even Inch to Degrees Chart on page 134:

Formula: TOA = Tan. = Opp./Adj. 1/12 = Tan. .08333 = 4.76°*
Formula: TOA = Tan. = Opp./Adj. 2/12 = Tan. .16667 = 9.46°
Formula: TOA = Tan. = Opp./Adj. 3/12 = Tan. .25 = 14.04°
And so on ....

*Carrying the decimal 2 places for this application is close enough.

How to Read the 100th Scale on a Lay Out Square and How to Use the Lay Out Square as a Scale:

Not all Lay Out Squares have a 100th scale on them. If yours does, see Info 11A, page 135 on how to read.

Most Lay Out Square have one side of the square in twelfths. That is each inch is divided into 12 equal parts. The main reason for this is for scaling. One increment of one inch represents 1 inch; two increments of 1 inch represents 2 inches, and so forth. Therefore 1 inch would equal 1 foot or 12 inches. This can be a handy tool for on-the-job sketching. See Info 11B, page 136 for more information.

Info #10 – Lay Out Angles
[with a Lay Out Square & Angle Tangents]

How to Use the Lay Out Square as a Protractor:

Example Problem 1.   Draw a 30° angle with a Lay Out Square.

Step 1.   Find the Tangent of 30°

Select: [3] [0] [TAN⁻¹ / TAN]

The display will show:

```
                    DEG
     0.577350269
         Display
```

[Note:

The Tan of 30° can be found in the book on the top of page 250. Therefore, a scientific calculator is not necessary.]

Step 2.   Multiply 0.577350269 X 12 = 6.92820323 inches

Step 3.   Convert 6.92 inches to inches and 16ths.
Use a decimal equivalent chart or multiply:

```
6 .92"
  X16
  552
   92
 14.72
```

Equals: 6 15/16–"

Step 4.   Measure 12" on the long side (blade)
of the square as shown.

Measure 6 15/16–" on the short side
(tongue] of the square as shown.

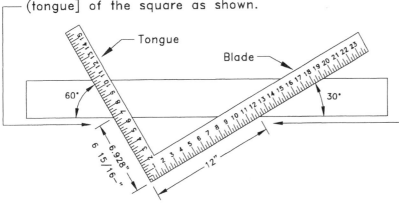

Step 5.   Draw the angle on the right, it will be 30°.   The angle on the left will be 60°.

Step 6.   Check the angles with a protractor. Do this until you are confident the angles are correct. See the protractor Cut–Out pattern on page 225.

Note: If 10" is used on the blade instead of 12", multiply the tangent of 30° by 10.

Example: 10 X .577350269 = 5.77350269 or 5 3/4+". The angle is still 30°. It works because 5.77350269 ÷ 10 = .577350269. Tangent = Adjacent side ÷ Opposite side.

Try: 6 X .577350269 = 3.464101614 or 3 7/16+". The angle is still 30°. Because 3.464101614 ÷ 6 = .577350269. 12 is most commonly used on the blade because it is the mid–point of the square. Also the wider the measurements on the square, the more accurate the angle will be. Use the method that works best for you.

The Lay Out Square as a Protractor (continued)

How to Use the Lay Out Square as a Protractor:

Example Problem 2. Draw a 15° angle with a Lay Out Square.

Step 1.   Find the Tangent of 15°

Select: [1] [5] [TAN⁻¹ / TAN]

The display will show:

$$\boxed{\begin{array}{c} \text{DEG} \\ 0.267949192 \end{array}}$$
Display

[Note:

The Tan of 15° can be found in the book on the top of page 235. Therefore, a scientific calculator is not necessary.]

Step 2.   Multiply 0.267949192 X 12 = 3.215390309 inches

Step 3.   Convert 3.215 inches to inches and 16ths.
Use a decimal equivalent chart or multiply:

```
  3 .215"
      X16
     1290
      215
    3.440
```

Equals: 3 3/16+"

Step 4.   Measure 12" on the long side (blade)
of the square as shown.

Measure 3 3/16+"" on the short side (tongue)
of the square as shown.

```
75°                              15°
         12"
3 3/16+"
```

Step 5.   Draw the angle on the right.
The angle will be 15°.

The angle on the left will be 75°.

Step 6.   Check the angle with a protractor. Do this until
you are confident the angles are correct.

Trade Trick #11 – Lay Out Angles

[How to Lay Out Angles using a Lay Out Square and a Chart]

How to Lay Out Angles using a Lay Out Square and an Even Degree to Inch Chart:

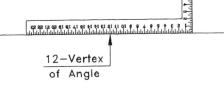

12–Vertex
of Angle

Example 1. Lay out a 36 degree angle with a lay out square and the chart below.

Step 1. Place the lay out square on the object or line, using the "12" on the Blade (long side of the square) as the vetex of the angle as shown on the right. The vertex 12 can be on either the <u>Blade</u> of <u>Tongue</u> of the square.

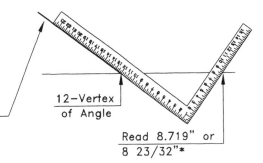

12–Vertex
of Angle

Read 8.719" or
8 23/32"*

Step 2. Rotate the square on the vertex 12, until the tongue measurement representing the desire angle (8.719" in this case) is reached.

Step 3. Mark the angle as shown with a sharp pencil or marker. Check the angle for accuracy with a <u>protractor</u>, if needed.

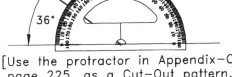

36°

*23/32" is 11/16+"
or 3/4–"

[Use the protractor in Appendix–C, page 225, as a Cut–Out pattern.]

[Note to lay out a 32 1/2° angle (angles by 1/2°) use <u>interpolation</u> as shown below.]

```
    33°  =      7.793"
    32°  =  –  7.498"
Difference  =  .295

Difference .295 ÷ 2 = .1475

  Add:   .1475
       +  7.498
Equals 7.6455"
```

12" and 7.6455" on the Lay Out Square = 32 1/2°

[See page 131 and 132 for more information.]

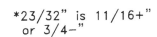

```
55° = 17.138" and 12"
54° = 16.517" and 12"
53° = 15.925" and 12"
52° = 15.359" and 12"
51° = 14.819" and 12"
50° = 14.301" and 12"
49° = 13.804" and 12"
48° = 13.327" and 12"
47° = 12.868" and 12"
46° = 12.426" and 12"
45° = 12." and 12"
44° = 11.588" and 12"
43° = 11.190" and 12"
42° = 10.805" and 12"
41° = 10.431" and 12"
40° = 10.069" and 12"
39° = 9.717" and 12"
38° = 9.375" and 12"
37° = 9.043" and 12"
36° = 8.719" and 12"
35° = 8.402" and 12"
34° = 8.094" and 12"
33° = 7.793" and 12"
32° = 7.498" and 12"
31° = 7.210" and 12"
30° = 6.928" and 12"
29° = 6.652" and 12"
28° = 6.381" and 12"
27° = 6.114" and 12"
26° = 5.853" and 12"
25° = 5.596" and 12"
24° = 5.343" and 12"
23° = 5.094" and 12"
22° = 4.848" and 12"
21° = 4.606" and 12"
20° = 4.368" and 12"
19° = 4.132" and 12"
18° = 3.899" and 12"
17° = 3.669" and 12"
16° = 3.441" and 12"
15° = 3.215" and 12"
14° = 2.992" and 12"
13° = 2.770" and 12"
12° = 2.551" and 12"
11° = 2.333" and 12"
10° = 2.116" and 12"
 9° = 1.901" and 12"
 8° = 1.686" and 12"
 7° = 1.473" and 12"
 6° = 1.261" and 12"
 5° = 1.050" and 12"
 4° = 0.839" and 12"
 3° = 0.629" and 12"
 2° = 0.419" and 12"
 1° = 0.209" and 12"
 0° (degrees)
```

[The complete <u>Even Degrees to Inch Chart</u> is in Appendix–C, page 226.]

Lay Out Angles using a Lay Out Square and an Even Degree to Inch Chart (Continued)

How to use the Lay Out Square and the Even Inches to Degrees Chart:

Example 2.   Lay out and determine the angle for a 4/12 roof slope.

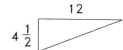

Step 1.   Note the chart indicates 18.43° for a 4/12 slope. Therefore a cut off saw would be set to approximately 18 1/2°. Or hold 4 and 12 on the square, and mark accordingly. This chart works well for most roof slopes. See the next example.

Example 3.   Lay out and determine the angle for a 4.5/12 roof slope. Use interpolation (also, see page 150).

Step 1.   Note the chart indicates 22.62° for a 5/12 slope and, the chart indicates 18.43° for a 4/12 slope. Therefore: Subtract: 22.62
                                                                                                                 − 18.43
                                                                                              Difference =   4.19°

Step 2.   Add 1/2 of the difference 4.19°; or 2.095° to 18.43°
          Therefore, the angle 4.5/12 =   20.525 or approx. 20.5°*

Step 3.   Rotate the square on the vertex 12, until the tongue measurement 4 1/2" intersects the reference line as shown on the right. Check the angle for accuracy with a protractor, if needed.

[Use protractor in Appendix−C, page 225, as a Cut−Out pattern.]

[CAUTION − Care must be used in reading the angle chart on the right. Always check your measurements before marking. There is also a chart in Appendix B in the back of the book.]

*The angle 20.5° will be close enough for most applications. However, the exact angle 20.556° would be needed for real fine work. See page 141 and 142 for more information.

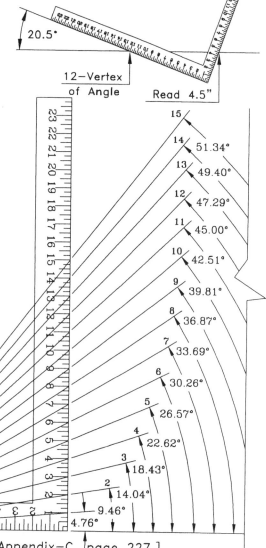

[The complete underline Even Inches to Degrees Chart is in Appendix−C, page 227.]

Info #11A – Conversion Made Easy
[Read the 100ᵗʰ Scale on the Lay Out Square]

How to Interpret the 100ths Scale on a Lay Out Square (Found on Stanley AR100 Square).

1. Convert .2187 to 16ths.

1st Locate, approximately, where 2187 ten thousandths are on the 100ths scale.

2nd Round off 2187 ten Thousandths to 22 Hundredths.

3rd Locate 22 Hundredths on the 100ths scale, as shown below.

4th Drop down and read the answer on the 16ths scale.

5th The answer is 3/16+" or 7/32" exact.

(Top Scale Divided into 100THS increments)

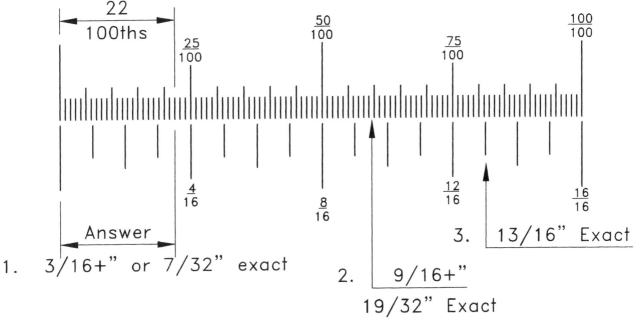

(Bottom Scale Divided into 16th Increments)

2. Convert .5937 to 16ths., and .5937 rounded off equals .59+ hundredths.

3. Convert .8125 to 16ths., and .8125 rounded off equals .81+ 100ths.

[Note: Not all lay out squares have the hundredths scale. See Appendix-C, page 228 for a cut-out that can be used for reference, or use this page.]

Info #11B - Scaling
[Use the 12th Side of the Lay Out Square as a Scale]

How to Use the Twelfth Side of the Lay Out Square as a Scale.

Use the twelfth side of the Lay Out Square as a scale to estimate the sizes of building components such as rafters, stairs, walls, etc. Or as a drawing scale to draw room sizes, small buildings, garages, etc.

Example 1.   Estimate the common rafters for a building with a 4/12 slope, a run of 10'– 0" and a total rise of 40".

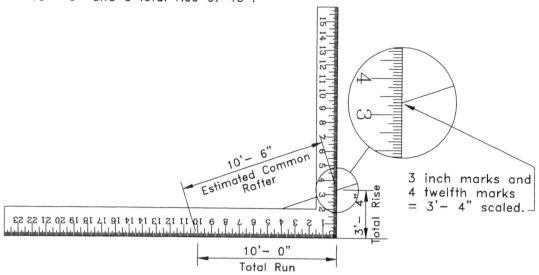

3 inch marks and 4 twelfth marks = 3'– 4" scaled.

[Turn to page 150 on how to carry out this example further. The Lay Out Square can be used for many different applications, too numerous to mention.]

Example 2.   Make a drawing of a small out building 12 ft. by 16 ft. for lawn tool storage. Suggestion: Make the drawing on a sheet of plywood. As the square can be used as a T–Square.

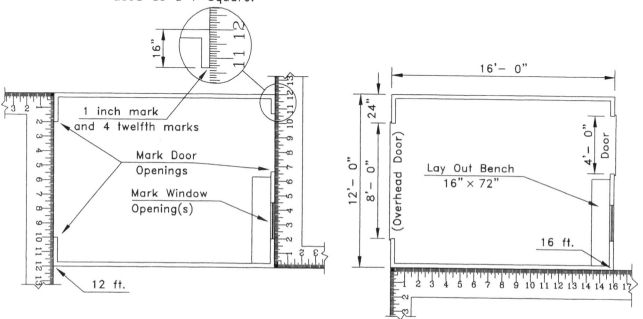

[Note this drawing is incomplete, it's main purpose is to illustrate how to use the Lay Out Square as a scale.]

Objective Practice Problems for Module #13

1. Lay out a 20° (degree) angle with a lay out square.

The Blade (long side of the square) will read _____ inches.
The Tongue (short side of the square will read _____ inches.
The angle opposite is ____°.

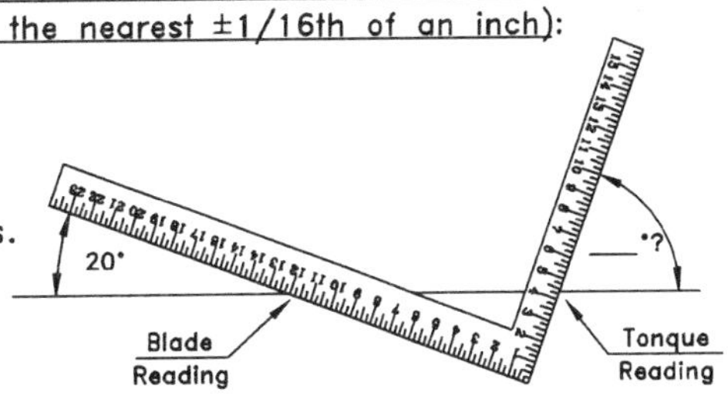

2. Lay out a 37 1/2° (degree) angle with a lay out square.

The Blade will read _____ inches.
The Tongue will read _____ inches.
The angle opposite is ____°.

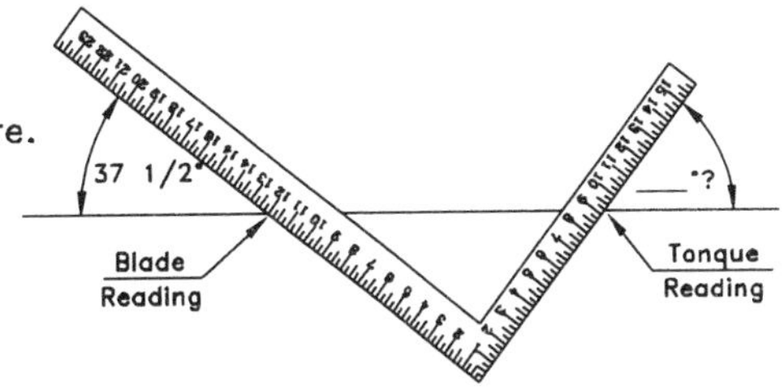

3. Lay out a 45° (degree) angle with a lay out square.

The Blade will read _____ inches.
The Tongue will read _____ inches.
The angle opposite is ____°.
Name another combination of the blade and the
tongue readings that will work. _____ and _____.

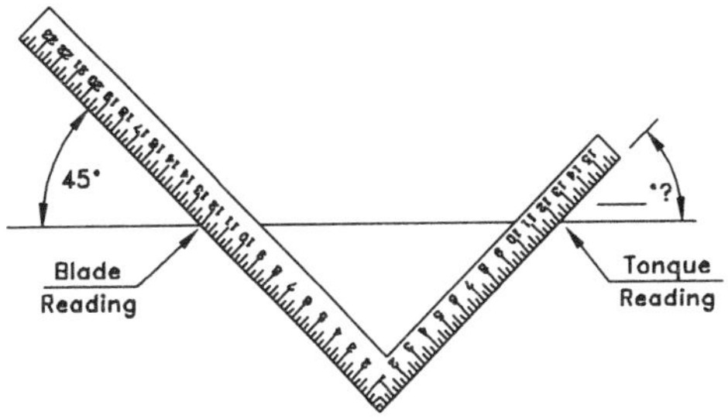

4. Lay out a 65° (degree) angle with a lay out square.

The Blade will read _____ inches.
The Tongue will read _____ inches.
The angle opposite is ____°.

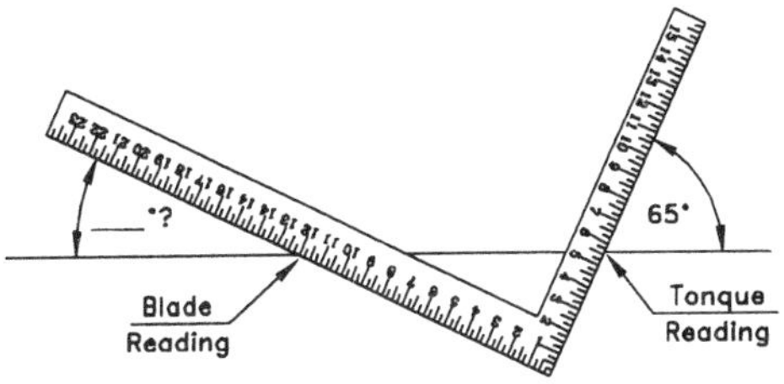

N1B Review Problems

5–10. Calculate the missing dimensions on the right
to feet, inches, and ±1/16th of an inch.

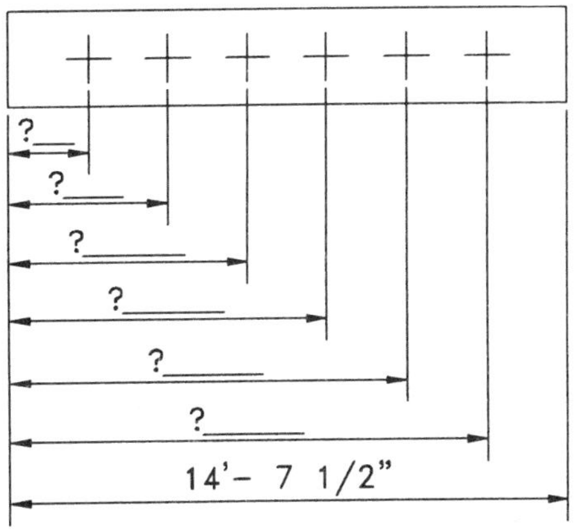

14'– 7 1/2"

Objective Practice Problems for Module #13

Lay Out Angles with a Lay Out Square and a Chart — Trade Trick #10:

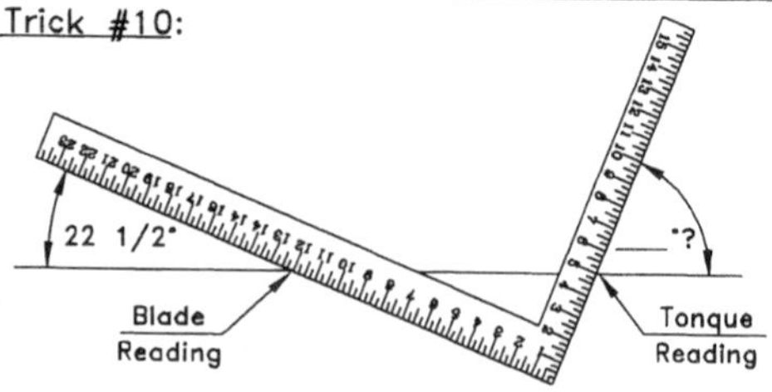

1. Lay out a 22 1/2° (degree) angle with a lay out square and the chart given below.

The Blade (long side of the square) will read _____ inches.
The Tongue (short side of the square will read _____ inches.
The angle opposite is ___°.

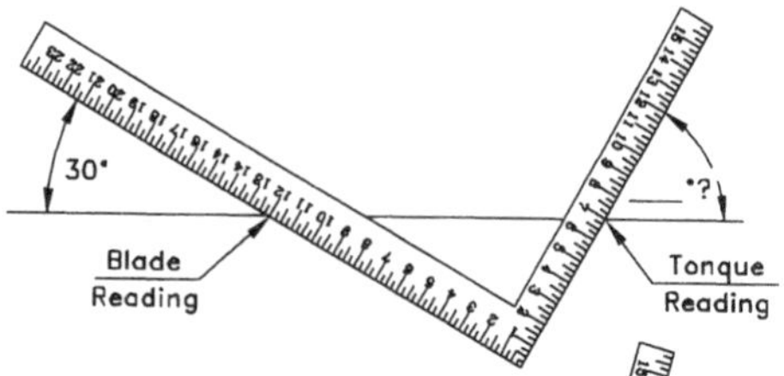

2. Lay out a 30° (degree) angle with a lay out square and the chart given below.

The Blade will read _____ inches.
The Tongue will read _____ inches.
The angle opposite is ___°.

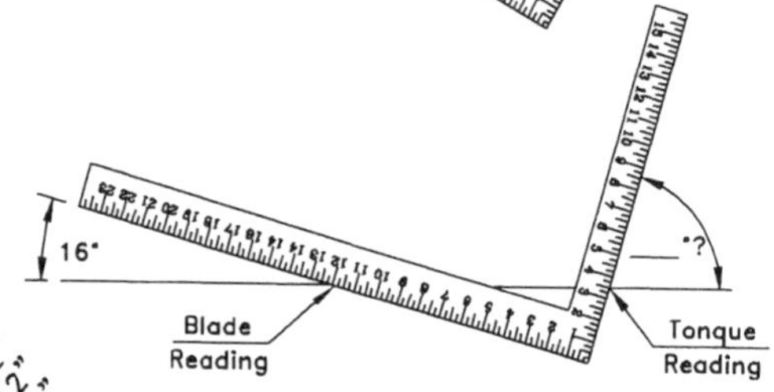

3. Lay out a 16° (degree) angle with a lay out square shown below and the chart on the right.

The Blade will read _____ inches.
The Tongue will read _____ inches.
The angle opposite is ___°.

55° = 17.138" and 12"
54° = 16.517" and 12"
53° = 15.925" and 12"
52° = 15.359" and 12"
51° = 14.819" and 12"
50° = 14.301" and 12"
49° = 13.804" and 12"
48° = 13.327" and 12"
47° = 12.868" and 12"
46° = 12.426" and 12"
45° = 12" and 12"
44° = 11.588" and 12"
43° = 11.190" and 12"
42° = 10.805" and 12"
41° = 10.431" and 12"
40° = 10.069" and 12"
39° = 9.717" and 12"
38° = 9.375" and 12"
37° = 9.043" and 12"
36° = 8.719" and 12"
35° = 8.402" and 12"
34° = 8.094" and 12"
33° = 7.793" and 12"
32° = 7.498" and 12"
31° = 7.210" and 12"
30° = 6.928" and 12"
29° = 6.652" and 12"
28° = 6.381" and 12"
27° = 6.114" and 12"
26° = 5.853" and 12"
25° = 5.596" and 12"
24° = 5.343" and 12"
23° = 5.094" and 12"
22° = 4.848" and 12"
21° = 4.606" and 12"
20° = 4.368" and 12"
19° = 4.132" and 12"
18° = 3.899" and 12"
17° = 3.669" and 12"
16° = 3.441" and 12"
15° = 3.215" and 12"
14° = 2.992" and 12"
13° = 2.770" and 12"
12° = 2.551" and 12"
11° = 2.333" and 12"
10° = 2.116" and 12"
9° = 1.901" and 12"
8° = 1.686" and 12"
7° = 1.473" and 12"
6° = 1.261" and 12"
5° = 1.050" and 12"
4° = 0.839" and 12"
3° = 0.629" and 12"
2° = 0.419" and 12"
1° = 0.209" and 12"
0° (degrees)

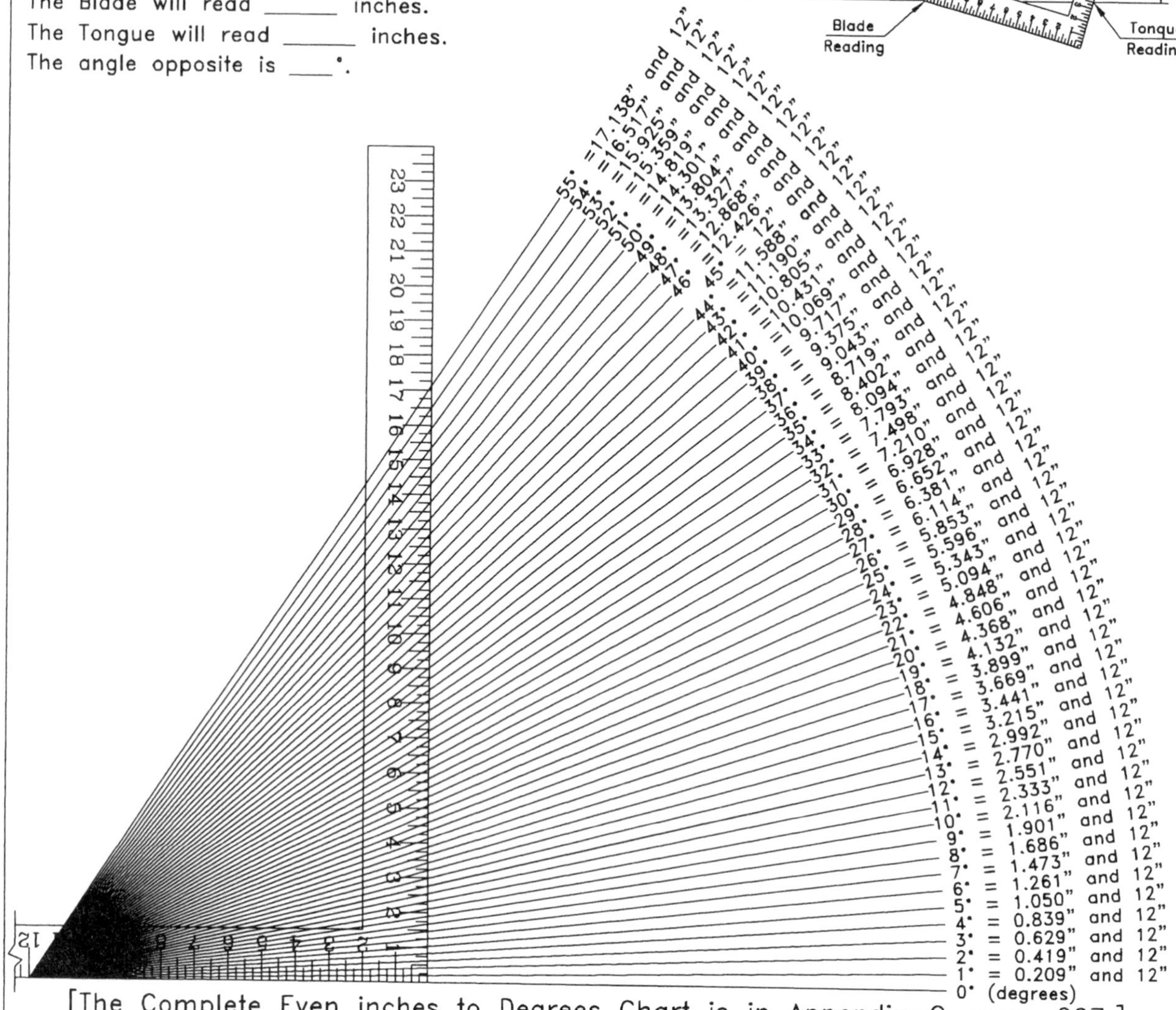

[The Complete Even inches to Degrees Chart is in Appendix−C, page 227.]

Math Training Module #14

Instructional Objectives:

Page No.

Hands On:

☐ *Application Problem* - Measure given angles with a Lay Out Square. Check with a Protractor.

☐ *Application Problem* - Practice Drawing Angles with the Lay Out Square.

☐ *Application Problem* - The Scientific Calculator and Trig Functions. Use in conjunction with the Text Book Trig Tables.

Basic Math Study Notes (Determine Angles with a Lay Out Square and Conversion of Angles – Degrees, Minutes, and Seconds):

How to Determine Angles from a Right Triangle:

Example 1.　Find missing angle in the triangle on the right.

Use the Formula:　(TOA) Tangent = Opposite/Adjacent

$$\text{Tan.} = \frac{\text{Opp.}}{\text{Adj.}}$$

Substitute:　$\text{Tan.} = \frac{3"}{12"}$

Calculate:　Tan. = .25*

[See page 181 and 184 for more information on the formula TOA. Remember it is a simple formula, but has to be written and manipulated properly to work correctly.]

$\text{Tan.}^{-1} = 14.03624°$

Answer:　14° (degrees)

*Note Tan. .25 can be found on page 234 in the text book. Tan. .25 is actually 14 degrees 3 minutes (approx.). However for most applications 14 degrees would be close enough. Use the method that works best for you. The easy way to calculate and measure angles is to use the charts on page 133 and 134. These charts are good for most applications, but are limited to the accuracy ±.5°. However, both methods are shown and demonstrated in this book. The next page will demonstrate how to to find the angle with a sciencfic calculator.

Basic Math Study Notes (Continued)

Use a Scientific Calculator to find the Angle from the Tan. (Function of an Angle).

To convert tan. .25 with a scienfic calculator: Select: [.] [2] [5] [2nd] [TAN⁻¹]

The display should show:

DEG
14.03624347

Display

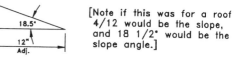

Determine/Measure Angles with a Lay Out Square:

Example 2.   The lines on the right measure 4" and 12" on the Lay Out Square as shown on the right. Find the angle of the lines to set up the cut off saw to saw the board.

Use the formula: (TOA) Tan. = Opp./Adj.

Substitute:	Tan. = 4/12
Calculate:	Tan. = .33333
Answer:	Tan.⁻¹ = 18.43478°

Set saw at: 18.5°** for Line A
Set saw at: 71.5°** for Line B (90° − 18.5° = 71.5°)

*Close enough for most applications − see Angle Conversion below for more accuracy.

[Note if this was for a roof 4/12 would be the slope, and 18 1/2° would be the slope angle.]

Or   Formula: (TOA) Tan. = Opp./Adj.

Substitute:	Tan. = 12/4
Calculate:	Tan. = 3
Answer:	Tan.⁻¹ = 71.56505°

Set saw at: 71.5° for Line A

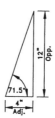

[Note the reference point to the angle being solved in each triangle determines the Opposite and the Adjacent sides. This will correspond with the Lay Out Square. In most cases, common sence (a sketch) will illustrate if you are correct or not. Practice makes perfect.]

Angle Conversion (manually):

Step 1.   Multiply by the desired denominator, 60, for 60 Minutes.

Step 2.   Multiply by the desired denominator, 60, for 60 Seconds.

Step 3.   Bring down the whole numbers and read, as shown on the right.

```
18.43478°
   x60 (for Minutes)
26 .08680'
   x60 (for Seconds)
5.208"
```

18° 26'5.208" or 18°26'5.208"
18° 26'5" (read 18 degrees 26 minutes 5.208 seconds)

Angle Conversion via a Scientific Calculator:

Select: [.] [3] [3] [3] [3] [3] [2nd] [TAN⁻¹]

The display should show:

DEG
18.43477694

Display

[See Info #12 on page 141 to Measure Angles with a Lay Out Square and Angle Conversion.]

Info #12 – Measure Angles
[with a Lay Out Square and the Formula TOA]

How to Use the Lay Out Square and TOA to Measure Angles:

Example Problem 1. Measure a "specific angle" with a Lay Out Square.

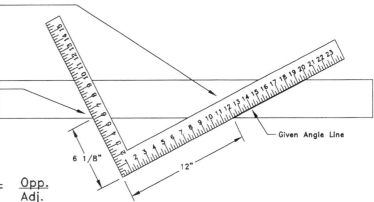

Step 1. Measure the Adjacent and the Opposite side with the square.

a) Measure 12" on the long side (blade) of the square as shown.

b) Measure and mark the point where the short side (tongue) of the square and the given line intersect. In this case 6 1/8".

Step 2. Use the Formula TOA: $Tan = \dfrac{Opp.}{Adj.}$

Substitute: $tan = \dfrac{6\ 1/8"}{12}$

Convert and Calculate: $Tan = \dfrac{6.125"}{12} = 12\overline{)6.125}\ \ .5104"$

$Tan = .5104"$

Step 3. Calculate the Angle from the Tan. (Function of an Angle).

Select: [.] [5] [1] [0] [4] [2nd] [TAN⁻¹ TAN]

The display should show:

> DEG
> **27.03976634**
> Display

[Note:

The Tan of 27° can be found in the book on the top of page 247. Therefore, a scientific calculator is not necessary.]

Step 4. For greater accuracy convert 27.03976634 to Degrees, Minutes, and Seconds'

Select: 27.03976634 and [3nd] [▷DMS ▷DD =]

The Display will Show:

> DEG
> **27° 02' 23"1**
> Display

Calculate Manually:

27 .03976634° ←— Times the Decimal Only
  X 60' ←— 60 Minutes
2 .3859804' ←— Times the Decimal Only
  X 60" ←— 60 Seconds
23.158824"

27° 2' 23.1"

Or: Multiply .03976634 X 60 = 2'.3859804"
     Then multiply .3859804" X 60 = 23.1" (Or 27° 02' 23"1)
     Read: 27 degrees 2 minutes 23.1 seconds

[Note: When measuring angles with the Lay Out Square, the accuracy of the angle(s) will depend on the accuracy of the measurements. Usually, the angle can be accurate to the nearest <u>whole degree</u> or <u>half degree</u>.]

Measure Angles with a Lay Out Square (Continued)

How a Degree is broken down into "Degree", "Minutes", and "Seconds".

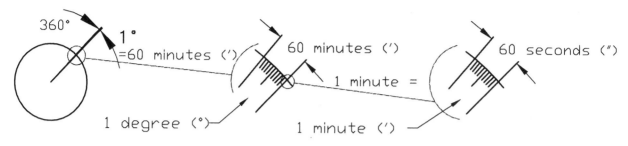

Review of Conversion of Decimals of Angles:

Example Problem 1. Convert 33.8333° to Degrees, Minutes, and Seconds.

Step 1. Multiply by the desired
denominator, 60, for 60 Minutes.

Step 2. Multiply by the desired
denominator, 60, for 60 Seconds.

Step 3. Bring down the whole numbers
and read, as shown on the right.

33 .8333°
　　x60 (for Minutes)
49 .998'
　　x60 (for Seconds)
59.880" = 1 Minute

33° 49'59.88" or 33°50"
33° 50' (read 33 degrees 50 Minutes)

Step 4. How to Convert using
a Scientific Calculator.

Select: 33.8333 and

[3nd] [▷DMS ▷DD =]

The Display will Show:

DEG
33° 49' 59"8
Display

[Note, for most practical purposes the above reading
would be close enough. However, in surveying and
other high accurate professions the reading would
be 33°49'59.88"]

Step 5. How to read 33° 50'
on a Vernier Scale.

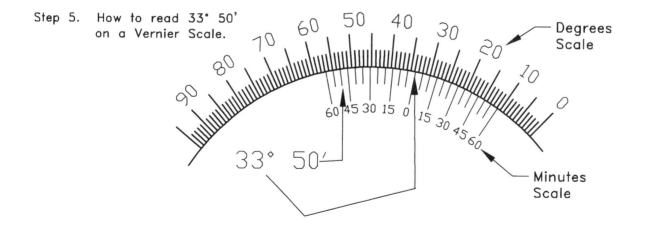

Objective Practice Problems for Module #14

Measure Angles with a Lay Out Square – Info #12 (carry decimal 3 places):

1. Angle A on the right measures 12" and 5" on the lay out square.

   Calculate angle A = _____°.

   Calculate angle B = _____°.

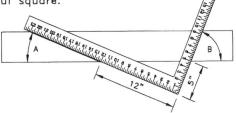

2. The slope of a roof is 9/12.

   The slope angle = _____°?

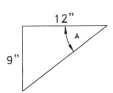

3. Angle A on the right measures 12" and 6 15/16".

   Calculate angle A = _____°.

   Calculate angle B = _____°.

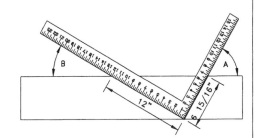

4. The stair angle A = _____°.

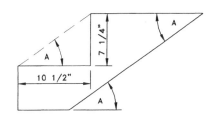

Review Problems (carry the decimal 5 places):

Use a scientific calculator (Info #6) and/or the textbook trig tables to find the sine, cosine, and tangent of the angles listed below.

5. Sin. 17° = _____   6. Cos. 27° = _____   7. Tan. 75° = _____

8. Sin. 21° = _____   9. Cos. 60° = _____   10. Tan. 45° = _____

11. Sin. 90° = _____   12. Cos. 42° = _____

Objective Practice Problems for Module #14

<u>Review Problems (carry the decimals 3 places):</u>

Use a scientific calculator and/or the textbook trig tables to find the angles of the angle functions listed below.

13. Sin. .8480 = _____ °   14. Tan. .9657 = _____ °   15. Sin. .7880 = _____ °

16. Cos. .8572 = _____ °   17. Sin. .4694 = _____ °   18. Cos. .4067 = _____ °

19. Tan. .1583 = _____ °   20. Sin. .1736 = _____ °

<u>Review Lay Out Angles with a Lay Out Square – Info #10 (answer to the nearest ±1/16th of an inch):</u>

21. Lay out a 14° (degree) angle with a lay out square.

The Blade (long side of the square) will read _____ inches.
The Tongue (short side of the square will read _____ inches.
The angle opposite is ____°.

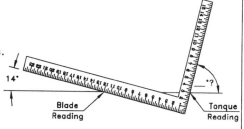

22. Lay out a 5° (degree) angle with a lay out square.

The Blade will read _____ inches.
The Tongue will read _____ inches.
The angle opposite is ____°.

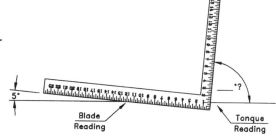

23. Lay out a 75° (degree) angle with a lay out square.

The Blade will read _____ inches.
The Tongue will read _____ inches.
The angle opposite is ____°.

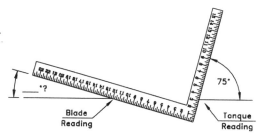

Math Training Module #15

Hands On:

☐   *Application Problem* - Practice Laying Out Common Rafters on a 2 × 4.

☐   *Application Problem* - Measure given angles with a Lay Out Square. Check with a Protractor.

Objective Practice Problems: Calculate the Practice Problems for Math Training Module #15

Basic Math Study Notes (Rafter Problems, Knee Walls, Slope Angles, Unequal Roof Slopes and Interpolation, and the Slant Line Method):

How to Calculate and Lay Out Different Types of Rafters:

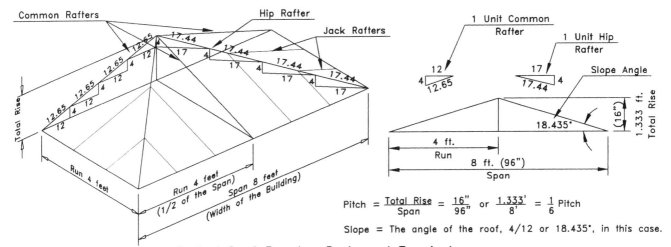

$$\text{Pitch} = \frac{\text{Total Rise}}{\text{Span}} = \frac{16"}{96"} \text{ or } \frac{1.333'}{8'} = \frac{1}{6} \text{ Pitch}$$

Slope = The angle of the roof, 4/12 or 18.435°, in this case.

Typical Roof Framing Parts and Terminology

Common Rafters: Common rafters are rafters that have a "run" and "total rise".
                      They are used in homes, garages, commerical buildings, etc.

The most common lay out methods are; <u>the step off method</u>, <u>the rafter tables method</u>, and <u>the Rule of Pythagoras method ($a^2 + b^2 = c^2$)</u>.

Step Off Method:

Note if you stepped off the rafter on
the right and were off 1/8" each
time, you would be off 3/8" total.

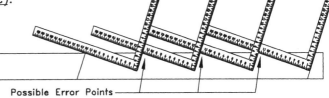

Possible Error Points

[Note, this method is okay for short rafters, but is not as accurate as the rafter tables method for longer rafters. Use the method that works best for you.]

Rafters (Continued)

Rafter Tables Method:

This is probably the most popular method because it is the most accurate. Multiply, <u>1 unit of common rafter</u> (13 in this case) times number of units of run (in feet).

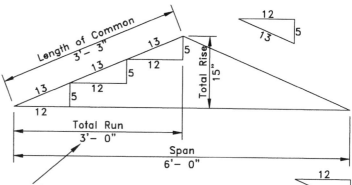

How to Calculate the Common Rafter:

To find the Common Rafter, multiply the RUN (in feet units) X the HYPOTENUSE of each specific unit in inches ————————————— Example:

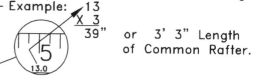

$$\begin{array}{r} 13 \\ \underline{X\ 3} \\ 39" \end{array}$$ or 3' 3" Length of Common Rafter.

The hypotenuse of each unit is found in the 1st column of the rafter tables. Look under The number that corresponds with the rise of the rafter unit for the rafter. 5 in this case.

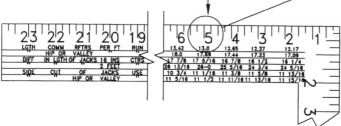

How to Calculate the Total Rise:

To find the Total Rise, multiply the RUN (in ft. units) X the rise of each specific unit in inches ————————————————— Example: 3 X 5 = 15"   Total Rise

Rule of Pythagoras Method:

This method proves that the rafter tables method works.

Calculate the rafter length by using the Rule of Pythagoras in all inches, or in all feet.

Formula: $a^2 + b^2 = c^2$
Substitute: $5^2 + 12^2 = c^2$
Calculate: $25 + 144 = c^2$
                  $169 = c^2$
                  $\sqrt{169} = c$
                  $13 = c$

Formula: $a^2 + b^2 = c^2$
Substitute: $15^2 + 36^2 = c^2$
Calculate: $225 + 1296 = c^2$
                  $1521 = c^2$
                  $\sqrt{1521} = c$
                  $39" = c$

$a^2 + b^2 = c^2$
$1.25^2 + 3^2 = c^2$
$1.5625 + 9 = c^2$
$10.5625 = c^2$
$\sqrt{10.5625} = c$
$3.25' = c$

Find the Slope Angle using TOA (Tan. = Opp./Adj.).   Or use the Lay Out Square.

Formula: $\text{Tan.} = \dfrac{\text{Opp.}}{\text{Adj.}}$

Substitute: $\text{Tan } A = \dfrac{5}{12}$

Calculate: $\text{Tan } A = .41666$

Find the Angle: $\text{Tan } A^{-1} = .41666$

             $\text{Angle } A = 22.62°$

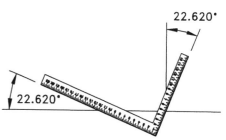

[For more information on TOA, see page 140 and 141, or Info #15, pages 183–186.]

Rafters (Continued)

Shed Rafters: Shed rafters are common rafters that have a "run" and and "total" rise. They are used in lean-to buildings.

The Shed Rafter and the Total Rise are calculated the same as common rafters.

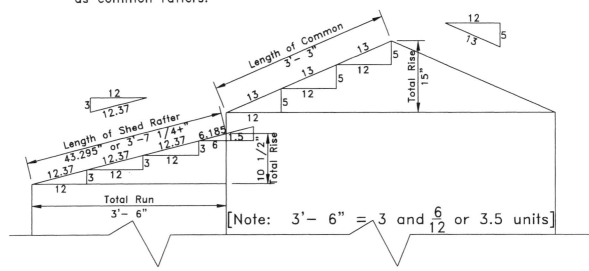

[Note: 3'- 6" = 3 and $\frac{6}{12}$ or 3.5 units]

[Common Rafter = RUN (in ft. units) X the HYPOTENUSE of each specific unit in inches.]

[Find _total rise_: Multiply the RUN X (times) the rise of each unit.

Example 3.5 X 3 = 10.5"]

Example: 12.37
X 3.5
43.295"   Length of Shed (Common) Rafter.

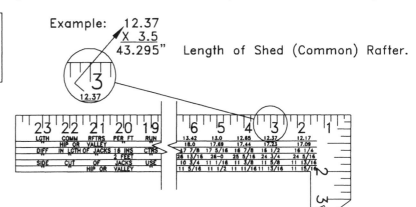

Rule of Pythagoras Method:

This method proves that the rafter tables method works.

Formula:	$a^2 + b^2 = c^2$
Substitute:	$3^2 + 12^2 = c^2$
Calculate:	$9 + 144 = c^2$
	$153 = c^2$
	$\sqrt{153} = c$
	$12.37 = c$

Find the Slope Angle using TOA (Tan. = Opp./Adj.). Or use the Lay Out Square.

Formula:	Tan. = $\frac{Opp.}{Adj.}$
Substitute:	Tan A = $\frac{3}{12}$
Calculate:	Tan A = .25
Find the Angle:	Tan A⁻¹ = .25
	Angle A = 14.036°

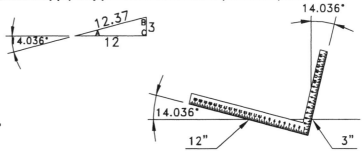

[For more information on TOA, see page 140 and 141, or Info #15, pages 183-186.]

Rafters (continued)

Knee Walls: A "Knee Wall" is a common rafter that has a "shorter run" and a total rise. They are used to reinforce rafters that have large overhangs.

The Knee Wall height is the total rise of it's run.

Common Rafter: 13.42"   Knee Wall Rafter: 13.42"
                   X 10   X 4.75
                   134.20"   63.745

Common Rafter Rise: 10 X 6 = 60"

Knee Wall Total Rise: 4.75 X 6 = 28.5"

$[4' - 9" = 4 \text{ and } \frac{9}{12} \text{ or } 4.75 \text{ units}]$

Find the Slope Angle using TOA:

Formula: $\text{Tan.} = \frac{\text{Opp.}}{\text{Adj.}}$

Substitute: $\text{Tan } A = \frac{6}{12}$

Calculate: $\text{Tan } A = .5$

Find Slope Angle: $\text{Tan } A^{-1} = .5$

Angle A = 26.565°

[Note, the purpose of this module is to demonstrate how to calculate different building components, not to demonstrate how to build them. Consult with local codes for that.]

Rafters (continued)

Hip Rafters: A "Hip Rafter" is a rafter that runs diagonally between the corners of a build-ing and intersects two common rafter at the peak (ridge), as shown below.

The "Hip Rafter" is calculated the same way as the common rafter. The only difference is that the hip rafter unit is larger than the common rafter unit.

Common Rafter: 12.65"
$$\underline{\times\ 5}$$
63.25" = 5'- 3 1/4"

Hip Rafter: 17.44"
$$\underline{\times\ 5}$$
87.20" = 7'- 3 1/4-"

Total Rise: 4"
$$\underline{\times\ 5}$$
20" = 1'- 8"

1 Unit of Common:

1 Unit of Hip: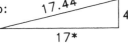

*Actually 16.97, but rounded off to 17.

[Note there are the same number of Hip Units as there are Common Units. However, the hip units are larger. Therefore the common rafter and the hip rafters are calculated the same way.]

Find the Common Slope Angle using TOA:

Formula: Tan. = $\dfrac{Opp.}{Adj.}$

Substitute: Tan A = $\dfrac{4}{12}$

Calculate: Tan A = .33333*

Find the Angle: Tan A⁻¹ = .33333

Angle A = 18.43478°

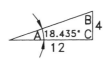

Find the Hip Slope Angle using TOA:

Formula: Tan. = $\dfrac{Opp.}{Adj.}$

Substitute: Tan A = $\dfrac{4}{17}$ $\left(\dfrac{4}{16.97}\right)$

Calculate: Tan A = .23529*   (.23571)

Find the Angle: Tan A⁻¹ = .23529   (.23571)

Angle A = 13.24052° (13.26310°)

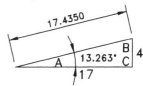

*Note the Scientific Calculators carry the decimal 7–9 places, and the textbook trig tables carry the decimal 5 places. However for this type of application, 3 places is close enough. Use your own discretion.

[Note, the purpose of this module is to demonstrate how to calculate different building components, not to demonstrate how to build them. Consult with local codes for that.]

149

Rafters (continued)

Unequal Roof Slopes and Interpolation:

[Note all rafter (common, hip, and jacks) values are from even units (3, 4, 5, etc.) of rise.]

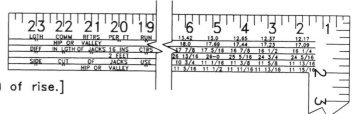

Unequal roof slopes are those slopes that have an unequal rise per foot run. Unequal roof slope rafters (common, hip, and jacks) are not shown on the square, but by subtracting the smaller even slope rafters from the upper even slope rafters will yield the difference between the two. Divide that difference by two and add that quotient (answer) to the lower even slope This will equal the unequal slope rafter. Check with the Rule of Pythagoras.

Example. Find rafter length for one unit of 4 1/2 and 12 slope.

[For Unequal Roof Pitches, see pages 56 and 186.]

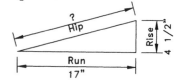

Common Rafters:

Step 1.   Upper even slope (5/12) rafter value =   13.00"

Step 2.   Lower even slope (4/12) rafter value =   − 12.65"

Step 3.   Subtract the two values ⟋ .35"

Step 4.   Divide that quotient (answer) by 2.   .35 ÷ 2 = .175"

Step 5.   Add that quotient to Step 2. value ——— + 12.65"
Answer (sum) = 12.825"

Step 6.   Check with the formula: $a^2 + b^2 = c^2$
Substitute: $4.5^2 + 12^2 = c^2$
Calculate: $20.25 + 144 = c^2$
$164.25 = c^2$
$\sqrt{164.25} = c$
$12.816 = c$

Answer Very Close Okay

Hip Rafters:

Upper value =   17.69"

Lower value =   − 17.44"

Subtract ⟋ .25"

Divide by 2.   .25 ÷ 2 =   .125"

Add Step 2 value − + 17.44"
Answer (sum) = 17.565"

Formula: $a^2 + b^2 = c^2$
$4.5^2 + 16.97^2 = c^2$
$20.25 + 287.98 = c^2$
$308.23 = c^2$
$\sqrt{308.23} = c$
$17.556 = c$

Answer Very Close Okay

Jack Rafters:

Interpolation can be used for the Jack Rafters, too. See page 156 to see how they are calculated. Interpolate the same as above, but use the desired jack rafter values instead.

The Slant Line Method:

The slant-line method of scaling for rafters (common, hip, and jacks) is a unique way of estimating their material sizes on-the-job or in the shop. It brings all the component parts together where they can be checked roughly for accuracy and be used to estimate the material list.

The drawing on the right is made by using the twelfth side of the Lay Out Square as a scale. It can be drawn on a piece of plywood, poster board, paper, etc.

[See page 136 and 158 for more details.]

© Copyright 2005 Chenier Educational Enterprises, Inc.

Info #13 - Calculate and Lay Out Rafters
(Common, Hip, and Jacks)

How to Calculate Common Rafters:

1. To find the length of the "Common Rafter", multiply the <u>run</u> times the <u>hypotenuse</u> of each specific unit.

One Unit Common

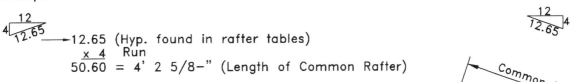

Example:

→12.65 (Hyp. found in rafter tables)
x 4   Run
50.60 = 4' 2 5/8-" (Length of Common Rafter)

[To find the Hypotenuse of each unit, see 2. below.]

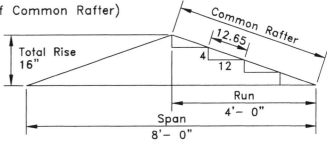

2. To find the "Hypotenuse" of each unit of "Common Rafter", use the rafter tables, shown below. Or, use the Formula: $a^2 + b^2 = c^2$

   a) Refer to the Length of Common Rafters Per Ft. Run Column (Column 1).

   b) Look, directly, under the 4 in that column. Read 12.65, this is the hypotenuse of 4 and 12.

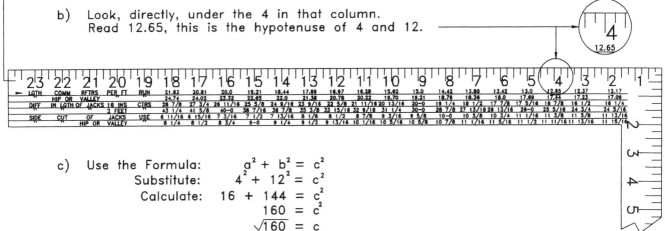

	23	22	21	20	19	18	17	16	15	14	13	12	11	10	9	8	7	6	5	4	3	2	1
LGTH COMM RFTRS PER FT RUN						21.63	20.81	20.0	19.21	18.44	17.69	16.97	16.28	15.62	15.0	14.42	13.89	13.42	13.0	12.65	12.37	12.17	
HIP OR VALLEY						24.74	24.02	23.32	22.65	22.0	21.38	20.78	20.22	19.70	19.21	18.76	18.36	18.0	17.69	17.44	17.23	17.09	
DIFF IN LGTH OF JACKS 16 INS CTRS						28 7/8	27 3/4	26 11/16	25 5/8	24 9/16	23 5/8	22 5/8	21 11/16	20 13/16	20-0	19 1/4	18 1/2	17 7/8	17 5/16	16 7/8	16 1/2	16 1/4	
2 FEET						43 1/4	41 5/8	40-0	38 7/16	36 7/8	35 3/8	33 15/16	32 9/16	31 1/4	30-0	28 7/8	27 13/16	26 13/16	26-0	25 5/16	24 3/4	24 5/16	
SIDE CUT OF JACKS USE						6 11/16	6 15/16	7 3/16	7 1/2	7 13/16	8 1/8	8 1/2	8 7/8	9 3/8	9 5/8	10-0	10 3/8	10 3/4	11 1/16	11 3/8	11 5/8	11 13/16	
HIP OR VALLEY						8 1/4	8 1/2	8 3/4	9-0	9 1/4	9 1/2	9 13/16	10 1/16	10 5/16	10 5/8	10 7/8	11 1/8	11 1/2	11 11/16	11 13/16	11 15/16		

   c) Use the Formula: $a^2 + b^2 = c^2$
      Substitute: $4^2 + 12^2 = c^2$
      Calculate: $16 + 144 = c^2$
                     $160 = c^2$
                   $\sqrt{160} = c$
             $12.6491 = c$
               $12.65 = c$ [12.65 inches = 1 unit of Common Rafter]

3. To find the "Total Rise", multiply the <u>run</u> times the height of each specific unit.

Example: →4 (rise of each unit)
                 x 4 Run
               16" = 1'4"   Total Rise

How to Lay Out Rafters — Common, Hip, and Jacks (continued)

How to Lay Out Common Rafters:

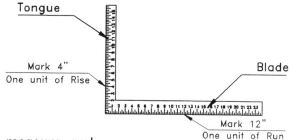

1. a) Mark (4"), the "Rise" of one unit on the <u>Tongue</u> of the Square, as shown.

   b) Mark (12"), the "Run" of one unit on the <u>Blade</u> of the Square, as shown.

2. a) Mark the Bow of the Rafter "UP". b) Then, measure and Mark (50 5/8—"), the Length of the Common Rafter", as shown below.

   c) Mark the "Center" of the Ridge Board.

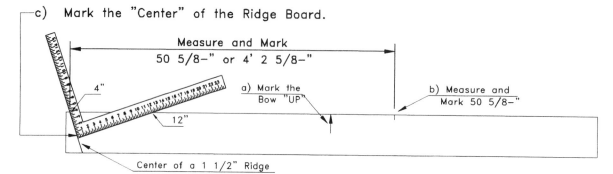

3. a) Mark the "Plumb Line (Building Edge)", as shown.

   b) Mark 1/2 the thickness of the Ridge.

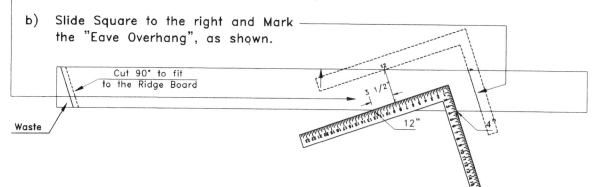

4. a) Mark the "Seat Cut (Width of Top Plate)", as shown.

   b) Slide Square to the right and Mark the "Eave Overhang", as shown.

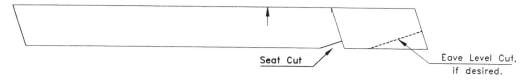

5. a) Mark final lines, and "Cut" the Common Rafter, as shown below.

© Copyright 2005 Chenier Educational Enterprises, Inc.

How to Lay Out Rafters – Common, Hip, and Jacks (continued)

How to Calculate Hip or Valley Rafters:

1. To find the length of the "Hip (or Valley) Rafter", multiply the <u>run</u> times the <u>hypotenuse</u> of each unit.

    Example:

    <u>**One Unit Hip**</u>

    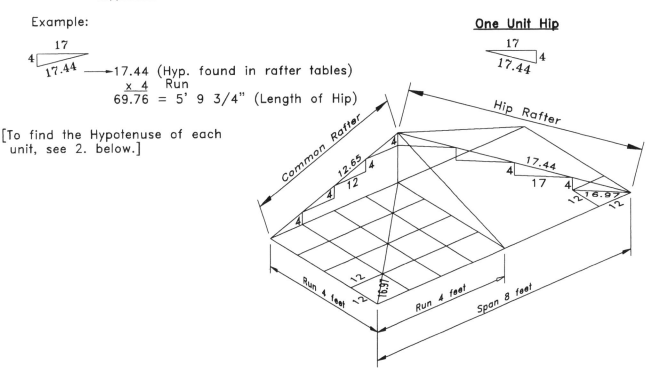

    17.44 (Hyp. found in rafter tables)
    x 4   Run
    69.76 = 5' 9 3/4" (Length of Hip)

    [To find the Hypotenuse of each unit, see 2. below.]

2. To find the "Hypotenuse" of each unit of "Hip Rafter", use the rafter tables, shown below. Or, use the Formula: $a^2 + b^2 = c^2$

    a) Refer to the Length of Hip or Valley Per Ft. Run Column (Column 2).

    b) Look, directly, under the 4 in that column.
        Read 17.44, this is the hypotenuse of 4 and 17.

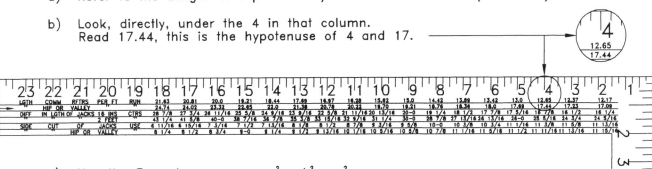

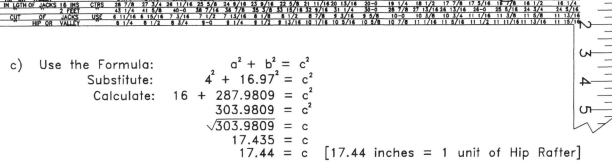

    c) Use the Formula: $a^2 + b^2 = c^2$
        Substitute: $4^2 + 16.97^2 = c^2$
        Calculate: $16 + 287.9809 = c^2$
                         $303.9809 = c^2$
                     $\sqrt{303.9809} = c$
                           $17.435 = c$
                            $17.44 = c$ [17.44 inches = 1 unit of Hip Rafter]

How to Lay Out Rafters — Common, Hip, and Jacks (continued)

How to Lay Out Hip or Valley Rafters:

1. a) Mark (4"), the "Rise" of one unit on the <u>Tonque</u> of the Square, as shown.

    b) Mark (17"), the "Run" of one unit on the <u>Blade</u> of the Square, as shown.

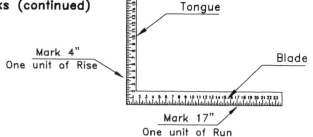

2. a) Mark the Bow of the Hip Rafter "UP". b) Then, measure and mark (69 3/4"), the Length of the Hip or Valley Rafter", as shown below.

    c) Mark the "Center" of the Ridge Board.

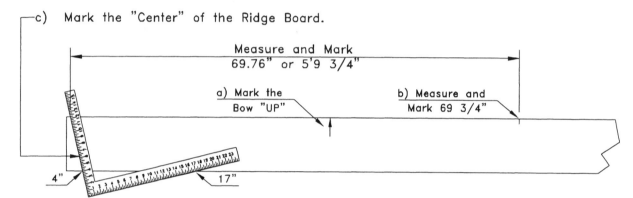

3. a) Mark the "Plumb Line (Building Edge)", as shown.

    b) Mark <u>1/2 the 45° thickness</u> of the Ridge.

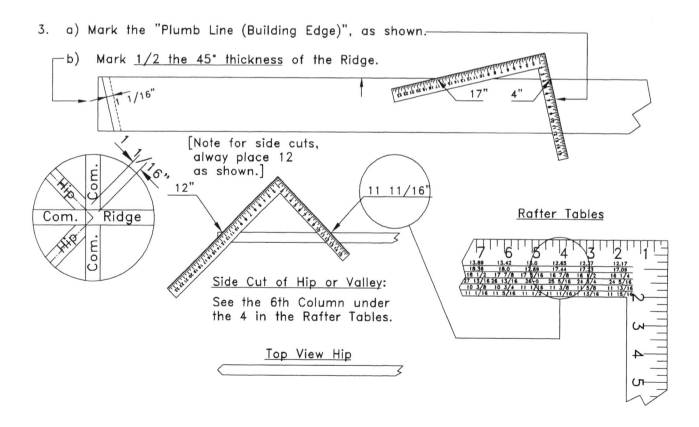

© Copyright 2005 Chenier Educational Enterprises, Inc.

How to Lay Out Rafters — Common, Hip, and Jacks (continued)

How to Lay Out Hip or Valley Rafters (continued):

4. a) Mark the "Seat Cut". The "Heel" will determine the size of the "Seat Cut" because it <u>must be</u> the same size as the "Heel" of the Common Rafter.

   b) Calculate the "Hip Drop", which is <u>the slope of 1/2 the thickness of the Hip Rafter</u>. In this case the Hip Drop is 3/16", as shown below.

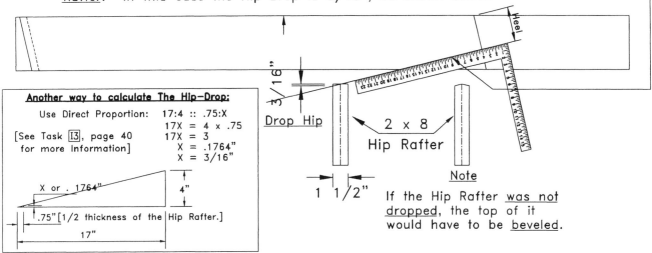

Another way to calculate The Hip-Drop:

Use Direct Proportion: 17:4 :: .75:X

[See Task 13, page 40 for more Information]

$$17X = 4 \times .75$$
$$17X = 3$$
$$X = .1764"$$
$$X = 3/16"$$

X or .1764"   4"

.75" [1/2 thickness of the Hip Rafter.]

17"

Drop Hip

2 x 8
Hip Rafter

1 1/2"

Note
If the Hip Rafter <u>was not dropped</u>, the top of it would have to be <u>beveled</u>.

5. a) Mark the Hip Drop (3/16" in this case) above the Seat Cut".

   b) Slide the Square to the right and Mark the "Eave Overhang", as shown.

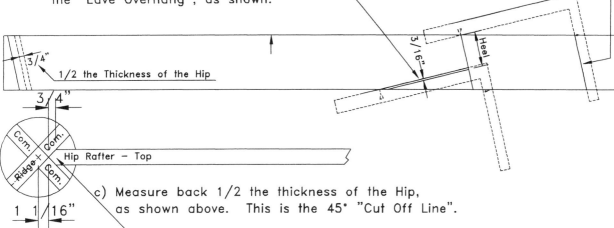

3/4"

1/2 the Thickness of the Hip

3/4"

Com. Com.
Ridge + Com.
Com.

Hip Rafter — Top

1 1/16"

   c) Measure back 1/2 the thickness of the Hip, as shown above. This is the 45° "Cut Off Line".

5. a) Mark final lines, and "Cut" the Rafter, as shown below.

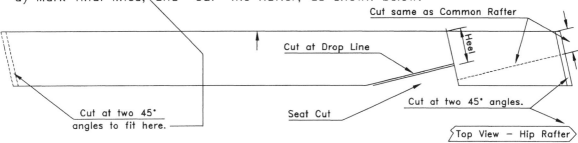

Cut same as Common Rafter

Cut at Drop Line

Heel

Cut at two 45° angles to fit here.

Seat Cut

Cut at two 45° angles.

Top View — Hip Rafter

How to Lay Out Rafters – Common, Hip, and Jacks (continued)

How to Calculate Hip or Valley Jack Rafters:

1. To find the length of the "Hip (or Valley) Jack Rafter", subtract the difference in in Centers (16" O.C. or 24" O.C.) from the Common Rafter.

   Example: The "Jacks" shown below are 16" O.C. Therefore, the difference is 16 7/8". [See 2. below.]

Com. Rafter = 50.600"
Jack Differ. = −16.875" (16 7/8")
Jack #1 = 33.725" (33 3/4")

Jack #1 = 33.725"
Jack Dif. = −16.875"
Jack #2 = 16.85" (16 7/8")

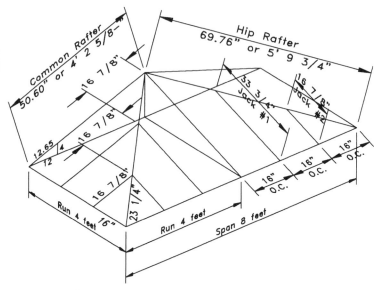

2. To find the Difference in Length of Jacks 16" (or 24") On Center is, use the rafter tables, shown below. Or, use "Direct Proportion" and the Formula: $a^2 + b^2 = c^2$.

   a) Refer to the Difference in Length of Jacks 16 in. On Centers Column (Column 3).

   b) Look, directly, under the 4 in that column.
   Read 16 7/8", this is how far a 4/12 slope extends 16", see c).

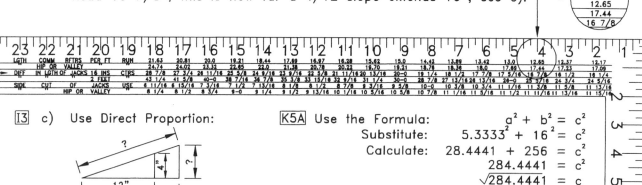

			4
			12.65
			17.44
			16 7/8

23	22	21	20	19	18	17	16	15	14	13	12	11	10	9	8	7	6	5	4	3	2	1
LGTH	COMM	RFTRS	PER FT	RUN	21.63	20.81	20.0	19.21	18.44	17.69	16.97	16.28	15.62	15.0	14.42	13.89	13.42	13.0	12.65	12.37	12.17	
	HIP OR	VALLEY			24.74	24.02	23.32	22.65	22.0	21.38	20.78	20.22	19.70	19.21	18.76	18.36	18.0	17.69	17.44	17.23	17.09	
DIFF	IN LGTH OF JACKS 16 INS CTRS				26 7/8	27 3/4	26 11/16	25 5/8	24 9/16	23 9/16	22 5/8	21 11/16	20 13/16	20-0	19 1/4	18 1/2	17 7/8	17 5/16	16 7/8	16 1/2	16 1/4	
		2 FEET			43 1/4	41 5/8	40-0	38 7/16	36 7/8	35 3/8	33 15/16	32 9/16	31 1/4	30-0	28 7/8	27 13/16	26 13/16	26-0	25 5/16	24 3/4	24 5/16	
SIDE	CUT	OF	JACKS	USE	6 11/16	6 15/16	7 3/16	7 1/2	7 13/16	8 1/8	8 1/2	8 7/8	9 3/16	9 5/8	10-0	10 3/8	10 3/4	11 1/16	11 3/8	11 5/8	11 13/16	
		HIP OR	VALLEY		8 1/4	8 1/2	8 3/4	9-0	9 1/4	9 1/2	9 13/16	10 1/16	10 5/16	10 5/8	10 7/8	11 1/16	11 5/16	11 1/2	11 11/16	11 13/16	11 15/16	

13 c) Use Direct Proportion:

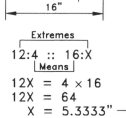

Extremes
12:4 :: 16:X
[Means]
12X = 4 × 16
12X = 64
X = 5.3333"

K5A Use the Formula: $a^2 + b^2 = c^2$

Substitute: $5.3333^2 + 16^2 = c^2$

Calculate: $28.4441 + 256 = c^2$

$284.4441 = c^2$

$\sqrt{284.4441} = c$

$16.8655 = c$

16 7/8" = c

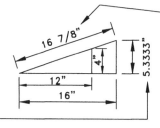

How to Lay Out Rafters — Common, Hip, and Jacks (continued)

How to Lay Out Hip or Valley Jack Rafters:

1. a) Mark (4") on the <u>tongue</u> of the Square, and Mark (12") on the <u>Blade</u> of the Square. This is the same procedure as laying out the Common Rafter. Mark the Bow "UP".

   b) Measure and Mark (33 3/4-"), the Length of the Jack Rafter, as shown below.

   c) Mark the "Center" of the Hip Rafter.

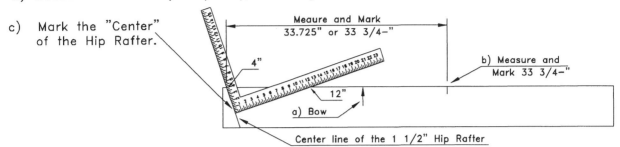

Meaure and Mark
33.725" or 33 3/4-"

4"

12"

a) Bow

b) Measure and Mark 33 3/4-"

Center line of the 1 1/2" Hip Rafter

3. a) Mark the "Plumb Line (Building Edge)", as shown.

1 1/16"

Jack Plumb Line

Hip

Jack Rafter

3/4"

1 1/16"
3/4"
12"
4"

b) Measure back 1 1/16" from the Hip Center Line to the center of the Jack. Then back from that line 3/4" to get the Jack Plumb Edge.

Rafter Tables

Side Cut of Jacks:
See the 5th Column under the 4 in the Rafter Tables.

[Note for side cuts always place 12 as shown.]

12"

11 3/8"

7	6	5	4	3	2	1
13.89	13.42	13.0	12.65	12.37	12.17	
18.36	18.0	17.69	17.44	17.23	17.09	
18 1/2	17 7/8	17 5/16	16 7/8	16 1/2	16 1/4	
27 13/16	26 13/16	26 0	25 5/16	24 3/4	24 5/16	
10 3/8	10 3/4	11 1/16	11 3/8	11 5/8	11 13/16	
11 1/16	11 5/16	11 1/2	11 11/16	11 13/16	11 15/16	

1
2
3
4
5

4. Mark the "Seat Cut" (same as the Common Rafter), then Mark the "Eave OverHang", as shown on the right.

Cut 45°

3 1/2"
12"
4"

5. a) Mark final lines, and "Cut" the Jack Rafter, as shown below.

Top View Jack

Seat Cut

Eave Level Cut, if desired.

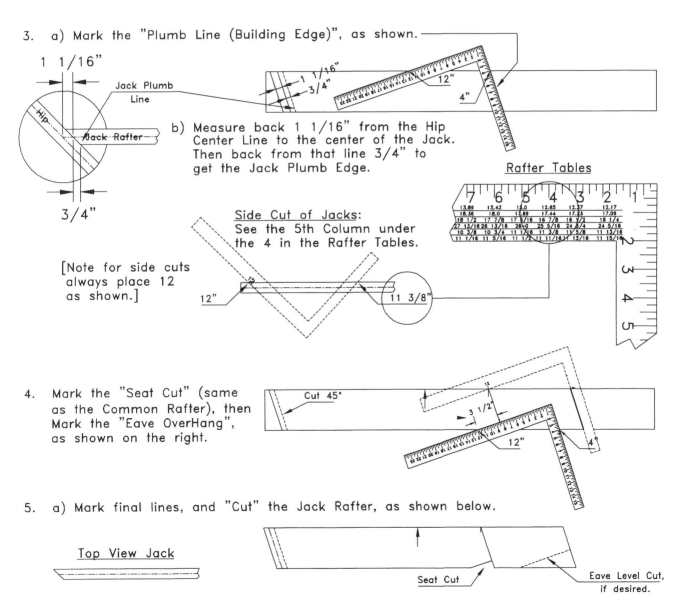

How to Lay Out Rafters — Common, Hip, and Jacks (continued)

The Slant Line Method:

The slant—line method of scaling for rafters (common, hip, and jacks) is a unique way of estimating their material sizes and making an actual parts size list. This can be done on—the—job or in the shop. An advantage of this technique is that it brings all the component parts together so they can be scaled, checked, and a material count can be made of them.

How to Estimate the Common, Hip, and Jack Rafters via the Slant—Line Method:

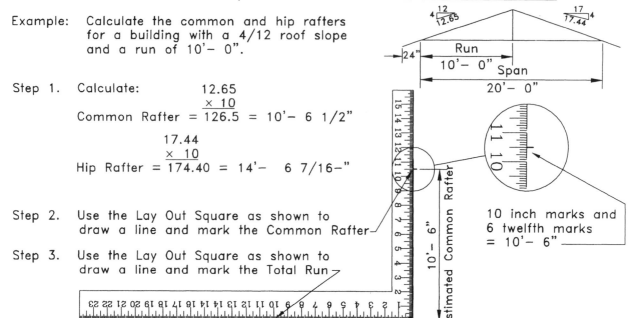

Example: Calculate the common and hip rafters for a building with a 4/12 roof slope and a run of 10'— 0".

Step 1. Calculate:

$$\begin{array}{r} 12.65 \\ \times\ 10 \\ \hline \end{array}$$
Common Rafter = 126.5 = 10'— 6 1/2"

$$\begin{array}{r} 17.44 \\ \times\ 10 \\ \hline \end{array}$$
Hip Rafter = 174.40 = 14'— 6 7/16—"

10 inch marks and
6 twelfth marks
= 10'— 6"

Step 2. Use the Lay Out Square as shown to draw a line and mark the Common Rafter

Step 3. Use the Lay Out Square as shown to draw a line and mark the Total Run

10'— 0" Total Run

Step 4. Mark the Jack Rafters 16" O.C. (On Center) in this case. 16" (1 in & 4 marks), 32" (2 in. & 8 marks), 48" (4 in. marks), 64" (5 in. & 4 marks), etc. Use "T" marks.

Step 5. Reposition the the Lay Out Square from the drawing surface shown above to: Measure, and mark the Hip Rafter as shown below on the left.

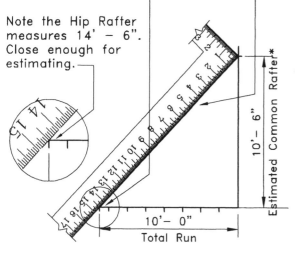

Note the Hip Rafter measures 14' — 6". Close enough for estimating.

10'— 0" Total Run

Step 6. Scale the Jacks with the Lay Out Square. Or calculate them to make a parts list. Don't forget to allow for the overhang.

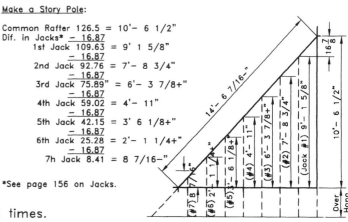

Make a Story Pole:

Common Rafter 126.5 = 10'— 6 1/2"
Dif. in Jacks* — 16.87
   1st Jack 109.63 = 9' 1 5/8"
        — 16.87
   2nd Jack 92.76 = 7'— 8 3/4"
        — 16.87
   3rd Jack 75.89" = 6'— 3 7/8+"
        — 16.87
   4th Jack 59.02 = 4'— 11"
        — 16.87
   5th Jack 42.15 = 3' 6 1/8+"
        — 16.87
   6th Jack 25.28 = 2'— 1 1/4+"
        — 16.87
   7h Jack 8.41 = 8 7/16—"

*See page 156 on Jacks.

*Accuracy can be difficult scaled down 12 times.

Objective Practice Problems for Module #15

How to Lay Out Rafters (Common, Shed, Hip, and Jacks) — Info #13 (carry decimals 3 places):

1. Calculate <u>the rafter lengths</u> and the <u>total rise</u> of the rafter drawings on the right.

   Common Rafter = _____

   Hip Rafter = _____

   Total Rise = _____

   Difference in Jacks (16" O.C.) = _____

   Slope Angle = _____ °

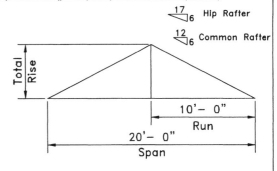

2. Calculate <u>the rafter lengths</u> and the <u>total rise</u> of the rafter drawings on the right.

   Common Rafter = _____

   Hip Rafter = _____

   Total Rise = _____

   Difference in Jacks (24" O.C.) = _____

   Slope Angle = _____ °

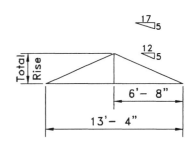

3. Calculate <u>the rafter lengths</u> and the <u>total rise</u> of the rafter drawings on the right.

   Shed (Common) Rafter = _____

   Total Rise = _____

   Slope Angle = _____ °

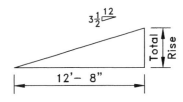

Objective Practice Problems for Module #15

Use a scientific calculator (Info #6) and/or the textbook trig tables to find the angles of the angle functions listed below.

4. Cos. .9205 = _____ °

5. Tan. .21255 = _____ °

6. Sin. .58778 = _____ °

7. Cos. .6018 = _____ °

8. Sin. .42261 = _____ °

9. Cos. .01745 = _____ °

10. Tan. 7.1153 = _____ °

11. Sin. .32556 = _____ °

Review Lay Out Angles with a Lay Out Square — Info #12 (change to the nearest 1/2 degree):

12. Angle A on the right measures 12" and 4 1/2" the lay out square.

   Calculate angle A = _____ °.

   Calculate angle B = _____ °.

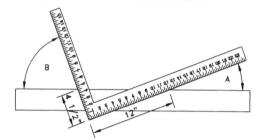

13. The slope of a roof is 6/12.

   The Slope Angle = _____ °?

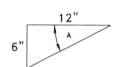

14. Angle A on the right measures 12" and 6 15/16".

   Calculate angle A = _____ °.

   Calculate angle B = _____ °.

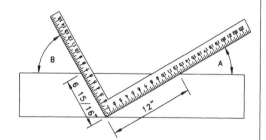

15. The Stair Angle A = _____ °.

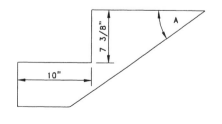

Math Training Module #16

Instructional Objectives:

Hands On:

☐ *Application Problem* - Practice Laying Out Basic Stairs on 1/4" plywood. Calculate the Stair Angles.

☐ *Application Problem* - Practice Laying Out Common Rafters on a 2 × 4. Calculate the Slope Degrees.

Objective Practice Problems: Calculate the Practice Problems for Math Training Module #16 ....

Basic Math Study Notes (Basic Stair Terminology, Parts, and Lay Out Tips):

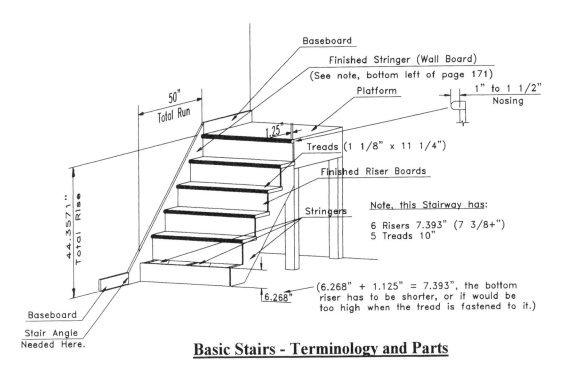

Basic Stairs - Terminology and Parts

Info #14 on the next 5 pages demonstrates how to calculate and lay out basic stairs. This module can also be used as reference for Math Training Module #17 page 169, Info #14B (Platform Stairs) page 171, Info #14C (Winder Stairs) page 173, and Info #14D (Spiral Stairs) page 175.

Basic Stair Study Notes (Continued)

Basic Stair Lay Out Tips:

Tip #1.   If are laying out stairs for the first time, make a sample pattern of the stairs on a piece of plywood or heavy cardboard. This can be much cheaper than practicing on a piece of expensive stringer board.

Tip #2.   When laying out the steps on the stringer, use square clips as a guide to step each step out. The clips enable the square to glide on the stringer so you don't have to re-measure the steps each time.

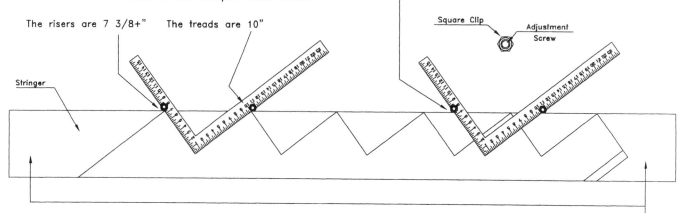

Tip #3.   The stair stringer, especially for beginners, should be purchased so it is long enough to be able to manipulate the Lay Out Square on both ends.

Tip #4.   For long stairs where precision is needed, make a story pole using the Rule of Pythagoras $a^2 + b^2 = c^2$. See page 166.

How to Calculate the Slope Angle of Stairs:

The slope angle is needed to set-up a cut-off saw to cut the stair angle for the finished stringer boards, hand rails, and the stair stringers.

Use the Formula: TOA (Tangent = Opposite/Adjacent)

Formula: Tan. = $\dfrac{\text{Opp.}}{\text{Adj.}}$

Substitute: Tan. = $\dfrac{7.393}{10}$

Calculate: Tan. = .7393

Tan.$^{-1}$ = 36.4755°

Answer =   36 1/2° (Close enough for this application)

[See Info #12, page 141, if more information is needed.]

A Protractor can also be used to find the slope angle of the stairs. It can also be used used to confirm the formula TOA works. Use the method that works best for you.

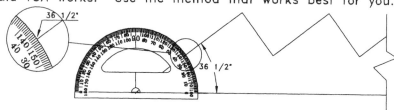

Info #14A – Calculate and Lay Out Basic Straight Stairs

How to Lay Out Basic Stairs in relation to Total Rise and Total Run:

Points to Remember:

1. The best combination for a stairway is between 17 and 18 inches, that means, the sum of the height of the riser and the width of the tread should add up to between 17 and 18 inches.

Example: Riser Height   7 1/2"
           +Tread Width   10"
            Equals   17 1/2" Ideal Stairs

2. If the riser would be 6 1/2" make the thread 11", or if the riser was 8", make the tread 9 1/2" to 10". Example adjust the riser and the tread so the sum adds up to 17–18 inches.

   In extreme cases this rule can be broken. For example, steep stairways to attics, steep stairs down cellars, steep stairs to mezzanines, etc.. However, make sure that local code rules are checked out and satisfied before construction.

3. To start, divide the total rise by the <u>key 7</u>. The figure 7 is a hypothetical height of a riser to start with.

Example: <u>Total rise 30"</u> divided by 7 equals 4, therefore, there are approximately 4 risers —— then divide the total rise by that figure 4, this will give you the exact height of each riser. 30" divided by 4 equals 7.5 or 7 1/2".

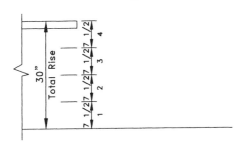

      4 approximate number of risers
Key 7/30" Total Rise

      7.5 or 7 1/2" height of each riser
4/30.0"
   28
   20
   20

Note: In some cases after dividing by the Key 7 results, the riser will be too high. Therefore, add one more riser and recalculate. the result will shorten all the risers. See the illustrations below.

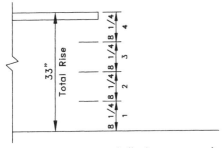

4 Risers 8 1/4" (too high*)

    4 approx.   8.25 = 8 1/4"
7/33   4/33.00
   28   32

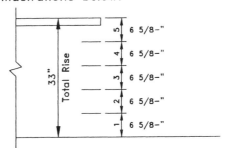

5 Risers 6 5/8-" (Risers OK)

      6.6 = 6 5/8-"
5/33.0
   30

*Most building code allow a maxium height of 8 1/4" for risers, and a minimum width of 9" for treads. An ideal stairs is considered to be 7 1/2" for the risers and 10" for the treads. See the next page for basic stair recommendations and rules.]

Lay Out Basic Straight Stairs (continued)
Points to Remember:

4. There is always one less tread than there is risers. Therefore, always divide the total run by the number of treads. [The only time that this rule would not be true is if the top step was used as a platform. This is unlikely and unsafe.]

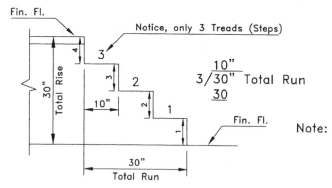

Risers 4   7 1/2"
+Treads 3   10 "
Combination 17 1/2" Excellent Stairs

Note: <u>Total Rise</u> is the "vertical distance from Finish Floor to Finish Floor". <u>Total Run</u> is the "horizontal distance the stairs will cover".

5. After the risers and treads are laid out, the thickness of the tread <u>must be subtracted off the bottom of the stringer</u>. This does not apply to masonry steps. See the illustrations below:

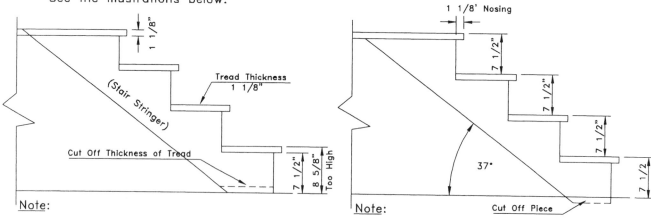

Note:

The first riser is <u>too high</u>. Therefore, <u>the thickness of the tread must be subtracted off the bottom of the stringer</u>. **This would be UNSAFE.**

Note:

The first riser is the same as all of the risers because the stringer dropped 1 1/8 inches, the thickness of the treads. **This is a SAFE Stairway.**

Basic Recommendations and Rules:

− The stair <u>nosing</u> should not exceed 1 3/4" (can vary from 1" to 1 3/4").
− The <u>preferred angle for a safe stairway</u> is approximately between 30° and 35°**.
− The recommended width of steps is 36", but 42" is preferred (32" is minimum).
− The minimum <u>headroom</u> for stairs is generally 6'− 8" (can vary by local codes and applications) vertical of the stairwell header to the <u>stair nosing line</u> . See page 170.

Rule #1 − The best riser and tread combination is between 17" and 18".
Rule #2 − The sum of 2 risers plus 1 tread should equal <u>approximately 25"</u>.
Rule #3 − The height of the riser times the tread should equal <u>approximately 75</u>.

*Stair angles can vary from 20° to 50°. It is up to the builder to insure a safe stairs and keep within the recommended proportions and rules stated above.

Lay Out Basic Straight Stairs (continued)

How to Lay Out the Stair Stringer:

1. a) Mark the "Riser" height on the Tongue of the Square as shown below.
   b) Mark the "Tread" width on the Blade of the Square as shown below.

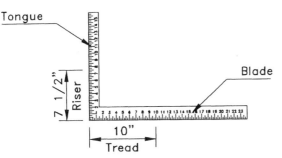

2. Step off the number or Risers (4) and Treads (3) as shown below.
   Line up the Risers and Treads carefully and use a sharp Pencil.

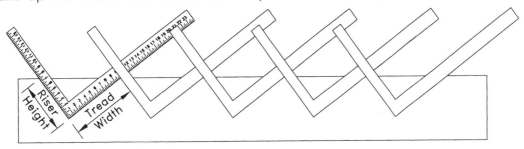

3. Finish the Lay Out of the Stair Stringer as shown below.

Mark the Crown (Bow) of the board up.

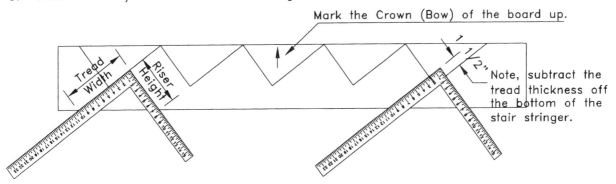

Note, subtract the tread thickness off the bottom of the stair stringer.

4. Cut out Riser and Tread lines as shown below.

Note to find the angle of the stairs, use TOA:

$$\text{Tan} = \frac{\text{opp}}{\text{adj}}$$

$$\text{Tan} = \frac{7.5"}{10"}$$

$$\text{Tan} = .75$$

$$\text{Tan}^{-1} = 36.86° \text{ or } 37°$$

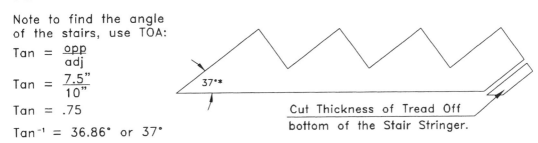

37°*

Cut Thickness of Tread Off bottom of the Stair Stringer.

*Note the stair angle of 37° will come in handy to cut the finish stringer and trim, if the strairs is to be finished later. See page 141 and 162 for more information on TOA.

Lay Out Basic Straight Stairs (continued)

How to make a "Stair Story Pole" using the Rule of Pythagoras:

This procedure is ideal for stairs that have to fit exactly between two platforms. Consider the stair stringer shown below had 14 treads instead of 5 as shown. And each time a 1/16 of an inch error was made. That would be 7/8" off. Realistically this can happen very easily. One way to help prevent this is to make a story pole of all the stair <u>hypotenuses</u> as shown below.

Use the Formula: $a^2 + b^2 = c^2$
Substitute: $7.393^2 + 10^2 = c^2$
Calculate: $54.656 + 100 = c^2$
$ 154.656 = c^2$
$ \sqrt{154.656} = c$
$ 12.436 = c$
$ 12\ 7/16" = c$

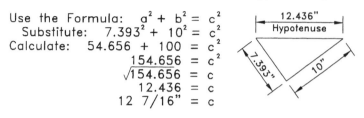

Make a Story Pole:

1st dimension 12.436 = 1'- 0 7/16"
$ + 12.436$
2nd dimension 24.872 = 2''- 0 7/8"
$ + 12.436$
3rd dimension 37.308 = 3'- 1 5/16-"
$ + 12.436$
4th dimension 49.744 = 4'- 1 3/4"
$ + 12.436"$
5th dimension 62.180 = 5'- 2 3/16"
and so on ......

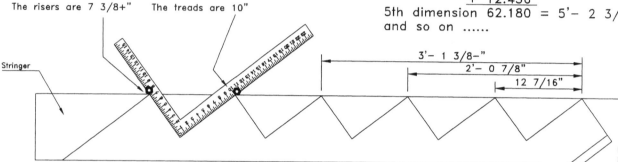

[Use the Step-Off Method shown above with the Story Pole Method and many mistakes can be alleviated. One method will check the other. Use the system that works best for you.]

Basic Steps and Hand Rails Heights:

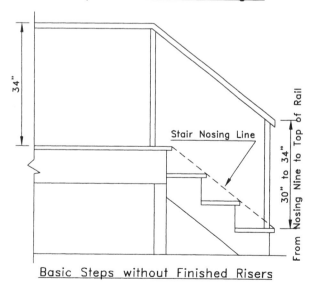

Basic Steps without Finished Risers

[Note there are many different variations of finished stairs. They can have mortised risers and treads, mortised stringers, mitered risers boards to the stringers, and so forth.]

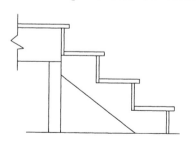

Basic Steps with Finished Risers

Basic Step Widths:

The recommended width of steps is 36 inches, but 42" is preferred (32" is minimum).

Objective Practice Problems for Module #16

<u>How to Calculate and Lay Out Basic Stairs – Info #14A (carry decimals 3 places)</u>:

1. Calculate the stairs shown on the right. Fill in the blanks below and give the answers to the nearest ±1/16th of an inch.

    Number of risers ____   Height of risers ____

    Number of treads ____   Width of treads ____

    Total Run _____

    Stair Angle = _____.°

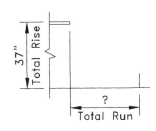

2. Calculate the Stairs shown on the right. Fill in the blanks below and give the answers to the nearest ±1/16th of an inch.

    Number of risers ____   Height of risers ____

    Number of treads ____   Width of treads ____

    Total Run _____

    Stair Angle = _____.°

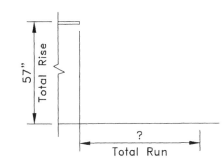

<u>Review How to Lay Out Rafters – Info #13 (carry decimals 3 places)</u>:

3. Calculate <u>the rafter lengths</u> and the <u>total rise</u> of the rafter drawings on the right.

    Common Rafter = _____

    Hip Rafter = _____

    Total Rise = _____

    Difference in Jacks (16" O.C.) = _____

    Slope Angle = _____.°

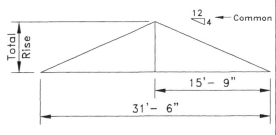

Objective Practice Problems for Module #16

1. A specific angle calculates to be 35.83765°.   Lay out the angle with a lay out square.

The Blade (long side of the square) will read _____ inches.
The Tongue (short side of the square will read _____ inches.
The angle opposite is _____°.

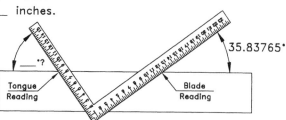

2. Draw a sketch and explain how to lay out a 10° angle with a lay out square in the space provided below.

The Blade will read _____ inches.
The Tongue will read _____ inches.
The angle opposite is ____°.

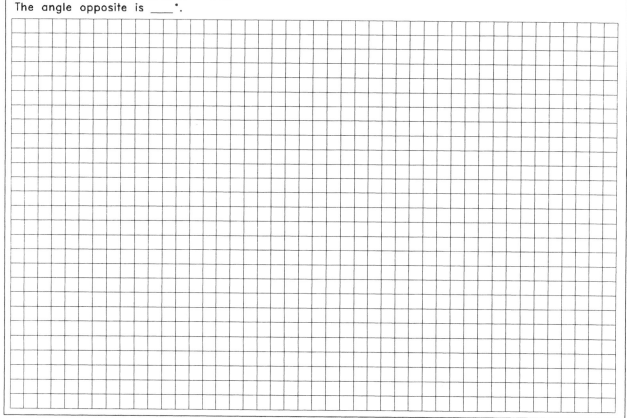

Math Training Module #17

Instructional Objectives:

Hands On:

☐   *Application Problem* - Practice Laying Out Different Kinds of Stairs on a sheet of paper. Calculate the Stair Angles.

☐   *Application Problem* - Practice Laying Out Basic Stairs on 1/4" plywood. Calculate the Stair Angles.

Objective Practice Problems: Calculate the Practice Problems for Math Training Module #17 .... 179, 180

Basic Math Study Notes (Types of Stairs and Minimum Headroom):

Types of Stairs:

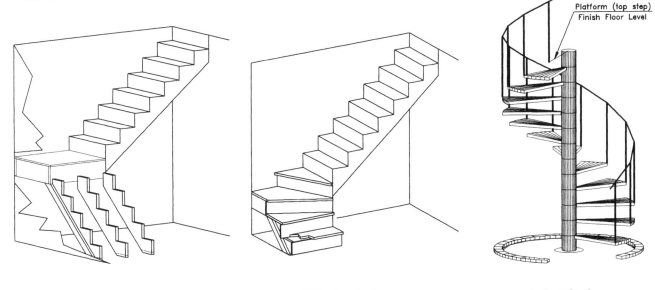

Straight and Platform Stairs
(See Info #14B, page 171)

Winder Stairs
(See Info #14C, page 173)

Spiral Stairs
(See Info #14D, page 175)

Note: Use Math Training Module #16 page 161, and Info #14A page 163, in conjunction with the different stairways shown above, as the basic rules of building stairs are applied toward all of them.

Basic Study Notes (Continued):

Minimum Headroom:

The minimum <u>headroom</u> for main stairs is 6'– 8" vertical of the stairwell header to the <u>stair nosing line</u>. Main stair headroom, basement headroom, and service headroom can vary. Check with local codes before constructing stairs, if in doubt.

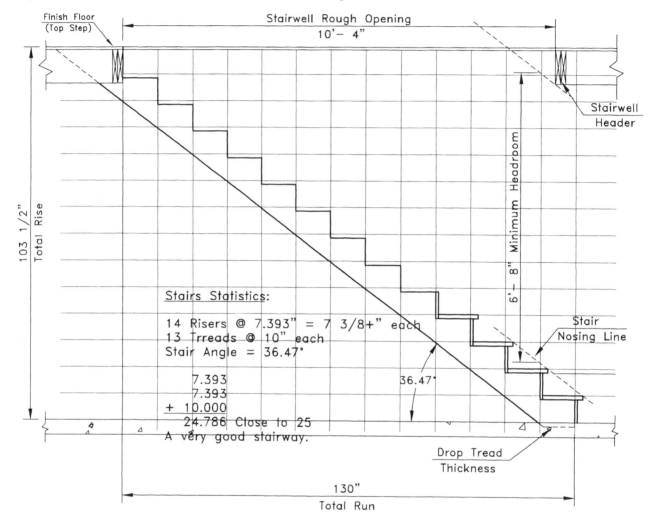

Stairs Statistics:

14 Risers @ 7.393" = 7 3/8+" each
13 Treads @ 10" each
Stair Angle = 36.47°

```
   7.393
   7.393
+ 10.000
  24.786 Close to 25
```
A very good stairway.

[Note the 12th side of the Lay Out Square can be used to draw a typical stairs. See Info #11B, page 136, and Trade Trick #3, page 77–78 for more information.]

1st — Use a Lay Out Square to draw all the dimensions lines for the stairs from the information shown above. Draw light lines then darken when ready. Use a piece of plywood, poster board, and/or a sheet of paper.

2st — Divide the vertical distance from Finish Floor to Finish Floor by 14 spaces.

3nd — Divide the horizontal distance from the first step to the last step by 13 spaces. Use light lines then darken when finished.

4th — Dimension and finish the drawing. Draw a rough sketch each time you build a stairway. It will become easier each time. Practice makes perfect.

Info #14B – Calculate Stairs
with Platforms

How to Calculate Stairs with Platforms. Use in Conjunction with the Basic Stairs Module:

Total Rise = 103.5" (Rise A 59.142856" + Rise B 44.357142" = 103.499998")

Rise A = 59.142856" (59 1/8+") Or 8 Risers   7.392857" (7 3/8+") each
Run A = 66" (5'– 6")   Or 7 Treads + 9.428571" (9 7/16–") each
                                           16.821428 = Close to 17*

Rise B = 44.357142" (44 5/16+") Or 6 Risers 7.392857" (7 3/8+")
Run B = 47.142857" (47 1/8+")   Or 5 Treads 9.428571" (9 7/16–")

Slope Angle: [Note, carry the decimal at least 3 places.]

Formula: TOA
Tan. = Opp./Adj.
Tan. = 7.393/9.429
Tan. = .784153
Tan.⁻¹ = 38.10°

38.10° / 9.428"   7.393"

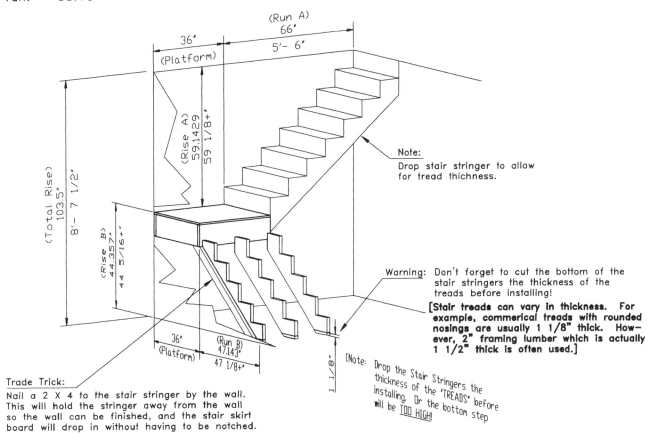

(Run A)
66'
5'– 6'

36'
(Platform)

(Rise A)
59.1429
59 1/8+"

(Total Rise)
103.5"
8'– 7 1/2"

(Rise B)
44.357"
44 5/16+"

36'
(Platform)

(Run B)
47.143'
47 1/8+"

1 1/8'

Note:
Drop stair stringer to allow
for tread thichness.

Warning: Don't forget to cut the bottom of the
stair stringers the thickness of the
treads before installing!

[Stair treads can vary in thickness. For
example, commerical treads with rounded
nosings are usually 1 1/8" thick. However, 2" framing lumber which is actually
1 1/2" thick is often used.]

[Note: Drop the Stair Stringers the
thickness of the 'TREADS' before
installing. Or the bottom step
will be TOO HIGH!

Trade Trick:
Nail a 2 X 4 to the stair stringer by the wall.
This will hold the stringer away from the wall
so the wall can be finished, and the stair skirt
board will drop in without having to be notched.

*See the Basic Straight Stairs Module in regards to the 17–18 combination, page 163.

How to Calculate Stair with Platform (Continued)

Types of Platform Stairs:

Listed below are some of the different types of platform stairs.

Straight Stairs with landing.

Used when the total rise is greater than 15 steps
The landing serves as a rest point (refer to local
codes if building this types of stairs).

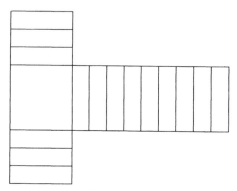

Platform with two Offset Stairs.

Occasionally used in foyers, basements, public
building, etc.

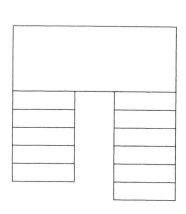

Single Platform 180° Turn.

Used in limited space areas, foyers, basements, etc.

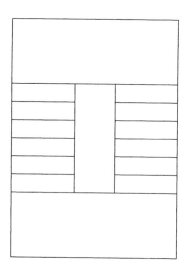

Double Platform 360° Turn.

Used in limited space areas to access
upper floors and for fire escapes.

Info #14C – Calculate Stairs with Winders

How to Calculate Stairs with Winders. Use in Conjunction with the Basic Stairs Module:

Total Rise = 94" (62.6664" + 23.4999" + 7.833")

Rise A = 62.6664" (62 5/8+") <u>Or</u> 8 Risers 7.8333" (7 13/16+")
Run A = 66" (5'– 6") <u>Or</u> 7 Treads 9.42857" (9 7/16")

Rise B = 23.4999" (23 1/2") <u>Or</u> 3 Risers 7.8333"
Run B = 32" (2'– 8") <u>Or</u> 3 Treads (varied sizes*)

Rise C = 7.833" (7 13/16+") <u>Or</u> 1 Riser
Run C = 9.429" (9 7/16") <u>Or</u> 1 Tread

*The winder square in most cases will be 32" or 36".

Slope Angle: [Note, carry the decimal at least 3 places.]

Formula: TOA
Tan. = Opp./Adj.
Tan. = 7.833"/9.429"
Tan.$^{-1}$ = .83073
Tan. = 39.718°

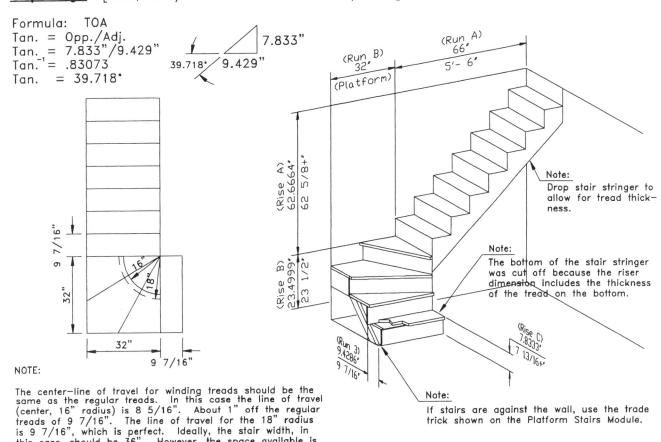

9 7/16"

32"

32"

9 7/16"

(Run B) 32" (Platform)

(Run A) 66" 5'– 6"

(Rise A) 62.6664" 62 5/8+"

(Rise B) 23.4999" 23 1/2"

(Run 3) 9.4286" 9 7/16"

(Rise C) 7.8333" 7 13/16+"

Note: Drop stair stringer to allow for tread thickness.

Note: The bottom of the stair stringer was cut off because the riser dimension includes the thickness of the tread on the bottom.

Note: If stairs are against the wall, use the trade trick shown on the Platform Stairs Module.

NOTE:

The center-line of travel for winding treads should be the same as the regular treads. In this case the line of travel (center, 16" radius) is 8 5/16". About 1" off the regular treads of 9 7/16". The line of travel for the 18" radius is 9 7/16", which is perfect. Ideally, the stair width, in this case, should be 36". However, the space available is sometimes the factor here. Use your own judgement on this and check local codes, if in doubt.

The circumference for the 16" arc is 25.1327" ÷ 3 = 8.378"
The circumference for the 18" arc is 28.2743" ÷ 3 = 9.425"

Note: These types of stairs are more dangerous because of the change of tread size (from normal to wedge shaped). However for lofts, basements, garages, etc. the the winders stairs are acceptable. Check with local codes before constructing.

How to Calculate Stair with Winders (Continued)

Types of Winder Stairs:

Listed below are some of the different types of winder stairs. Note how the winder treads are located toward the bottom of the stairs. This is a safe practice to follow.

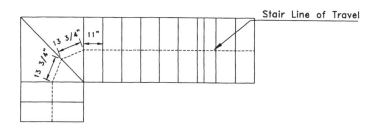

Two Tread Winders.

Note the line of travel on the two tread winders can vary more, but if the treads are wider and the risers are lower (17-18 combo), as shown on the right, this can be a very comfortable and safer stairway.

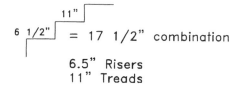

= 17 1/2" combination

6.5" Risers
11" Treads

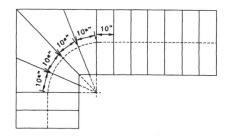

Four Tread Modified Winders.

Note how the tread width is closer to the treads on the straight line of travel.

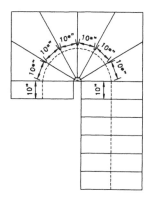

Six Tread "U" Shaped Winders.

Note if laid out correctly, the winder treads can be close to the straight line of travel treads.

*Care must be taken when designing winder stairs to be consistant with the tread sizes.

Info #14D – Calculate and Lay Out Spiral Stairs

How to Calculate Spiral Stairs. Use in Conjunction with Basic Stairs Module:

Step 1.   Calculate stair risers in relation to the total rise.   Example:

$$\frac{15}{7 \overline{)105.5}} \text{ Approx. Steps} \qquad \frac{7.0333"}{15 \overline{)105.5"}} \text{ Too narrow for most applications.}$$

$$\frac{7.5357"}{14 \overline{)105.5"}} \text{ Perfect for most applications.}$$

Stairs:
13 Risers 8.115"
12 Treads (Special)

$$\frac{8.1153"}{13 \overline{)105.5"}}$$ Good for this project because the stairs are going in a basement. One less tread will make the circumference less.

105 1/2" Total Rise

Step 2.   Lay out risers on 1/4" plywood as shown.   Chalk lines, <u>or</u> use a "T" Square.

(Hint: Make a story pole of all the dimensions for greater accuracy.

8.115"	=	8 1/8–"
+ 8.115"		
16.230"	=	16 1/4–"
+ 8.115"		
24.345"	=	24 3/8–"
+ 8.115"		
32.460"	=	32 7/16+"
+ 8.115"		
40.575"	=	40 9/16+"
+ 8.115"		
48.690"	=	48 11/16"
+ 8.115"		
56.805"	=	56 13/16–"
+ 8.115"		
64.920"	=	64 15/16–"

And so on ....

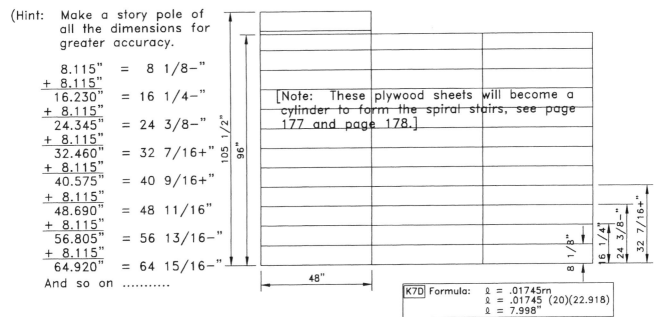

[Note: These plywood sheets will become a cylinder to form the spiral stairs, see page 177 and page 178.]

105 1/2"   96"   48"

8 1/8"   16 1/4–"   24 3/8–"   32 7/16+"

K7D Formula: ℓ = .01745rn
ℓ = .01745 (20)(22.918)
ℓ = 7.998"

Step 3.   Determine the "Tread Length", Center-Line Width, and the Tread Depth.

a)   The "Tread Length", in this case is 36" – 4" = 32".

b)   The tread "Travel Center-Line Length" from the center-line arc is 20".
Find the Circumference: ──────

$C = \pi d$
$C = 3.1416 \times 40$
$C = 125.664"$

c)   Determine center-line (tread arc in degrees)
125.664" ÷ 360° = .34907" per each degree (°).

d)   Tread arc should be approximately 8 – 10"* including the nosing. Therefore: 8 ÷ .34907 = **22.918° Tread Angle.**
The "Center-Line Width" is approximately 9 3/16".

*Most applications require the 17–18 combination. However, spiral stairs will vary. This combo is 8"+ 8.115" = 16 1/8".

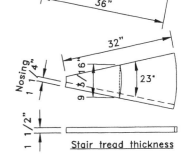

Arc Length 7.998"
8" dia. Pipe or Pole
20"r Travel Center-Line (40" dia.)
36"
32"
Nosing 1 1/4"
9 3/16"
23°
1/2"
1 1/4"
Stair tread thickness

Spiral Stairs (Continued)

Step 4. Determine the "Large end of the Tread Arc Length" as shown.

Use the Formula: $\ell = .01745rn$

[See Task No. K7D page 144 of the textbook.]

$\ell = .01745 (36)(22.918)$

$\ell = .01745 \times 825.048$

$\ell = 14.397"*$ (Large end of Tread)

Arc Length 14.397"

Arc Length 7.998"

14.397"

20"r Travel Center-Line

36"

*This dimension does not include the nosing, but should be marked on the treads. As the nosing will overhang this mark.

Step 5. Lay out treads on 1/4" plywood or a good grade of 1/4" wood paneling. Use a Lay Out Square or drafting triangle to do a neat job.

(Hint: Make a story pole of all the dimensions for greater accuracy.

$$
\begin{array}{ll}
14.397" & = \quad 14\ 3/8+"" \\
+\ 14.397" & \\
\hline
28.794" & = \quad 28\ 13/16-" \\
+\ 14.397" & \\
\hline
43.191" & = \quad 43\ 3/16+" \\
+\ 14.397" & \\
\hline
57.588" & = \quad 57\ 9/16+" \\
+\ 14.397" & \\
\hline
71.985" & = \quad 71\ 15/16+" \\
\end{array}
$$

And so on ....

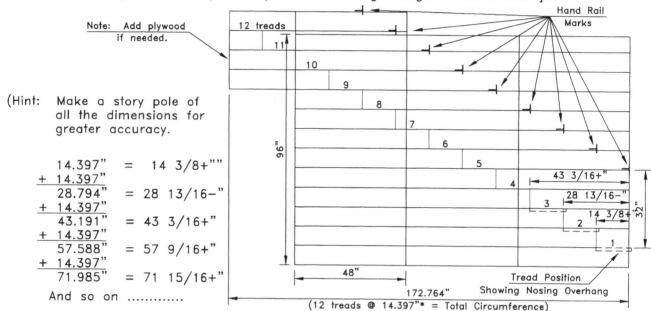

Note: Add plywood if needed.

Hand Rail Marks

12 treads

11

10

9

8

7

6

5

4

3

2

1

96"

48"

172.764"

(12 treads @ 14.397"* = Total Circumference)

43 3/16+"

28 13/16-"

14 3/8+"

37"

Tread Position Showing Nosing Overhang

Step 6. Mark the stair railing heights above the tread marks. Most stair railing heights are as shown on the right.

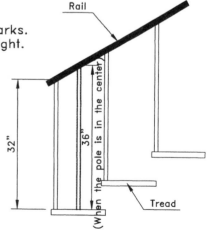

Rail

32"

36" (When the pole is in the center)

Tread

Step 7. Machine the outside of treads with a disc sander and a pivot point. Machine the inside arc of the treads with a drum sander and a pivot point.

Mark the Circumference without the nosing mark.

Plywood Jig for Machining Treads

Pivot Screw

15.647"

14.397"

Spiral Stairs (Continued)

Step 8. a) Lay out "Stair Center Post" and "Tread Outer Circle" as shown.

b) Construct a bottom base, use scrap Lumber. This will serve, as a nailing base for the 1/4" plywood cylinder. Make sure to allow for the 1/4" plywood. If two layers of plywood are used allow 1/2".

c) Prepare the top of the stairs as needed. Not shown as each stairs will differ.

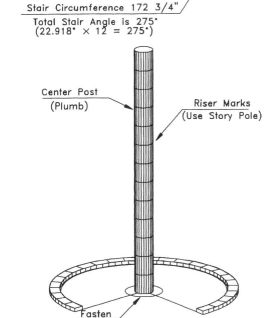

Tread Outer Circle

Stair Circumference 172 3/4"
Total Stair Angle is 275°
(22.918° × 12 = 275°)

Step 9. a) Install the stair "Center Post" to the bottom as shown. Fasten with custom made brackets. Note the risers are all marked on the post.

b) Install the stair "Center Post" to the top. Fasten with custom made brackets (not shown).

Center Post
(Plumb)

Riser Marks
(Use Story Pole)

Fasten

Step 10. a) Install the 1/4" plywood to the base. The base can be made permanent if the plywood/paneling is to stay.

b) Prepare top of stairs, if needed, and fasten the 1/4" plywood to a temporary top base. If a top base cannot be prepared, use temporary tread and railing spacers*.

Step 11. Fasten treads to the center pole and the inside of the 1/4" plywood where they belong.

a) If the treads are wooden, fasten with screws. Or if metal, fasten with brackets.

b) If 1/4" plywood or paneling is to be permanent, fasten accordingly.

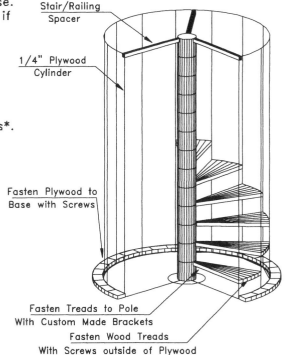

Stair/Railing
Spacer

1/4" Plywood
Cylinder

Fasten Plywood to
Base with Screws

Fasten Treads to Pole
With Custom Made Brackets
Fasten Wood Treads
With Screws outside of Plywood

*The spacers should be the same size as the treads. Use whatever is takes to form the cylinder, accurately. <u>Use two layers of 1/4" plywood if the cylinder is to be permanent.</u>

Spiral Stairs (Continued)

Finish Stairs inside of Cylinder:

Step 12. a) Finish installing stair treads inside
the stair cylinder, as shown.

b) Install "Spacer Blocks*" for the Hand
Railing. Adjust according to the Hand
Rail marks located on the stair cylin-
er as shown on page 176.

c) Mold the Hand Rail to the spacer blocks
by fastening thin strips of plywood or
lumber to the spacer blocks. Repeat
this process until the Hand Rail is completed.

d) Install "Hand Rail Post" to support the
Hand Rail above the finish foor.

e) Finish the stairs by adding finished riser
boards (optional). Also, reinforce the
treads by fastening ledger (support)
strips of lumber below them. Glue, if
necessary.

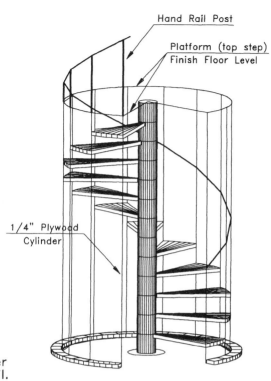

Hand Rail Post

Platform (top step)
Finish Floor Level

1/4" Plywood
Cylinder

*When the Hand Rail is attached to the cylinder, spacer
blocks will be needed to fit your hand around the rail.

Stairs without Cylinder: [Construct Tread Support Beam — Not Shown.]

Step 13. a) Construct a "Tread Support Beam" by
using the same technique as building
the Hand Rail. The Beam can be built
by laminating thin plywood or lumber
together using glue and fastners. However, this can be a TEDIOUS and timely
process. Constructing a metal support
beam would be another way. Whatever
type of beam is selected, make sure to
use the cylinder as a pattern to build it.

b) Once the support beam is constructed,
special brackets may be needed to
to support the beam.

[Note: The intent of this module is to demonstrate
how to calculate the components of a spiral
stairs. Also, to demonstrate how these component parts can be molded together in this
cylinder. This procedure has been proven,
but it can be a very challenging process. If
care is taken in the construction of the cylinder,
machining of all the parts, and assembly, the
end results will yield a beautiful staircase.]

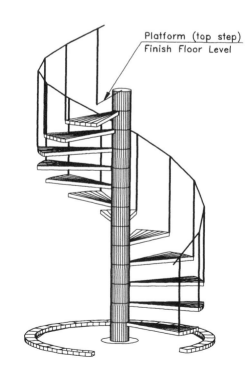

Platform (top step)
Finish Floor Level

Objective Practice Problems for Module #17

How to Calculate and Lay Out   Stairs with Platforms — Info #14B (carry decimals 3 places):

1. Calculate the risers and the treads for the stairs shown below. Then calculate the number of risers and the number of treads to make a platform stairs. The platform is 36" square. All calculations must be to the nearest ±1/16th of an inch. Make a sketch of the stairs in the drawing provided (each square represents 4 inches).

Total number of risers ____   Height of risers ____

Total number of treads* ____   Width of treads ____

Rise #1 = _____ risers _____ treads. Rise #1 = _____ inches. Run #1 = _____ inches.

Rise #2 = _____ risers _____ treads. Rise #2 = _____ inches. Run #2 = _____ inches.

Stair Angle = _____°

*One Tread will be the platform.

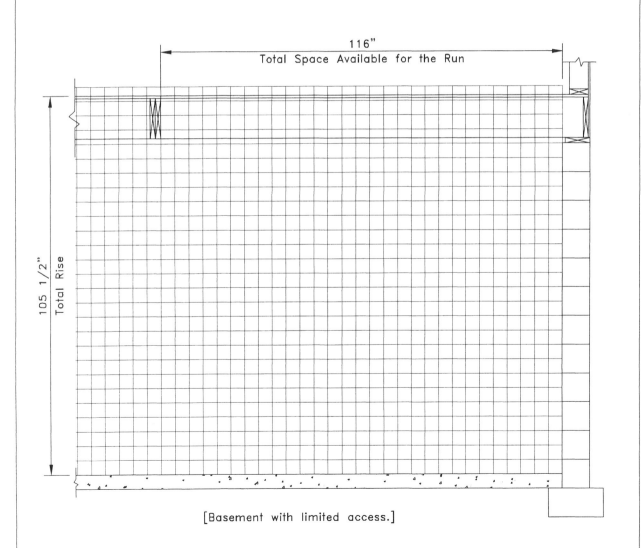

116"
Total Space Available for the Run

105 1/2"
Total Rise

[Basement with limited access.]

Objective Practice Problems for Module #17

How to Calculate and Lay Out Stairs with Winders — Info #14C (carry decimals 3 places):

2. Calculate the risers and treads for the stairs below. Then calculate the number of regular treads and winder treads to make a winder stairs. The stairs will be 32" wide with 3 winder treads. All calculation must be to the nearest ±1/16th of an inch. Make a sketch of the stairs in the drawing provided (each square represents 4 inches).

Number of Risers ____ Height of Risers ____ [Hint: Make risers close to 8 inches.]

Number of regular Treads ____ Width of Treads ____

Run #1 = _____

Run #2 = _____·

Stair Angle = _____·

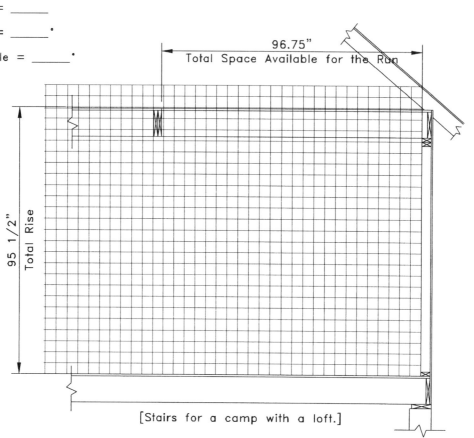

96.75"
Total Space Available for the Run

95 1/2" Total Rise

[Stairs for a camp with a loft.]

How to Calculate and Lay Out Spiral Stairs — Info #14D (carry decimals 3 places):

3. In reference to the above drawing, calculate the number of risers and treads in would take to build a spiral stairs. The finished treads will be 36" wide with a 10" diameter center post. All calculation must be to the nearest ±1/16th of an inch. Make a sketch* of the stairs on a separate sheet of engineer paper (1/4" squares) found in Appendix–C, page 230–232.

Number of Risers ____ Height of Risers ____ [Hint: Make risers close to 8 inches.]

Number of regular Treads ____ Width of Treads ____

Center–line arc length = _____

Large tread end arc length = _____

*Use Info #14D as a guide to make the proper sketches.

Math Training Module #18

Instructional Objectives:

Hands On:

□ *Application Problem* - Practice Laying Out and Checking Trig Problems on a sheet of paper.

□ *Application Problem* - Practice Laying Out an Octagon on a sheet of paper.

Basic Math Study Notes (Basic Right TriangleTrig Problems and Lay Out an Octagon Problem):

Right Triangles and the Formula, SOH CAH TOA:

SOH (Sine = Opposite/Hypotenuse):

Set up as: Sin. $= \dfrac{Opp.}{Hyp.}$

Sin. A $= \dfrac{a}{c}$ or $\dfrac{3}{5}$

Sin. $a = .6$

Sin.$^{-1} a = 36.86989°$

CAH (Cosine = Adjacent/Hypotenuse):

Set up as: Cos. $= \dfrac{Adj.}{Hyp.}$

Cos. A $= \dfrac{b}{c}$ or $\dfrac{4}{5}$

Cos. $a = .8$

Cos.$^{-1} a = 36.86989°$

TOA (Tangent = Opposite/Adjacent):

Set up as: Tan. $= \dfrac{Opp.}{Adj.}$

Tan. A $= \dfrac{a}{b}$ or $\dfrac{3}{4}$

Tan. $a = .75$

Tan.$^{-1} a = 36.86989°$

Set up as: Cos. $= \dfrac{Adj.}{Hyp.}$

Cos. A $= \dfrac{b}{c}$ or $\dfrac{3}{5}$

Cos. $a = .6$

Cos.$^{-1} a = 53.13010°$

Note, how the triangle is viewed and the given values available will determine the proper formula to use. In this case CAH will be needed to find <u>Angle A</u>.

Check by adding the angles:

```
   53.13010°
 + 36.86989°
   89.99999°   Answer OK
(90° + 90° = 180°)
```

Note how the Sine, Cosine, and the Tangent can be used to solve for the <u>same angle</u>. However in each case a different value (one of the sides) is missing. Therefore, if any two values are known, angles or sides, the missing value can be found. The 3–4–5 triangle is used to illustrate this concept because it is easy to solve and to check. Check also by using the Rule of Pythagorás, $a^2 + b^2 = c^2$. Try different combinations using this example, until, you are confident on the use of the formulas.

[Refer to Info #15 pages 183–186, and Task No. M1 pages 170 thru 185, in the textbook if more information should be needed.]

Lay Out Octagons:

Many decks, gazebos, screen rooms, etc. are made up of octagons. An octagon is made up of eight equal sides and angles as shown below.

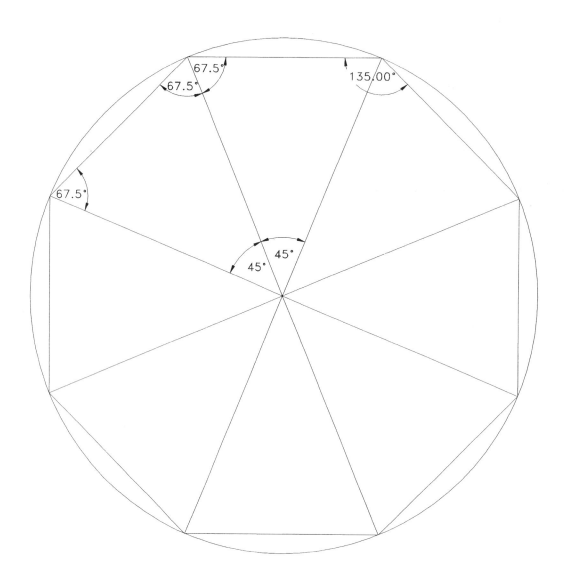

Suggestion:

An easy way to lay out an octagon is with the lay out square that has octagon tables (measurement) on it, see page 187 and 188. This method makes it easier to lay out an octagon. However, the octagon should be checked for accuracy by measuring, and/or by using one of the mathematical methods found in Task No. K6G page 139, or Task No. O8 page 309, in the textbook. The bigger the octagon, the more need there is to check it for accuracy. Use whatever works best for you.

Info #15 – Right Angles & Trig.
[Trigonometry Formulas SOH, CAH, & TOA]

Functions (Formulas) of Angles: Sine $= \dfrac{Opp.}{Hyp.}$ Cosine $= \dfrac{Adj.}{Hyp.}$ Tangent $= \dfrac{Opp.}{Adj.}$

Abbreviations:
Sine = Sin.	Hypotenuse = Hyp.
Cosine = Cos.	Side Opposite = Opp.
Tangent = Tan.	Side Adjacent = Adj.

Formula: **SOH - CAH - TOA** [see p. 179 & 180 in the textbook]

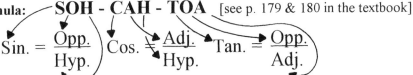

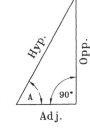

$Sin. = \dfrac{Opp.}{Hyp.}$ $Cos. = \dfrac{Adj.}{Hyp.}$ $Tan. = \dfrac{Opp.}{Adj.}$

<u>NOTE</u>:
Angle A is also known as θ (Theta).
The angle being sought (depends
where you are standing (point of
view) in relation to the angle.

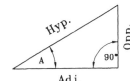

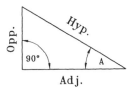

Example 1.   The angle and the Hyp. are
known. Find the side Opp.
and the side Adj.

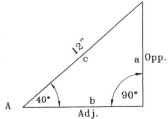

a)   Find the side opposite, use SOH.

Formula:	Sin. =	$\dfrac{Opp.}{Hyp.}$
Substitute:	Sin 40° =	$\dfrac{Opp}{Hyp}$
	(12) Sin 40° =	$\dfrac{Opp \;(\cancel{12})}{\cancel{12}}$
	(12) (.6428) =	Opp
	7.7135 =	Opp

b)   Find the side adjacent, use CAH.

Formula:	Cos =	$\dfrac{Adj.}{Hyp.}$
Substitute:	Cos 40° =	$\dfrac{Adj}{Hyp}$
	(12) (.7660) =	$\dfrac{Adj. \;(\cancel{12})}{\cancel{12}}$
	(12) (.7660) =	Adj
	9.1925 =	Adj

Check the above calculations by using the Rule of Pythagoras, Task No. $\boxed{\text{K5A}}$.

Formula: $a^2 + b^2 = c^2$

$(7.7135)^2 + (9.1925)^2 = c^2$

$144 = c^2$

$\sqrt{144} = c$

$12 = c$ Answer OK

How to Manipulate the Trigonometry Formulas SOH, CAH, and TOA (Continued)

Example 2.   The hyp and the side adj are known. Find
the reference angle (A) and the side opp.

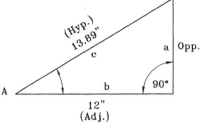
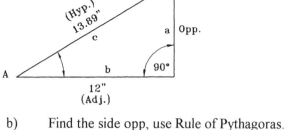

a)   Find the reference angle (A), use CAH.

Formula: $\cos A = \dfrac{\text{Adj.}}{\text{Hyp.}}$

Substitute: $\cos A = \dfrac{12}{13.89}$

$\cos A = .8639$

$\cos^{-1} = 30.2392°$ (.2392) decimal only
$\underline{\times 60}$
14.3520 min.
$\underline{\times 60}$
21.1200 sec.

b)   Find the side opp, use Rule of Pythagoras.

$a^2 + b^2 = c^2$

$a^2 + (12)^2 = (13.89)^2$
$\underline{- (12)^2 = \qquad\qquad - (12)^2}$
$a^2 \qquad = (13.89)^2 - (12)^2$

$a^2 = 48.9321$

$a = \sqrt{48.9321}$

$a = 6.995$ or 7 inches

Angle A = 30°14'21"   (Read 30 degrees 14 minutes 21 seconds)

Example 3.   The side adj and the side opp are known.
Find the reference angle (A) and the hyp.

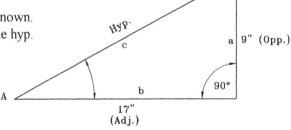

a)   Find the reference angle (A), use TOA.

Formula: $\tan A = \dfrac{\text{Opp.}}{\text{Adj.}}$

Substitute: $\tan A = \dfrac{9}{17}$

$\tan A = .5294$

$\tan^{-1} = 27.897°$ (.897) decimal only
$\underline{\times 60}$
53.820 min.
$\underline{\times 60}$
49.200 sec.

b)   Find the hyp, use Rule of Pythagoras.

$a^2 + b^2 = c^2$

$(9)^2 + (17)^2 = c^2$

$370 = c^2$

$\sqrt{370} = c$

$19.2354" = c$

Angle A = 27°53'49 sec.   (Read 27 degrees 53 minutes 49 seconds)

How to Manipulate the Trigonometry Formulas SOH, CAH, and TOA (Continued)

Example 4.   The reference angle
and the side adj are
known. Find the side
opp and the hyp.

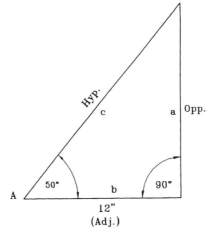

a)   Find the hyp, use CAH.

Formula: $Cos = \dfrac{Adj}{Hyp.}$

Substitute: $Cos\ 50° = \dfrac{12}{Hyp.}$

(Hyp) $Cos\ 50° = \dfrac{12\ (Hyp)}{Hyp.}$

(Hyp) $\dfrac{Cos\ 50°}{Cos\ 50} = \dfrac{12}{Cos.\ 50}$

$Hyp = \dfrac{12}{.64279''}$

$Hyp = 18.6686''$

b)   Find the side opp, use Rule of Pythagoras.

$$a^2 + b^2 = c^2$$

$$a^2 + (12)^2 = (18.6686)^2$$

$$\underline{-(12)^2 = -(12)^2}$$

$$a^2 = (18.6686)^2 - (12)^2$$

$$a^2 = 204.5166$$

$$a = \sqrt{204.5166}$$

$$a = 14.3009''$$

<u>OR</u> use TOA to find the side Opp.

Formula: $Tan = \dfrac{Opp}{Adj.}$

Substitute: $Tan\ 50° = \dfrac{Opp}{12}$

(12) $Tan\ 50° = \dfrac{Opp\ (12)}{12}$

(12) (1.1918) $= Opp$

$14.3010 = Opp$

<u>OR</u> manipulate the formula then calculate.

$$a^2 + b^2 = c^2$$

Substract both sides by b^2 ➤ $\underline{-b^2 = -b^2}$ ◄

New Formula ⟶ $a^2 = c^2 - b^2$

$$a^2 = (18.6686)^2 - (12)^2$$

$$a^2 = 348.5166 - 144$$

$$a^2 = \sqrt{204.5166}$$

$$a = 14.3009''$$

185

How to Manipulate the Trigonometry Formulas SOH, CAH, and TOA (Continued)

More Practical Application of SOH, CAH, and TOA:

Example 5. **Unequal roof pitches and the formula SOH, CAH, and TOA**. Illustrated below is an example of how to calculate the side cuts (angles) of the common rafter jacks and the hip rafter for a roof that has unequal roof pitches. Use this page in conjunction with page 56, unequal roof pitches and the Rule of Pythagoras ($a^2 + b^2 = c^2$). Note **PV** = the angle formula **P**oint of **V**iew.

Slope Angles: 4/12 = 18.43°, 6/12 = 26.57°, and 6/21.63″ = 15.50° (also, see page 149)

[Note this illustration depicts the line length of the rafters, only!]

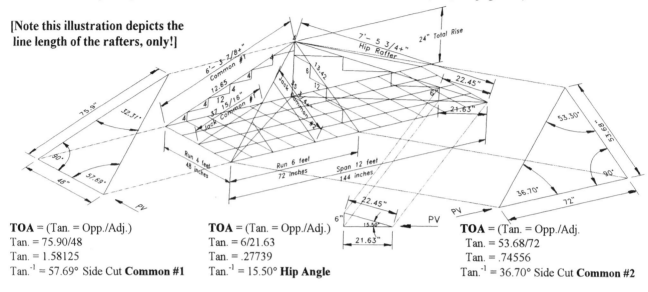

TOA = (Tan. = Opp./Adj.)
Tan. = 75.90/48
Tan. = 1.58125
Tan.$^{-1}$ = 57.69° Side Cut **Common #1**

TOA = (Tan. = Opp./Adj.)
Tan. = 6/21.63
Tan. = .27739
Tan.$^{-1}$ = 15.50° **Hip Angle**

TOA = (Tan. = Opp./Adj.
Tan. = 53.68/72
Tan. = .74556
Tan.$^{-1}$ = 36.70° Side Cut **Common #2**

CAH = (CAH. = Adj./Hyp.)
Cos. (57.69°) = .75/H
.53450 = .75/H
.75/.5345 = H
1.40″ = H
1 7/16-″ = H
(1 7/16-″ = length to deduct off of hip)

Note the Hip Drop for unequal roof pitches can be calculated by using the method shown on page 155, if the two roof slopes are close to the same. However if there is a big difference in the slopes, the Hip may have to be dropped and backed on one edge at the same time, so that the sheathing will lay flat.

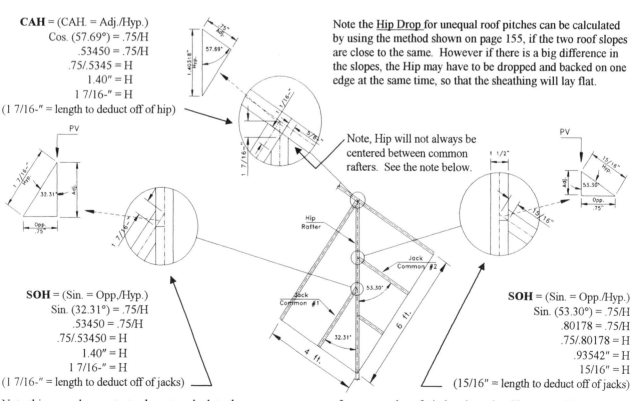

Note, Hip will not always be centered between common rafters. See the note below.

SOH = (Sin. = Opp./Hyp.)
Sin. (32.31°) = .75/H
.53450 = .75/H
.75/.53450 = H
1.40″ = H
1 7/16-″ = H
(1 7/16-″ = length to deduct off of jacks)

SOH = (Sin. = Opp./Hyp.)
Sin. (53.30°) = .75/H
.80178 = .75/H
.75/.80178 = H
.93542″ = H
15/16″ = H
(15/16″ = length to deduct off of jacks)

Note this page demonstrates how to calculate the component parts of an unequal roof pitch using trig. However, this page should be used in conjunction with a lay out of your specific unequal roof. The lay out can be made by using the lay out square as a scale, see Info #11B, page 136.

Info #16 – Lay Out an Octagon
[with a Lay Out Square]

Problem 1: Lay Out an Octagon for a 36" square.

1. Measure "36 Dots" on the Lay Out
   Square Octagon Scale as shown below.

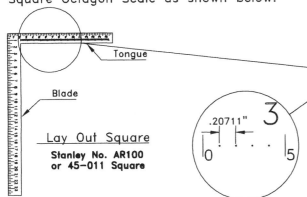

Tongue

Blade

Lay Out Square
Stanley No. AR100
or 45–011 Square

.20711"

3

0   5

OCTAGON TABLES ON
THE TONGUE OF THE SQUARE.

36 dots or 7 7/16–"
(.20711" × 36 = 7.456")

Final results will depend on how accurate
the dots are measured. Check by using
.20711" between the dots. See page,
229.

[Note; not all Lay Out Squares have Octagon Tables.]

2. Measure 7 7/16" from the center
   line (each way) of the square
   shown below.

3. Connect the 7 7/16" off center
   marks to each other as shown.

4. Measure each side of the octagon
   (14 7/8") as shown.

   Note, this is a pretty accurate
   method for laying out most
   octagons. However, when greater
   accuracy is needed, use .20711"
   times (×) the total number of dots,
   or use the checking methods shown.

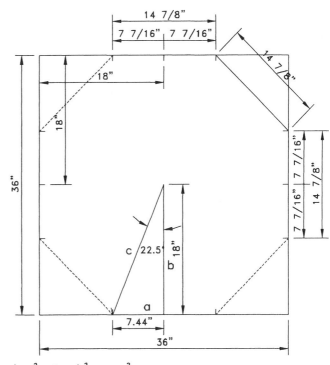

5. Check by using the formulas: CAH and $a^2 + b^2 = c^2$

$$Cos. = \frac{Adj.}{Hyp.}$$

$$Hyp. = \frac{Adj.}{Cos.} \quad Hyp. = \frac{18"}{.923879533}$$

$$Hyp. = 19.48"$$

$$a^2 = c^2 - b^2$$

$$a^2 = 19.48^2 - 18^2$$

$$a = \sqrt{55.4704}$$

$$a = 7.45" \quad or \quad 7\ 7/16" \quad Very\ Close$$

[To Lay Out Larger Octagons, See the Next page.]

Problem 2:   Lay Out an Octagon for a 16 foot square.

1. Change 16 feet to all
    inches: 16 x 12 = 192"

2. Measure "192 Dots",
    to do this most
    accurately, divide 192
    Dots by 3 = 64 Dots.
    [64 x .20711 = 13.255"]

3. Multiply: 13.255"
                  x 3
        equals 39.765"*

    [Note, another way to
    calculate 192 Dots, is
    measure "12 Dots", and
    multiply that sum 2.48532
    times (x) 16 = 39.765".
    (192 divided by 12 = 16)]

4. Measure 39 3/4+"
    off center each
    way as shown.

5. Connect the 39 3/4+"
    marks to each other.

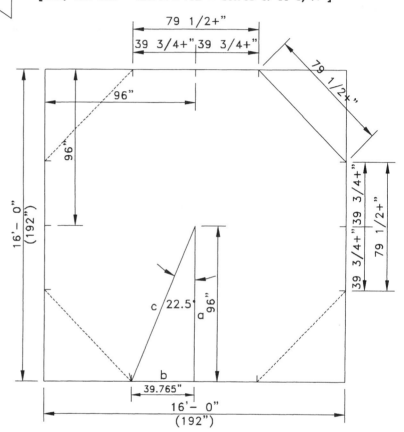

6. Check by using the formula: CAH and $a^2 + b^2 = c^2$

    Cos. = $\dfrac{Adj.}{Hyp.}$

    Hyp. = $\dfrac{Adj.}{Cos.}$ Hyp. = $\dfrac{96"}{.923879533}$

                    Hyp. = 103.9096512"

    $a^2 = c^2 - b^2$

    $a^2 = 103.9096512^2 - 96^2$

    $a = \sqrt{1581.215618}$

    $a = 39.7645"$ or 39 3/4+"   very Close

*Note when measuring just dots (without checking with .20711"), the accuracy will
depend on how accurate the dots are measured.

Objective Practice Problems for Module #18

Right Angles and Trig [Trig Formulas SOH CAH TOA] – Info #15 (carry decimals 3 places):

Use a scientific calculator and/or the Trig Tables in the textbook to solve the unkown right triangle angles and sides shown below. Use the formulas: $a^2 + b^2 = c^2$

$$SOH = [Sin. = \frac{Opp.}{hyp.}]$$

$$CAH = [Cos. = \frac{Adj.}{hyp.}]$$

$$TOA = [Tan. = \frac{Opp.}{adj.}]$$

1. Angle B = _____°

   Opp. = _____

   Adj. = _____

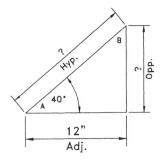

2. Angle B = _____°

   Hyp. = _____

   Opp. = _____

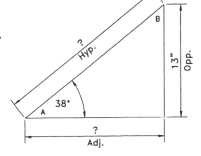

3. Angle B = _____°

   Hyp. = _____

   Adj. = _____

Objective Practice Problems for Module #18

4.   Angle A = _____ °

    Hyp. = _____

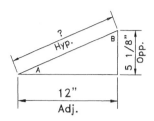

How to Lay Out an Octagon using a Lay Out Square — Info #16:

5.   Use a Lay Out square with the octagon tables to lay out an octagon for a 6" square in the space provided below, or use .20711" as the space between each dot. The results can be checked by using the formulas CAH and $a^2 + b^2 = c^2$.

Math Training Module #19

Instructional Objectives:

Hands On:

☐ *Application Problem* - Practice Converting English to Metrics, and Vice-Versa, Convert Metrics to English. Make a Story Pole (MILLIMETERS and INCHES), Problem 8: 8′- 0″ Stick (5 Centers)

☐ *Application Problem* - Practice Laying Out and Checking Trig Problems on a sheet of paper.

☐ *Application Problem* - Practice using the Lay Out Square as a Scale.

Objective Practice Problems: Calculate the Practice Problems for Math Training Module #19

Basic Math Study Notes (Basic Metrics and Conversion):

Basic Metric (Linear Measure): [For more information on Metric Linear Measure, see page 371, 372, and the inside of the back cover in the textbook.]

Basic Metrics – Linear Measure:

The basic metric linear measure unit is the <u>meter</u>. The meter is 1000 millimeters long.

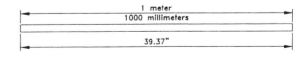

In comparison:

<u>One inch</u> is 25.4 millimeters long.
If you divide 1000mm ÷ 25.4 = 39.37″.   Or
if you multiply, 1000 × .03937 = 39.37″.
Therefore a meter is 39.37 or 3'– 3 3/8″ long.

$[1mm = \dfrac{1}{25.4}$ inch or .03937 inch.]

[Change inches to millimeters, multiply number of inches times 25.4]
[Change millimeters to inches, multiply number of millimeters times .03937]

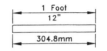

<u>One foot</u> = 12 × 25.4 or 304.8mm.

$[1 \text{ foot} = \dfrac{304.8mm}{1000mm}$ feet or .3048 meter]

$[1 \text{ meter} = \dfrac{1000mm}{304.8mm}$ meter or 3.28083 feet]

[Change feet to meters, multiply number of feet times .3048]
[Change meters to feet, multiply number of meters times 3.28083]

Basic Metrics – Linear Measure (Continued):

<u>One yard</u> = 36 × 25.4 or 914.4mm.

[1 Yard = $\dfrac{914.4mm}{1000mm}$ meter or .9144 meter]

[1 meter = $\dfrac{1000mm}{914.4mm}$ Yard or 1.09361 Yards]

[Change Yards to meters, multiply number of yards times .9144]
[Change meters to Yards, multiply number of meters times 1.09361]

<u>Convert Inches to Millimeters</u>: [See Info #17, page 194 for more information.]

Probably the easiest way to convert from the <u>English system</u> of measure to the <u>metric system</u> of measure is to multiply by 25.4mm for each inch. This way you don't have to remember the other conversion factors. See the examples below.

25.4mm × 1" = 25.4mm

25.4mm × 12" = 304.8mm

25.4mm × 36" = 914.4mm

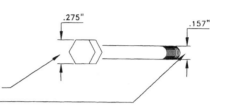

<u>The metric bolt on the right measures:</u>

What size wrench and nut are needed:
.275" × 25.4mm = 6.985 or 7mm wrench
.157" × 25.4mm = 3.9878 or 4mm nut

<u>American (English) Tape Measure and Conversion:</u>

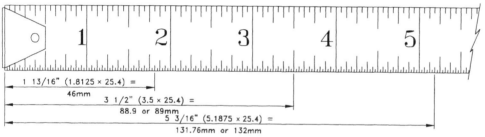

<u>Convert Millimeters to Inches</u>: [See Info #18, page 195 for more information.]

Probably the easiest way to convert from the <u>metric system</u> of measure to the <u>English system</u> of measure is to divide the number of millimeter by 25.4mm. Or use the inverse of 1/25.4 = .03937, and multiply that product times the number of millimeters. In this case, you only have to remember the reciprocal of 1/25.4 = .03937 or calculate it out.

.03937" × 25.4mm = 1 inch

.03937" × 304.8mm = 12 inches

.03937" × 914.4mm = 36 inches

<u>The English bolt on the right measures:</u>

What size wrench and nut are needed:
.03937 × 15.88mm = .625 or 5/8" wrench
.03937 × 11.11mm = .4374 or 7/16" nut

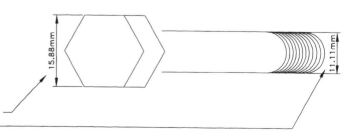

Basic Metrics — Linear Measure (Continued):

Metric Tape Measure and Conversion:

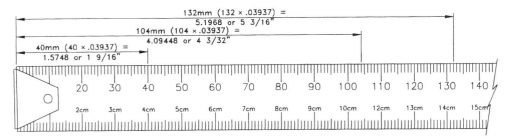

Convert Metric Objects that are in Meters:

The object on the right measures 7.5 meters by 12.2 meters. Convert to the English system of measure.

1 meter = 39.37 inches, Therefore:
12.2 × 39.37" = 480.314" or 40'– 0 5/16"
7.5 × 39.37 = 295.275" or 24'– 7 1/4+"

Or
12.2 meters = 12200mm ÷ 25.4 = 480.314"
7.5 meters = 7500mm÷ 25.4 = 295.275"

Use the system that works best for you.

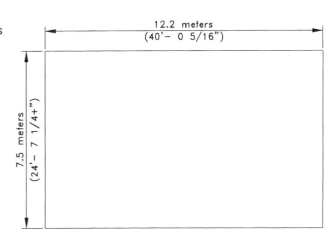

[Note to convert metric surface measure, metric cubic measure, metric liquid measure, metric mass and weight measure, and temperature, see the Appendix or the inside back cover in the textbook.]

Squaring Techniques and Metrics:

The metric object on the right can be squared with the 3–4–5 and the 5–12–13 combination.

Some of the combinations are:

6 meters – 8 meters – 10 meters

7.5 meters – 10 meters – 12.5 meters

5 meters – 12 meters – 13 meters.

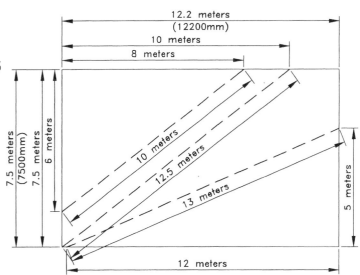

[See Trade Trick #2, page 51 and 52 in this book, or Task No. P1 and P1A in the textbook, pages 312–317. Use the same concepts, but use metric measure instead.]

Info #17 – Linear Metrics
[Convert Inches to Millimeters]

[To Change Inches to Millimeters, Multiply Inches by 25.4]

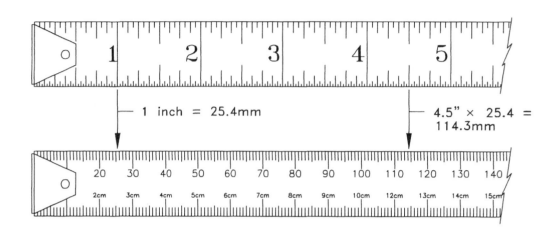

1 inch = 25.4mm

4.5" × 25.4 = 114.3mm

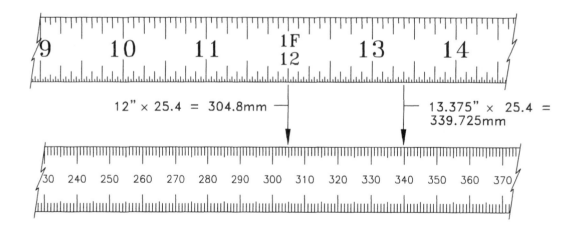

12" × 25.4 = 304.8mm

13.375" × 25.4 = 339.725mm

Info #18 – Linear Metrics
[Convert Millimeters to Inches]

[To Change Millimeters to Inches, Divide by 25.4 or Multiply by .03937]

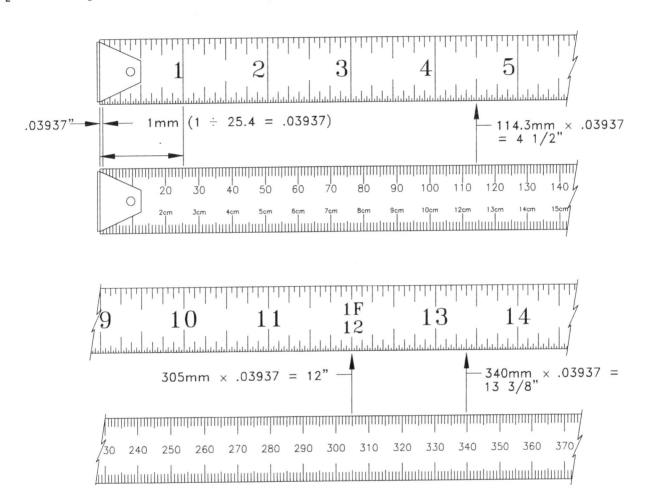

.03937"   1mm (1 ÷ 25.4 = .03937)

114.3mm × .03937 = 4 1/2"

305mm × .03937 = 12"

340mm × .03937 = 13 3/8"

Trade Trick #1 – Make a Story Pole

[Problem 8: 2 Meter Stick (Millimeters and Inches) - 5 Centers]

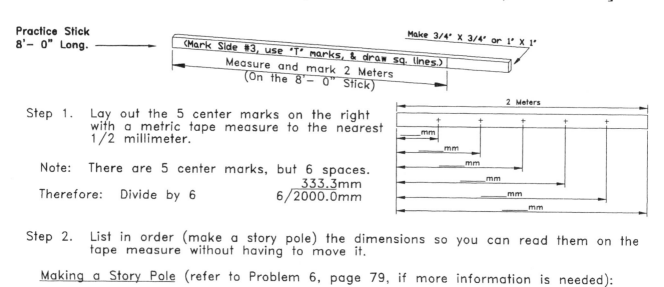

Practice Stick 8'- 0" Long.

Make 3/4" X 3/4" or 1" X 1"

(Mark Side #3, use "T" marks, & draw sq. lines.)
Measure and mark 2 Meters
(On the 8'- 0" Stick)

2 Meters

Step 1. Lay out the 5 center marks on the right with a metric tape measure to the nearest 1/2 millimeter.

Note: There are 5 center marks, but 6 spaces.

Therefore: Divide by 6

$$\frac{333.3mm}{6/2000.0mm}$$

Step 2. List in order (make a story pole) the dimensions so you can read them on the tape measure without having to move it.

Making a Story Pole (refer to Problem 6, page 79, if more information is needed):

1. 333.3mm   333.3mm
                  +333.3mm   +333.3mm   +333.3mm   +333.3mm   +333.3mm
        2. 666.6mm   3.   4.   5.   6.

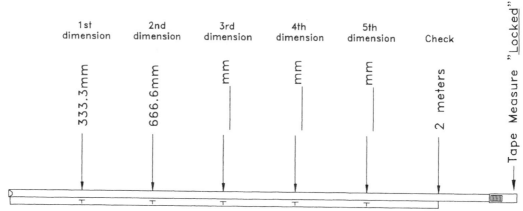

1st dimension	2nd dimension	3rd dimension	4th dimension	5th dimension	Check	
333.3mm	666.6mm	mm	mm	mm	2 meters	Tape Measure "Locked"

Step 3. Lay out the center marks (use "T" marks) on the 2 meter stick. Do not move the tape measure. Leave in the locked positon as shown above.

Step 4. Check by measuring _____mm between each "T" mark.

Step 5. Convert the metric measure to ft. in. and ±1/16 of an inch accuracy. Check these dimensions on the story pole with an American (English) tape measure.

333.3mm   666.6mm
 .03937   .03937
13.122"   26.244"

1. = <u>13 1/8"</u>   2. = <u>26 1/4"</u>   3. _____   4. _____   5. _____   6. _____

Which measuring system is more accurate and easier to use? Explain.

Objective Practice Problems for Module #19

<u>Convert Inches to Millimeters — Info #17 (carry decimals 3 places):</u>

Convert the American (English) measurements below to millimeters.

<u>The metric bolt on the right measures:</u>

1. What size wrench is needed? _____

2. What size nut is needed? _____

<u>The metric bolt on the right measures:</u>

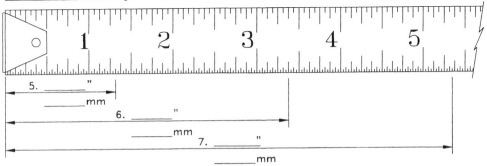

3. What size wrench is needed? _____

4. What size nut is needed? _____

<u>Fill in the missing dimensions below in English and in metric measure:</u>

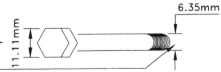

5. _____ "
   _____ mm

6. _____ "
   _____ mm

7. _____ "
   _____ mm

<u>Convert Millimeters to Inches — Info #18 (carry decimals 3 places):</u>

Convert the millimeters measurements below to English measurements.

<u>The English bolt on the right measures:</u>

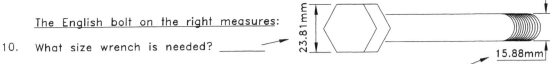

8. What size wrench is needed? _____

9. What size nut is needed? _____

<u>The English bolt on the right measures:</u>

10. What size wrench is needed? _____

11. What size nut is needed? _____

<u>Fill in the missing dimensions below in metric and in English measure:</u>

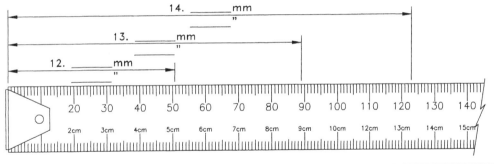

14. _____ mm
    _____ "

13. _____ mm
    _____ "

12. _____ mm
    _____ "

Objective Practice Problems for Module #19

Use a scientific calculator and/or the Trig Tables in the textbook to solve the unknown right triangle, angles and sides shown below.   Use the formulas: $a^2 + b^2 = c^2$

1.   Angle B = _____ °

   Hyp. = _____

   Adj. = _____

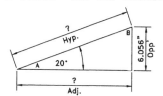

$SOH = [Sin. = \dfrac{Opp.}{hyp.}]$

$CAH = [Cos. = \dfrac{Adj.}{hyp.}]$

$TOA = [Tan. = \dfrac{Opp.}{adj.}]$

2.   Angle B = _____ °

   Hyp. = _____

   Opp. = _____

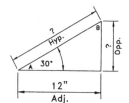

3.   Angle B = _____ °

   Opp. = _____

   Adj. = _____

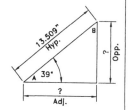

4.   Use a Lay Out Square with the octagon tables to lay out an octagon for a 3 inch square in the space provided below, or use .20711" as the space between each dot. The results can be checked by using the formulas CAH and $a^2 + b^2 = c^2$.

Math Training Module #20

Basic Math Study Notes (Scribing Tips, Lay Out Pipe Saddle Tips, and Straighten Fences/Wall Tips):

Scribing Tips:

Scribing can actually be considered a trick of the trades. Many building materials such as lumber, metal, masonry blocks, etc. are not always installed perfectly plumb (level) or true in dimension. Therefore to fit these materials to one another, or fitting other materials to them, can be extremely difficult and time consuming. By knowing how to scribe properly, the fit problems can be alleviated. With the proper tools and practice, the art of scribing can be easily mastered.

Scribe Horizontal or Scribe Vertical:

Note to scribe horizontally or vertically, being scribed should be plumb (level).

Tools for scribing:

Scribe or Compass:
(Always use a sharp pencil or marker.)

Compass No. 843/1
UPC CODE 24132 0
GENERAL TOOLS, Mfg. Co. LLC
New York, NY 10013-3567

Spirit Level:

Shim

[Object made of Metal, Wood, Plastic, etc.]

Irregular Surface

Shim or Nail to hold Scribe Object in place.

Adjust to Widest Point

Vile on the "Spirit Level" indicating "Level or Plumb".

Scribe Mark

Basic Math Study Notes (Continued)

Lay Out Pipe Saddle (3 ½ Pipe Example) Tips:

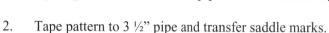

Cut → ← Tape

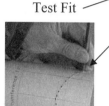

Test Fit

1. Cut pattern out (90° "T" in this case) with a scissors, tape together, and test on the pipe as shown on the right.

2. Tape pattern to 3 ½" pipe and transfer saddle marks.

    Note on metal, center punching the saddle marks works real good. This makes it easier to transfer the saddle curve marks with a soap stone or marker.

    — Center Punch

3. Mark the saddle curve marks with a soap stone*, pencil, or marker.

*Soap stone works good for marking most unpainted metals.

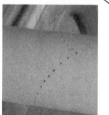
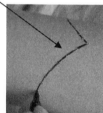

4. Cut out pipe saddle with a torch.

    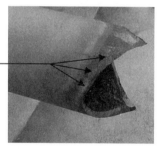

    Note, stay far enough away from the pipe saddle punch marks when cutting with the torch. This will make it much easier to grind the saddle arc with a disc grinder for fitting to the next piece of pipe.

5. Fit the pipe pieces together. Grind to fit to your satisfaction.

    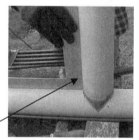

6. Mark to make a quick pipe "T", if desired. Then cut, grind, and weld.

7. Square up the pipe saddle, tack and weld, and finish the pipe saddle as shown on the right.

    Lay Out Square

Straighten Fences/Walls Tips):

Use <u>Mason line blocks</u> to hold the line for fences.

Use <u>space blocks</u> to space the line for fences/walls.

Use <u>8d duplex nails</u> and <u>½ hitches</u> to secure the line opposite the line block.

Use a <u>2 sided level</u> to get post in the ball park level.

Check with <u>a good 4 foot level</u> and/or <u>a level and a straight edge</u>.

Info #19 - Scribing
[as related to Welding, Sheet Metal, Carpentry, etc.]

How to Scribe (fit an object to an irregular surface) horizontally:

1. Use a Spirit level and "Level the Object" that is to be scribed. Shim the object, if necessary, as shown below.

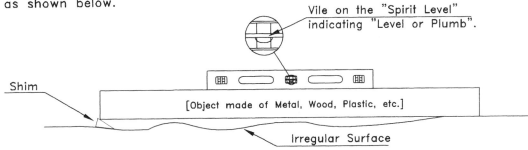

Vile on the "Spirit Level" indicating "Level or Plumb".

Shim

[Object made of Metal, Wood, Plastic, etc.]

Irregular Surface

2. Scribe with a "Scribe" or "Compass". Adjust (open) the "Scribe" at the widest point. Scribe (follow the irregular surface) through the length of the object. Make sure to hold the "Scribe" Perpendicular (90°) to the object at all times.

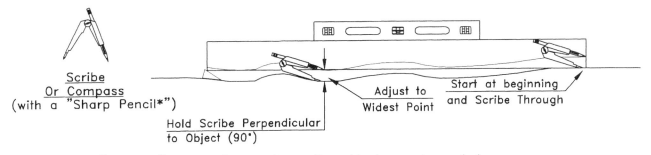

Scribe
Or Compass
(with a "Sharp Pencil*")

Adjust to Widest Point

Start at beginning and Scribe Through

Hold Scribe Perpendicular to Object (90°)

3. Carefully "Cut Out" the scribe mark on the object, as shown below.

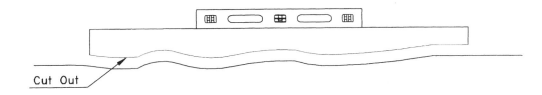

Cut Out

4. Position the object on the irregular surface. The object should fit tight to the surface, and be level. If the object <u>does not</u> fit tight to the surface, or is <u>not level</u>, make the necessary adjustments.

*Note felt markers, soap stone, ink pens etc. can also be used to scribe.

How to Scribe as related to the Trades (continued)

How to Scribe Vertically (Scribe Paneling):

1. Level the "Panel" being scribed. Use a Spirit level and shim (or tack) the "Sheet" in place. See Figure A.

   1st   Find the widest "Gap (15/16")" between the wall and the sheet of paneling after the panel is level (plumb).

   2nd   Measure the distance from the wall "at the widest gap" plus the distance to the center of the nearest stud. Add these two dimensions together (12 1/2"), and cut the panel that wide.

   3nd   Secure the "Panel" in position by using small tacks or finish nails.

2. Scribe with a "Scribe" or "Compass". Adjust (open) the "Scribe (15/16)" at the widest point. Scribe (follow the irregular surface) through the height of the sheet. Make sure to hold the "Scribe" Perpendicular (90°) to the wall at all times. See Figure B.

3. Carefully "Cut Out" the scribe mark on the Sheet. See Figure C.

4. Place the "Sheet" in position against the wall. The panel should fit tight and the opposite edge should be in the middle of the stud for nailing. Make necessary adjustments, if necessary. See Figure D.

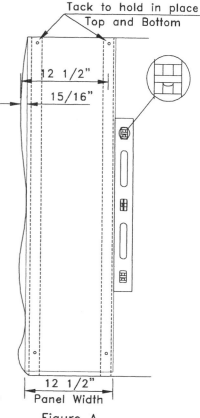

Tack to hold in place
Top and Bottom

12 1/2"
15/16"

12 1/2"
Panel Width

Figure A

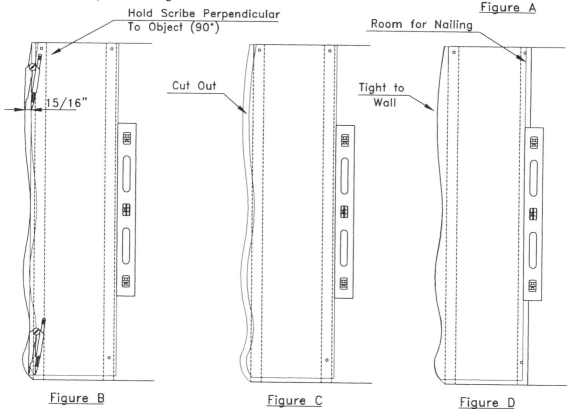

Hold Scribe Perpendicular
To Object (90°)

15/16"

Figure B

Cut Out

Figure C

Room for Nailing

Tight to Wall

Figure D

Info #20 – Draw and Lay Out Pipe Saddles

How to make a "Pipe Saddle" or a 90° "T" for a 3 1/2" dia. pipe:

1. Draw an "Elevation" drawing of a piece of 3" pipe. The actual size of the pipe is 3 1/2" (see chart inside of back cover). Make the drawing full size.

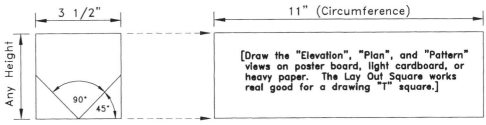

[Draw the "Elevation", "Plan", and "Pattern" views on poster board, light cardboard, or heavy paper. The Lay Out Square works real good for a drawing "T" square.]

Elevation   Pattern Length

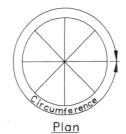

Plan

2. Project "Pattern" lines to the right of the "Elevation" drawing, and draw the "Pattern Length" as shown above. The "Length" of the pattern is the circumference of the pipe. In this case pi or 3.1416 x 3.5" or 10.9956" or 11".

3. Draw the "Plan" View (Diameter) of the pipe, from the elevation drawing, as shown on the left. Divide the circle into eight (8) equal segments.

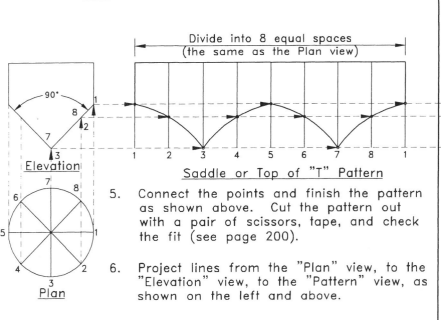

Elevation

Plan

Divide into 8 equal spaces
(the same as the Plan view)

Saddle or Top of "T" Pattern

5. Connect the points and finish the pattern as shown above. Cut the pattern out with a pair of scissors, tape, and check the fit (see page 200).

6. Project lines from the "Plan" view, to the "Elevation" view, to the "Pattern" view, as shown on the left and above.

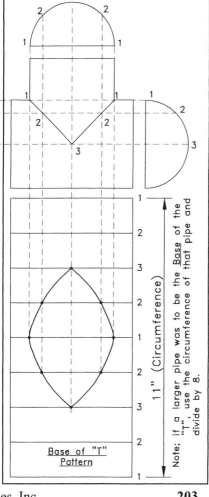

Base of "T"
Pattern

Note; if a larger pipe was to be the Base of the "T", use the circumference of that pipe and divide by 8.

Make the Base of the "T" Joint:

1. Project lines from the "Pattern" view, to drawings shown within the "Bold Lines" on the right. Make the base patterns the same size as the Saddle Patterns.

2. Refer to page 200 for information on how to cut, mark, and lay out the pattern. To make a quick "T" base pattern, see Step 6.

How to make Pipe Saddles — 90° and 45° (continued)

How to make a 45° "T" or "Pipe Saddle" for a 3 1/2" dia. pipe:

1. Draw an "Elevation" drawing of a piece of 3" pipe.
   Actual size of pipe 3 1/2" diameter. Make the
   drawing full size. Use a Lay Out Square if Needed.

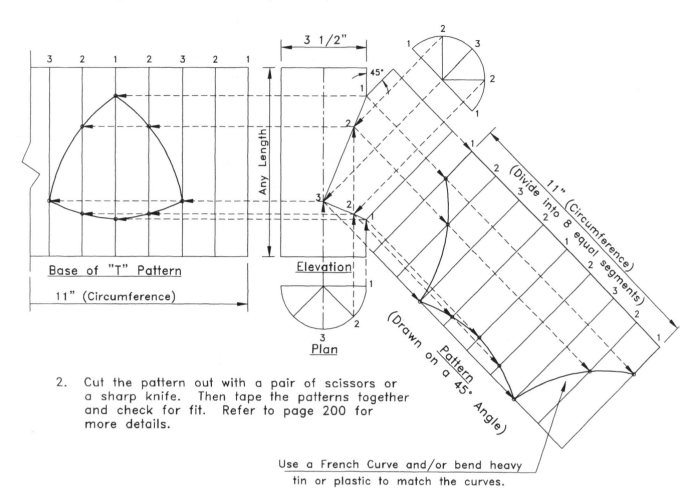

Base of "T" Pattern

11" (Circumference)

Elevation

Plan

2. Cut the pattern out with a pair of scissors or
   a sharp knife. Then tape the patterns together
   and check for fit. Refer to page 200 for
   more details.

Use a French Curve and/or bend heavy
tin or plastic to match the curves.

[Note, to make a pattern for a 45° saddle in very similar to a 90° saddle. The only
difference is the position of the pipe. Refer to the preceding page, if necessary.]

Try other angles: Now that you know how to draw angles with a square, try laying
out some pipe saddles on poster board, card board, or heavy paper.
After a few trys, making pipe saddles will be a piece of cake.

Helpful HInts: Make a drawing board out of plywood (sanded smooth one side).
Tape the card board or paper to the plywood. Then use a dry wall
T—Square and a Lay Out Square to draw the pipe saddle patterns.
Draw the pipe saddle patterns full size.

This module demonstrates how to manually develop pipe saddles, but there are also
computer programs (software) available for all kinds of pipe saddles and angles. Use
the method that works best for you.

Trade Trick #12 – Straighten Fences/Walls
[How to Straighten Fences and Walls with a Taut Line]

How to Align and Plumb Fences:

1) Space post holes according to your property lines, buildings, survey stakes, etc. Make a story pole of the proper spacing. In this example; 4 ft., 8 ft., 12 ft., 16 ft., etc. Run fence, in sections of 25 ft. to 50 ft. because of the wind effect on the line.

2) Dig the beginning post and the end post first of the 1st section. For long fences a transit may be needed to line up the last post of each section. Make the holes big enough to make adjustments when leveling.

3) Plumb the ends vertically as shown below. Take care to observe the desired property reference lines. These two post are the most critical, so take care when installing. Anchor in place with concrete, dirt, gravel, etc.

4) Nail a spacer block (3/4" × 1 1/2" × 4"*) to the top and bottom of the two end posts. Then fasten a nylon line on the starting end (make a simple loop knot) to a double headed nail. String the line over the beginning post spacer block and the ending post spacer block. Fasten the line to a masonry line block as shown. Or use a couple of small nails to wrap the string around. The line must be real tight. Repeat the above to the bottom of the two posts as shown below.

5) Space and dig the remaining post holes. Pencils make good markers to space the post. Also use a 50 ft. or 100 ft. tape measure if you have one.

6) Position the next post by leveling it perpendicular to the fence, and checking the space between the line and the post (top and bottom) with a spacer block as shown below.

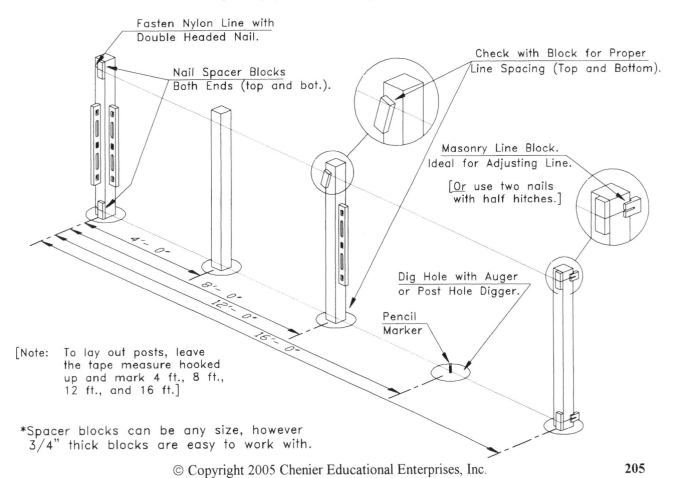

Fasten Nylon Line with Double Headed Nail.

Nail Spacer Blocks Both Ends (top and bot.).

Check with Block for Proper Line Spacing (Top and Bottom).

Masonry Line Block. Ideal for Adjusting Line.

[Or use two nails with half hitches.]

Dig Hole with Auger or Post Hole Digger.

Pencil Marker

4'- 0"

8'- 0"

12'- 0"

16'- 0"

[Note: To lay out posts, leave the tape measure hooked up and mark 4 ft., 8 ft., 12 ft., and 16 ft.]

*Spacer blocks can be any size, however 3/4" thick blocks are easy to work with.

How to Align Fences and Walls with a Taut Line (Continued)

How to Align and Plumb Walls:

1.) Plumb both ends of a wall by using a spirit level (4 foot or longer) or a plumb bob in oil*, as shown below. Another way is to use prepared braces, then check with a spirit level and/or a plumb bob in oil. Use the method that works best for you.

2) Once the bottom sole plate is nailed to the floor, and the walls are plumb, nail the end braces to the header joist or floor (use double headed nails). Make sure the wall is secure and safe before continuing.

3) Nail a spacer block (3/4" × 1 1/2" × 4") to the double top plate, one on each end, as shown below. Then attach a nylon line over each spacer block as shown below. Tighten the line real tight.

4) Check the space between the nylon line with a spacer block. Nail braces where needed to keep the wall in alignment. The braces can be precut and nailed to 2 × 4 blocks (any scrap 2" lumber) nailed to the floor. The top of the braces can be nailed to the studs or window/door trimmers.

5) The same principle, as shown above, can be used to align machines, sawmills, and other objects. Piano wire is some-times used instead of nylon line.

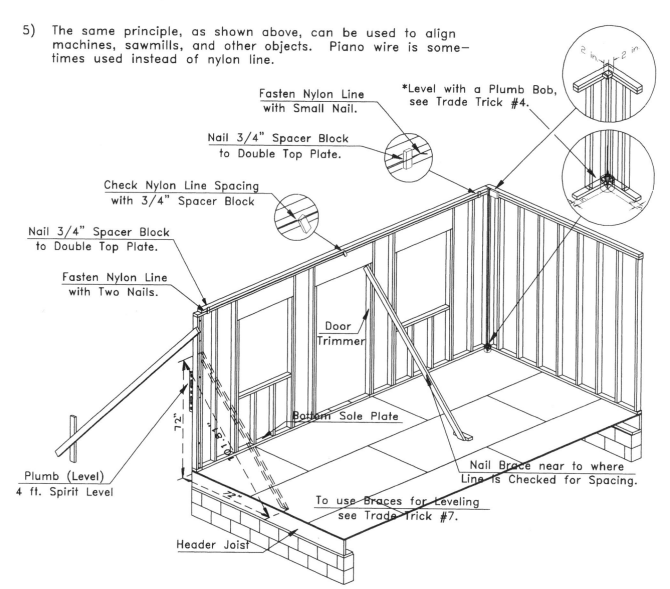

Fasten Nylon Line with Small Nail.

*Level with a Plumb Bob, see Trade Trick #4.

Nail 3/4" Spacer Block to Double Top Plate.

Check Nylon Line Spacing with 3/4" Spacer Block

Nail 3/4" Spacer Block to Double Top Plate.

Fasten Nylon Line with Two Nails.

Door Trimmer

Bottom Sole Plate

72"

Plumb (Level)
4 ft. Spirit Level

2"

Nail Brace near to where Line is Checked for Spacing.

To use Braces for Leveling see Trade Trick #7.

Header Joist

2 in. 2 in.

Trade Trick #1 – Make a Story Pole

[Problem 9: 2.032 Meter Stick (Millimeters and Inches) - 6 Centers]

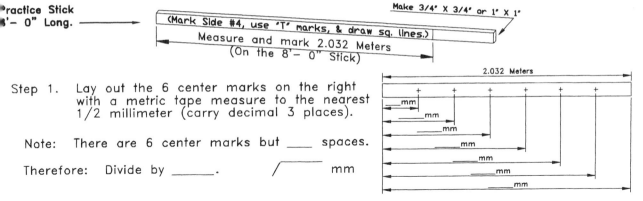

Practice Stick 8'– 0" Long.

(Mark Side #4, use 'T' marks, & draw sq. lines.)
Measure and mark 2.032 Meters
(On the 8'– 0" Stick)

Make 3/4" X 3/4" or 1" X 1"

2.032 Meters

Step 1. Lay out the 6 center marks on the right with a metric tape measure to the nearest 1/2 millimeter (carry decimal 3 places).

Note: There are 6 center marks but ____ spaces.

Therefore: Divide by _____. ____/ mm

Step 2. List in order (make a story pole) the dimensions so you can read them on the tape measure without having to move it.

Making a Story Pole (refer to Problem 8, page 196, if more information is needed):

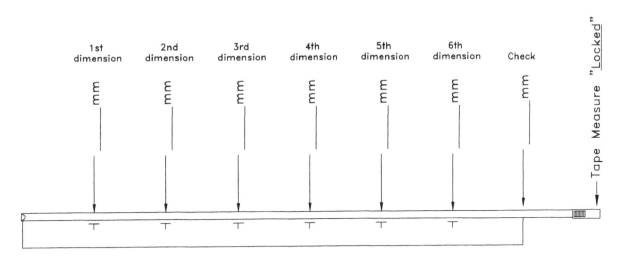

| 1st dimension | 2nd dimension | 3rd dimension | 4th dimension | 5th dimension | 6th dimension | Check |
| mm | mm | mm | mm | mm | mm | mm |

Tape Measure "Locked"

Step 3. Lay out the center marks (use "T" marks) on the 2.032 meter stick. Do not move the tape measure. Leave in the locked positon as shown above.

Step 4. Check by measuring _____ mm between each "T" mark.

Step 5. Convert the metric measure to ft. in. and ±1/16 of an inch accuracy. Check these dimensions on the story pole with an American (English) tape measure.

Objective Practice Problems for Module #20

Scribe the upper drawing in each problem shown below to the rectangle below each problem.

1. Scribe the upper figure to the lower figure with a compass.

2. Scribe the upper figure to the lower figure with a compass.

Draw and Lay Out Pipe Saddles — Info #20:

3. Complete the pipe pattern shown below. Use a 45° drafting triangle and a French Curve.

Elevation

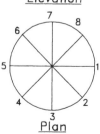

Plan

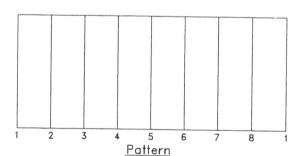

Pattern

Math Training Module #21

Instructional Objectives:

Hands On:

☐ *Application Problem* - Practice Laying Out and Bending Tubing (if applicable).

☐ *Application Problem* - Practice Calculating Material Sizes from Centerline Blueprints.

☐ *Application Problem* - Practice Laying Out Pipe Saddles.

☐ *Application Problem* - Practice Converting English to Metrics, and Vice-Versa, Convert Metrics
          to English.

Objective Practice Problems: Calculate the Practice Problems for Math Training Module #21............

Basic Math Study Notes (Mark and Bend Tubing with Tubing Benders, Fasten Tubing with Tubing Fittings, Level Tubing, Fasten Tubing with different Tubing Clamps, and Center line Drawings):

How to Mark and Bend Tubing with Tubing Bender Tips:

Center of Bend Mark*
Lined up with "L" (for Left) on Bender Handle.

90° Bend
Bend slightly past 90° for spring back (2°- 3°)

*For accuracy use a ferrule as a guide, or carefully mark
  all the way around the tubing with a sharp pencil or marker.

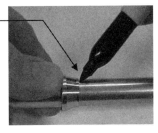

Bend Tubing with Tubing Benders (Continued)

<u>**How to Fasten Tubing with Tubing Fittings:**</u>

1. Carefully mark around the back ferrule with a sharp pencil or marker.

2. Pull tubing back 1/16" to 1/8" before tightening. This will help alleviate binding the tubing to the fitting*.

3. Tighten tubing nut with a wrench.

*Failing to pull the tubing back 1/16" to 1/8" will cause the tubing beyond the ferrule to expand too much. This would make it difficult to remove the fitting later to service the instrument or device for maintenance.

<u>**How to Level Tubing:**</u>

4. Level with a <u>spirit level</u>, <u>plumb bob (check at 90° angles)</u>, <u>line of sight</u> (<u>off blocks</u>, beams, columns, etc.), or by measuring off of floors, beams, blocks, etc.

 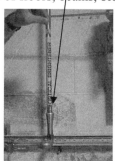  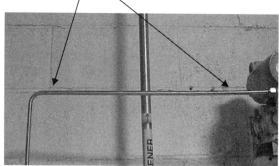

<u>**How to Fasten Tubing with Different Tubing Clamps:**</u>

5. Fasten the tubing with tubing clamps. Below are three popular manufactured clamps available.

<u>A Wall Clamp:</u>   <u>A Unistrut Clamp:</u>   <u>An Instrument Tray Clamp:</u>

[Refer to Info #21 on the next pages for more information.]

Bend Tubing with Tubing Benders (Continued)

Custom Built Tubing Clamps:

2 Single Clamps

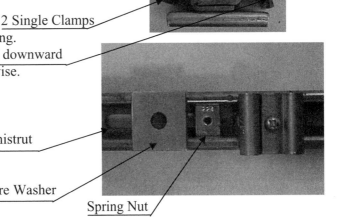

6. Simple way to fasten and reinforce 2 runs of tubing.

Bend downward in a vise.

Unistrut

Square Washer

Spring Nut

7. Simple method of fastening multiple runs of tubing.

Drill and Tap*

¼" Stove Bolt

¼" × 1" Flat Iron

Drill ¼+" dia.

Tubing Cutter Tips:

- When running hot and cold water lines, space the water lines far enough apart so the tubing cutters will clear. If you add a fixture later, the tubing lines can be easily cut to add a tee. The tubing lines on the right are 6 inches apart.

- Small cutters can be used for narrow spaced lines.

Cutters Clear

- Use a guide to mark for tubing cuts.

Use a hanging strap or ferrule as a marking guide

- Measure twice and cut once.

- For critical cuts, test the tubing cutters on a scrape piece of tubing. Sometimes the cutters will wander and not cut properly. In this case, reverse the cutting direction. If this doesn't work you may need new cutters.

*See the Tap and Drill Sizes For American Std. Bolts Chart, inside back cover.

Bend Tubing with Tubing Benders (Continued)

Center Line Drawings:

Basically, the center line method of drawing is to <u>increase accuracy</u>, make it <u>easier to measure</u>, and to <u>decrease errors</u>.

Increase Accuracy:

Can use the Story Pole Concept with the measurements much easier, either with the tape measure alone and/or by adding all the dimensions and using the tape measure.

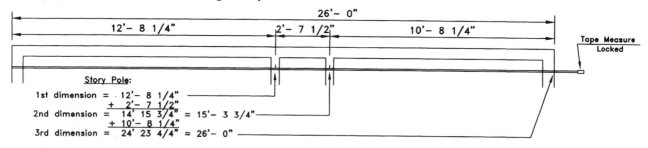

Easier to Measure:

Because the measurements are to the center of the object*. Therefore fewer dimensions are needed and materials can be added or changed later with no effect on the drawings or prints.

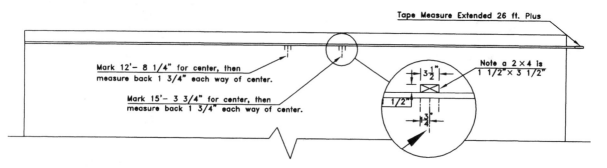

*After the center line is marked, just measure ½ each way of the center line and mark the object.

Decrease Errors:

The fewer dimensions there are, the fewer errors there will be. Note there are 7 dimensions on the drawing below, whereas the first drawing above has only 3 dimensions.

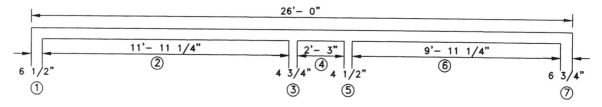

[See Trade Trick #13 – Center Line Drawings, page 221 for more information.]

Info #21 – Bend Tubing
[with Tubing Benders (90°, 45°, and 30°)]

How to Measure and Bend Tubing 90°:

The best way to "Measure" and "Bend" tubing, is to measure and bend as you go. Example, measure for the 1st bend, then make that bend. Then measure for the 2nd bend and make that bend. And so on.

1. "Measure" and "Mark" the tubing (From Left to Right).

[Measure Left ⟶ to Right]

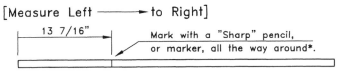

13 7/16"

Mark with a "Sharp" pencil, or marker, all the way around*.

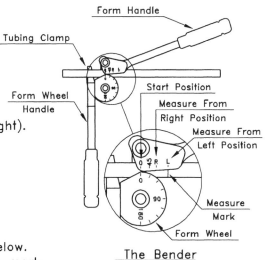

Form Handle

Tubing Clamp

Form Wheel Handle

Start Position

Measure From Right Position

Measure From Left Position

Measure Mark

Form Wheel

The Bender

2. Insert the "Tubing" into the "Bender", as shown below. Make sure "0" and "0", and "L" and the measure mark line up. The "L" is used when measuring from the "Left".

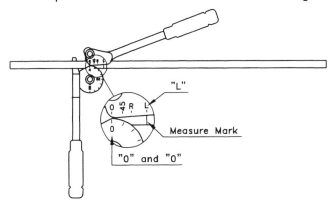

"L"

Measure Mark

"0" and "0"

3. Make the "First" Bend, as shown below. Make sure "0" and "90°" marks line up.

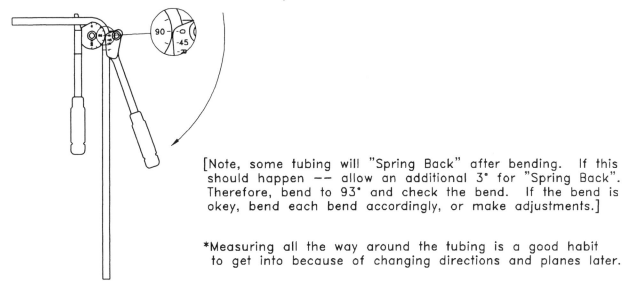

[Note, some tubing will "Spring Back" after bending. If this should happen —— allow an additional 3° for "Spring Back". Therefore, bend to 93° and check the bend. If the bend is okey, bend each bend accordingly, or make adjustments.]

*Measuring all the way around the tubing is a good habit to get into because of changing directions and planes later.

Bending Tubing with Tubing Benders — 90°, 45°, and 30° (Continued)

4. "Measure" and "Mark" the Tubing (From Left to Right) for the "2nd Bend".

1st Measure from the center of the tubing to the right 18 1/4".

2nd Insert tubing into the bender. Make sure "0" and "0", and "L" and the mark line up.

3rd Flip the "bender 180°", as shown below. Make sure "0" and "0", and "L" and the mark line up.

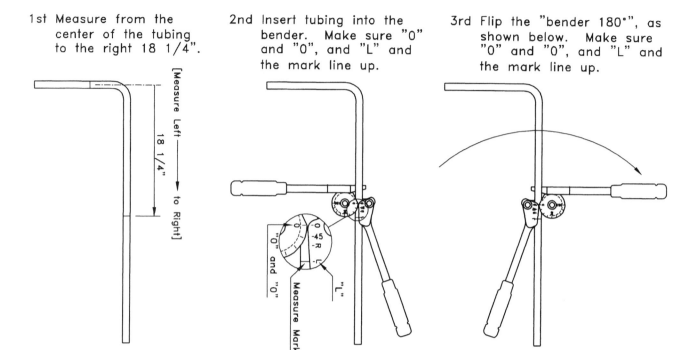

4th Make the "Second" bend, as shown below. Make sure "0" and "90°" marks line up.

5th Check the "Measurement" for accuracy. Prepare for the next bend. See 5.

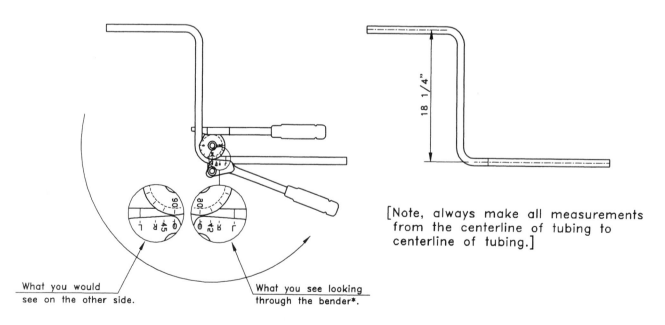

[Note, always make all measurements from the centerline of tubing to centerline of tubing.]

What you would see on the other side.

What you see looking through the bender*.

*Remember the bender was flipped over in the 3rd step, so in reality, you would be reading from the other side. The reason for mirroring the picture.

Bending Tubing with Tubing Benders – 90°, 45°, and 30° (Continued)

5. "Measure" and "Mark" the tubing (from Right to Left) for the "3rd Bend".

1st Measure from the "End" of the tubing to the "Left" (Right to Left) this time.

[There will be times the measurement direction will have to change. Therefore, the "R" scale on the bender will be used.]

2nd Insert tubing into the bender. Make sure "0" and "0", and "R" and the mark line up.

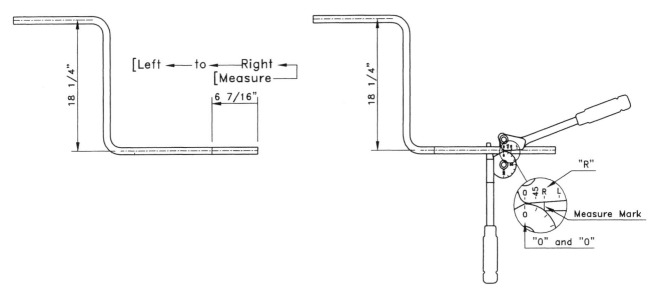

4th Make the "Second" Bend, as shown below. Make sure "0" and "90° marks line up.

5th Check the "Measurement" for accuracy. [This final bend should fit the fixture or fitting, exactly.]

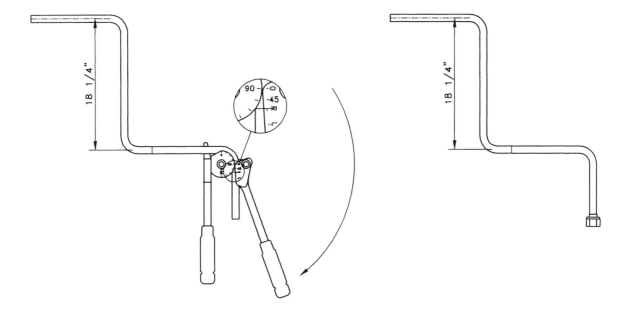

Bend Tubing with Tubing Benders — 90°, 45°, and 30° (Continued)

How to Measure and Bend Tubing 45°:

To bend tubing 45°, use the same concept to "Measure" and "Bend" tubing as you go. However, the "Offset" must be calculated 1st. To do this, multiply the "Offset" x "1.414". 2nd Measure that product (length of offset), and mark the positions of both bends. 3rd Make the 1st bend. 4th make the 2nd bend. [Follow the procedure shown below.]

1. "Measure" and "Mark" a "Tubing Offset" of 6 1/2".

1st   Multiply: 1.414 (the hypotenuse of 1 unit)
           x 6.5 (Offset — 6.5 units)
           9.191" = 9 3/16" (length of offset)

1 Unit of 45° Offset

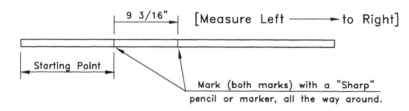

[See Task R1 if more information is needed.]

2nd   Measure from the "Starting Point", Left to Right, the Length of the Offset (9 3/16") Mark both lines, as shown below.

9 3/16"   [Measure Left ———→ to Right]

Starting Point

Mark (both marks) with a "Sharp" pencil or marker, all the way around.

3rd   Make the 1st Bend.

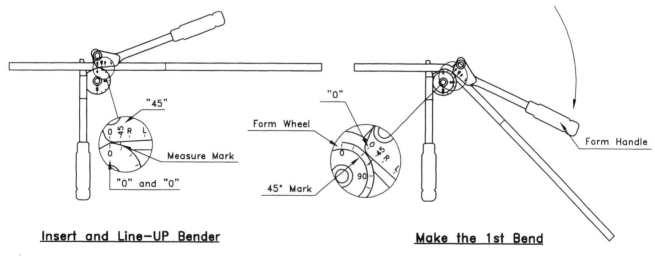

Insert and Line—UP Bender

Insert bender and make sure "0" and "0", and 45° and the measure mark line up.

Make the 1st Bend

Bend until the "0" in the Form Handle lines up with the "45° mark in the "Form Wheel".

Bend Tubing with Tubing Benders — 90°, 45°, and 30° (Continued)

4th   Make the 2nd Bend.

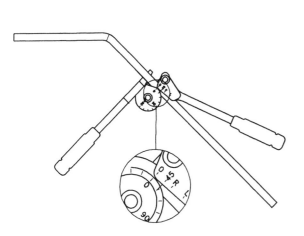

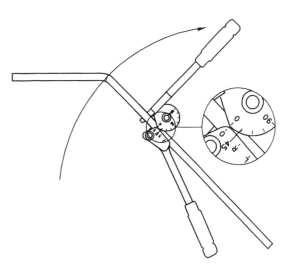

Insert and Line-Up Bender:

Insert bender and make sure "0" and "0", and "45" and the measure mark line up.

Flip Bender 180°:

Flip bender and make sure "0" and "0", and "45" and the measure mark line up.

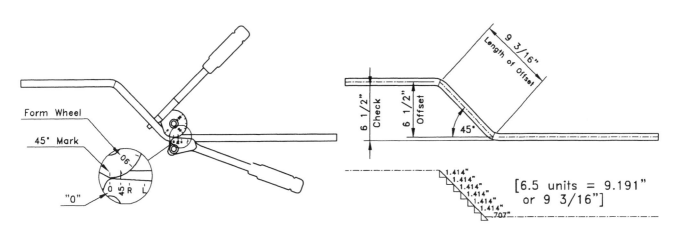

Form Wheel

45° Mark

"0"

9 3/16"
Length of Offset

6 1/2" Check

6 1/2" Offset

45°

1.414"
1.414"
1.414"
1.414"
1.414"
1.414"
.707"

[6.5 units = 9.191" or 9 3/16"]

Make the 2nd Bend

Bend until the "0" in the Form Handle lines up with the "45° mark in the "Form Wheel".

Check the Bend for Accuracy

Lay the tubing as shown above, and measure from the bottom of the tubing to the under side of the top bend.   The measurement should be very close to 6 1/2".

Bend Tubing with Tubing Benders — 90°, 45°, and 30° (Continued)

How to Measure and Bend Tubing 30°:

To bend tubing 30°, use the same concept to "Measure" and "Bend" tubing as you go. However, the length of the "Offset" must be calculated 1st. To do this, determine the calculated "Offset" of 1 unit first, then multiply it by the offset of 5.5 units (in this case). 2nd Measure that product (length of offset), and mark the positions of both bends. Make the 1st bend. 4th make the 2nd bend. [Follow the procedure shown below.]

1. "Measure" and "Mark" a "Tubing Offset" of 5 1/2".

   1st   Multiply: 2.0 (the hypotenuse of 1 unit)
            x 5.5 (Offset — 5.5 units)
            11.0" = 11" (length of offset)

<u>1 Unit of 30° Offset</u>

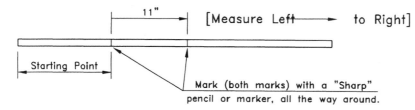

Sin. = Opp./Hyp.

Sin. 30° = Opp./Hyp.

.5 = 1/Hyp.

Hyp. = 1/.5

Hyp. = 2"

   2nd   Measure from the "Starting Point", Left to Right, the "Length of the Offset (11")". Mark both lines, as shown below.

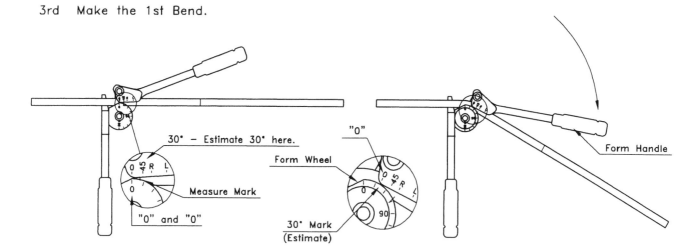

3rd   Make the 1st Bend.

Insert and Line—UP Bender

Insert bender and make sure "0" and "0", and 30° and the measure mark line up.

Make the 1st Bend

Bend until the "0" in the Form Handle lines up with the "30° mark in the "Form Wheel".

Bend Tubing with Tubing Benders — 90°, 45°, and 30° (Continued)

4th   Make the 2nd Bend.

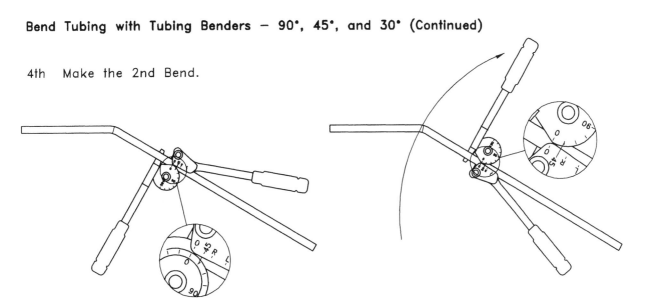

Insert and Line-Up Bender:

Insert bender and make sure "0" and "0", and "30" and the measure mark line up.

Flip Bender 180°:

Flip bender and make sure "0" and "0", and "30" and the measure mark line up.

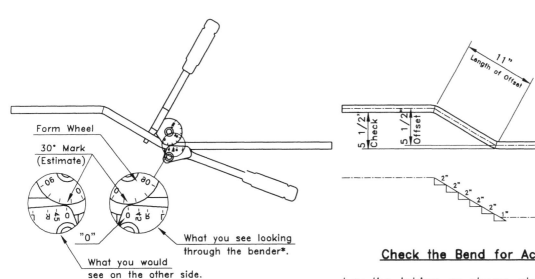

Make the 2nd Bend

Bend until the "0" in the Form Handle lines with the "30°" mark on the "Form Wheel".

Check the Bend for Accuracy

Lay the tubing as shown above, and measure from the bottom of the tubing to the under side of the top bend. The measurement should be very close to 5 1/2".

[Note, use the above example for any specific angle, for example 22 1/2°. However do the math first to get the bend length and estimate the angle on the protractor of the bender.]

*Remember the bender was flipped over in the 4th step, so in reality, you would be reading from the other side. The reason for mirroring the picture.

Bend Tubing with Tubing Benders (Continued)

How to Calculate Tubing Bends:

Example 1. Calculate the tubing bends for tubing the fixture on the right. the bends will be 45°.

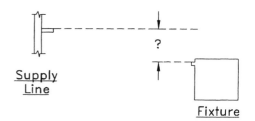

1. Measure the vertical distance between the tubing and the fixture with a spirit level as shown.

    a) Use a spirit level and a straight edge (tubing works good).

    b) Measure the vertical distance as shown.

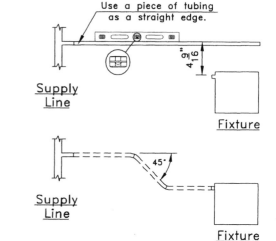

2. Change 4 9/16" to a decimal.

    a) $4.5625 \times 1.414 = 6.451"$ or 6 7/16"

    b) Measure 6 7/16" on the tubing as shown below.

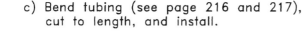

    c) Bend tubing (see page 216 and 217), cut to length, and install.

Example 2. Calculate the tubing bends to tube the fixture on the right. The bends will be 30°.

1. Measure the horizontal distance between the tubing and the fixture with a spirit level as shown.

    a) Use a spirit level and a straight edge tubing works good).

    b) Measure the horizontal distance as shown on the right.

2. Change 12 7/8" to a decimal.

    a) $12.875 \times 2 = 25.75"$ or 25 3/4"

    b) Measure 25 3/4" on the tubing as shown below.

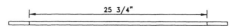

    c) Bend tubing (see page 218 and 219), cut to length, and install.

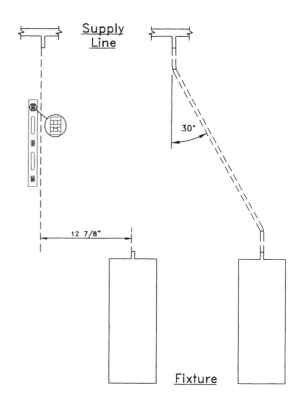

Trade Trick #13 – Center Line Drawings
[The Center Line Method of Drawing Prints]

This module illustrates the "Center–Line" method of drawing prints, verses a more traditional method. The center–line method increases accuracy (especially using the story pole concept) plus makes it easier to eliminate costly errors.

The Center–Line Method of Drawing Prints:

Example 1. [Note, in this example there are only 3 dimensions used to lay out 4 walls.]

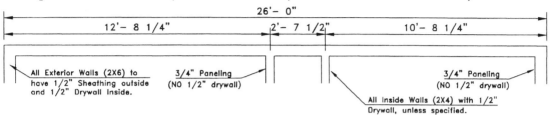

A Traditional Method of Drawing Prints:

Example 2. [Note, in this example there are 7 dimensions used to lay out 4 walls.]

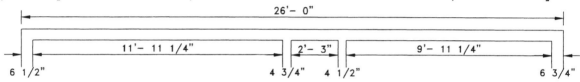

1. The reason only 3 dimensions are needed in Example 1 is that the first dimension is drawn to the center of the stud, the second dimension is drawn to the center of the stud, and the third dimension is drawn to the outside of the building. Once these dimensions are marked, it is just a matter of measuring (on–the–job), either side of the 2X4 wall, 1 3/4", or one half of the standard 2X4 which is 3 1/2". Most important, if a particular wall covering is changed, there is no need to change the prints. See the example in step 3 below.

2. In Example 2, if you decide to change the thickness of a wall covering, it would make it much harder to figure on–the–job. Also, observe how many different measurements are involved with this method. The more measurements, the greater chance for error.

3. From the drawing in Example 1, it is real easy to make a story pole of all the dimensions as shown below. This is another effective way to help eliminate errors, as it is not necessary to move the tape measure, in most cases.

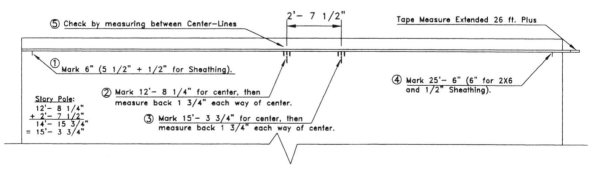

3. Try laying out the dimensions for Example 2. Hopefully, this will illustrate the difference between the two examples.

Objective Practice Problems for Module #21

Bend Tubing with Tubing Benders (90°, 45°, and 30°) – Info #21 (carry decimals 3 places):

Calculate the length of the tubing bends for the jobs listed below.
Accuracy must be ±1/16th of an inch accuracy.

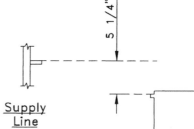

Job #1

1. Calculate the 45° tubing bend
length for the job on the right. Bend Length = _____

2. Calculate the 30° tubing bend
length for the job on the right. Bend Length = _____

Job #2

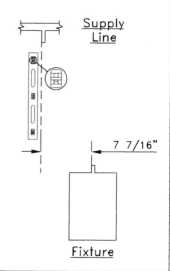

3. Calculate the 45° tubing bend
length for the job on the right. Bend Length = _____

4. Calculate the 30° tubing bend
length for the job on the right. Bend Length = _____

Center Line Drawings [The Center Line Method of Drawing Prints] – Trade Trick #13:

5. Given the Floor Plan shown below, draw how to lay out the walls (rough walls only) on the
Blank Floor shown below. A 2 × 4 is 1 1/2"× 3 1/2" and a 2 × 6 is 1 1/2"× 5 1/2".

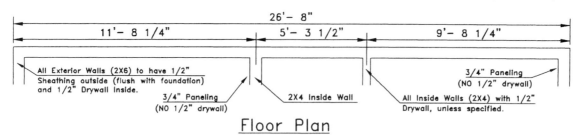

Floor Plan

Blank Floor

Appendix - A
List of Information Sheets - by Page Numbers and Module Numbers:

Appendix - B
List of Trade Tricks – by Page Numbers and Module Numbers:

APPENDIX – C

Protractor – Master Copy for Reproducing

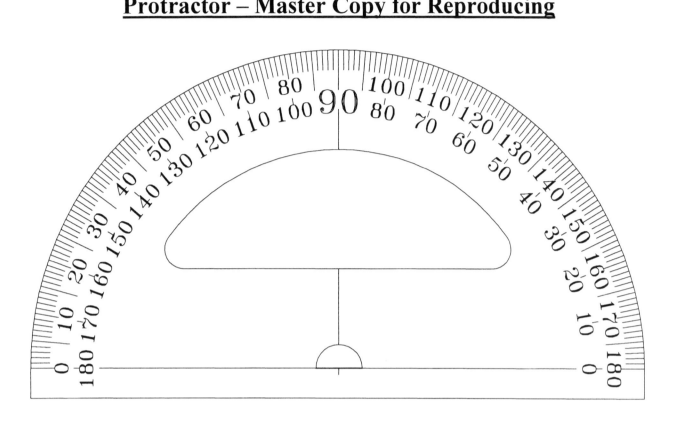

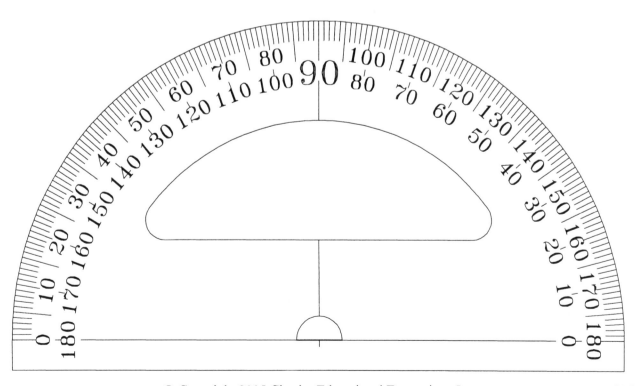

Lay Out Square
[Even Degree to Inch Chart]

Interpolation:

[Note to lay out a 22 1/2° angle (angles by 1/2°), use interpolation as shown below.]

$$23° = \quad 5.094"$$
$$22° = -\ 4.848"$$
Difference = .246

Difference .246 ÷ 2 = .123

Add: .123
\+ 4.848
Equals 4.971"

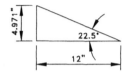

12" and 4.971" on the Lay Out Square = 22 1/2°

[See page 131 and 132 for more information.]

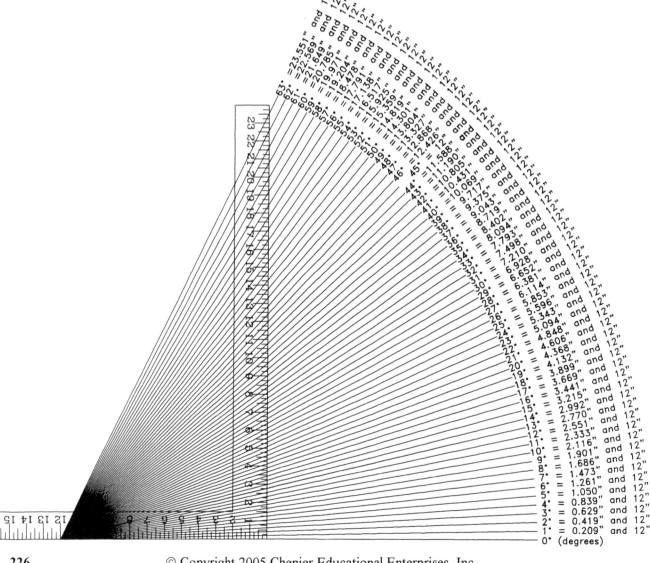

63° = 23.551" and 12"
62° = 22.569" and 12"
61° = 21.649" and 12"
60° = 20.785" and 12"
59° = 19.971" and 12"
58° = 19.204" and 12"
57° = 18.478" and 12"
56° = 17.791" and 12"
55° = 17.138" and 12"
54° = 16.517" and 12"
53° = 15.925" and 12"
52° = 15.359" and 12"
51° = 14.819" and 12"
50° = 14.301" and 12"
49° = 13.804" and 12"
48° = 13.327" and 12"
47° = 12.868" and 12"
46° = 12.426" and 12"
45° = 12" and 12"
44° = 11.588" and 12"
43° = 11.190" and 12"
42° = 10.805" and 12"
41° = 10.431" and 12"
40° = 10.069" and 12"
39° = 9.717" and 12"
38° = 9.375" and 12"
37° = 9.043" and 12"
36° = 8.719" and 12"
35° = 8.402" and 12"
34° = 8.094" and 12"
33° = 7.793" and 12"
32° = 7.498" and 12"
31° = 7.210" and 12"
30° = 6.928" and 12"
29° = 6.652" and 12"
28° = 6.381" and 12"
27° = 6.114" and 12"
26° = 5.853" and 12"
25° = 5.596" and 12"
24° = 5.343" and 12"
23° = 5.094" and 12"
22° = 4.848" and 12"
21° = 4.606" and 12"
20° = 4.368" and 12"
19° = 4.132" and 12"
18° = 3.899" and 12"
17° = 3.669" and 12"
16° = 3.441" and 12"
15° = 3.215" and 12"
14° = 2.992" and 12"
13° = 2.770" and 12"
12° = 2.551" and 12"
11° = 2.333" and 12"
10° = 2.116" and 12"
9° = 1.901" and 12"
8° = 1.686" and 12"
7° = 1.473" and 12"
6° = 1.261" and 12"
5° = 1.050" and 12"
4° = 0.839" and 12"
3° = 0.629" and 12"
2° = 0.419" and 12"
1° = 0.209" and 12"
0° (degrees)

Lay Out Square
[Even Inch to Degree Chart]

Interpolation:

[Note to calculate the angle for a 7 1/2" by 12" slope, use interpolation as shown below.]

$$8" = 33.69°$$
$$7\text{ }" = - 30.26°$$
Difference $= 3.43$

Difference $3.43 \div 2 = 1.715$

Add: 1.715
$+ 30.26°$
Equals $31.975°$

12" and 7 1/2" on the
Lay Out Square = 31.975 or 32**

[See page 133, 134, 141, and 142
for more information.]

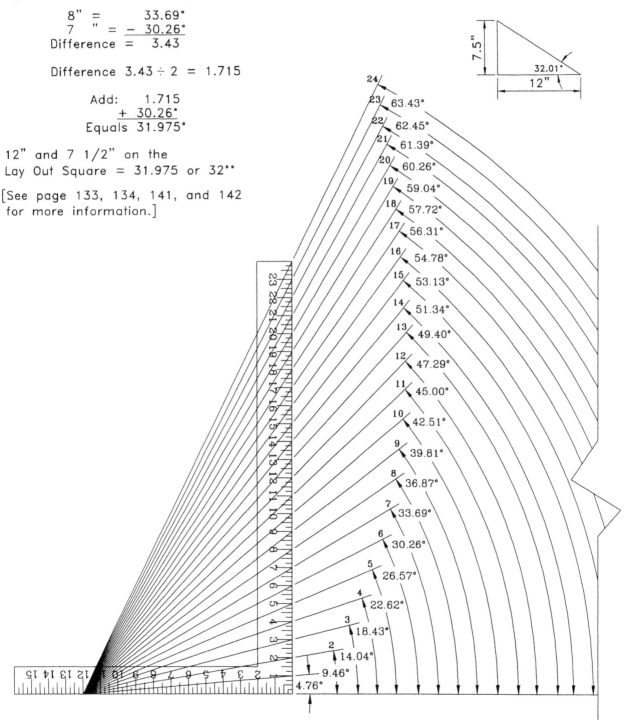

Lay Out Square
[100th to 16th Conversion Made Easy Chart]

(Top Scale Divided into 100THS increments)

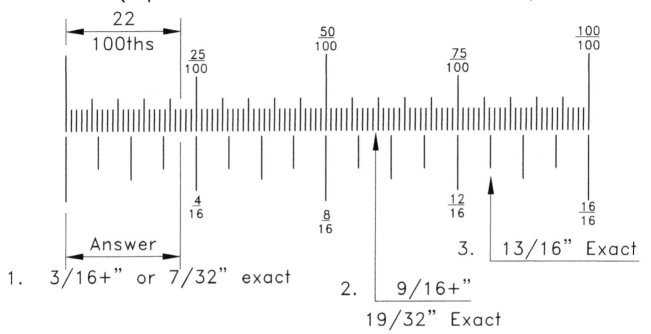

(Bottom Scale Divided into 16th Increments)

[Note this chart was taken from a Stanley AR100 Lay
Out Square. The chart can be used without the square.]

Lay Out Square
[Octagon Scale, Brace Measure, Lumber Measure, etc.]

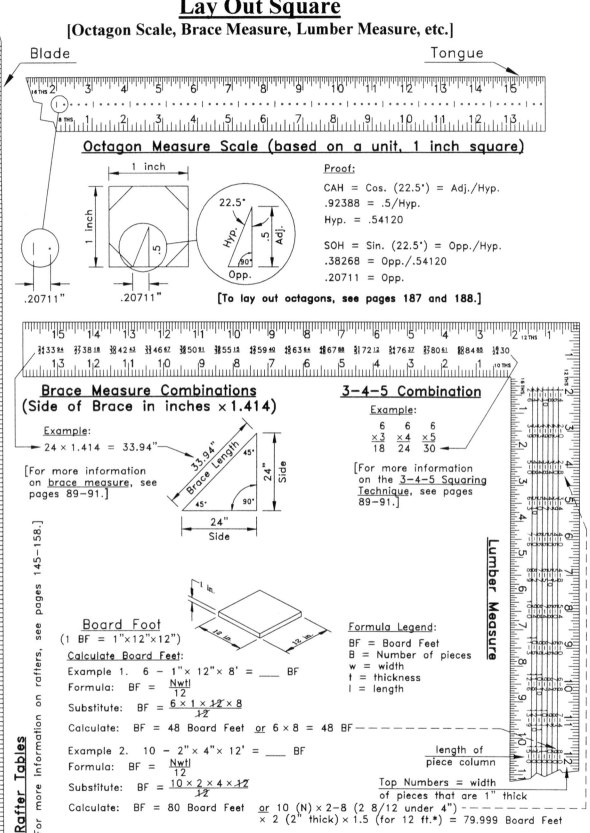

Blade

Tongue

Octagon Measure Scale (based on a unit, 1 inch square)

1 inch

1 inch

.5

.20711"

.20711"

Proof:

CAH = Cos. (22.5°) = Adj./Hyp.

.92388 = .5/Hyp.

Hyp. = .54120

SOH = Sin. (22.5°) = Opp./Hyp.

.38268 = Opp./.54120

.20711 = Opp.

22.5°

Hyp. / Opp. / Adj. / .5 / 90°

[To lay out octagons, see pages 187 and 188.]

Brace Measure Combinations
(Side of Brace in inches × 1.414)

Example:
24 × 1.414 = 33.94"

[For more information on brace measure, see pages 89-91.]

33.94" Brace Length
24" Side
24" Side
45° 45° 90°

3-4-5 Combination

Example:

6	6	6
×3	×4	×5
18	24	30

[For more information on the 3-4-5 Squaring Technique, see pages 89-91.]

Lumber Measure

Board Foot
(1 BF = 1"×12"×12")

1 in.
12 in.
12 in.

Calculate Board Feet:

Example 1.   6 – 1"× 12"× 8' = ___ BF

Formula: BF = $\dfrac{Nwtl}{12}$

Substitute: BF = $\dfrac{6 \times 1 \times 12 \times 8}{12}$

Calculate: BF = 48 Board Feet or 6 × 8 = 48 BF

Example 2.   10 – 2"× 4"× 12' = ___ BF

Formula: BF = $\dfrac{Nwtl}{12}$

Substitute: BF = $\dfrac{10 \times 2 \times 4 \times 12}{12}$

Calculate: BF = 80 Board Feet   or 10 (N) × 2-8 (2 8/12 under 4")
× 2 (2" thick) × 1.5 (for 12 ft.*) = 79.999 Board Feet

Formula Legend:

BF = Board Feet
B = Number of pieces
w = width
t = thickness
l = length

length of piece column

Top Numbers = width of pieces that are 1" thick

Rafter Tables

[For more information on rafters, see pages 145-158.]

*The scale on the square has an 8 ft. length, therefore use 12/8 or 1.5 of 8 ft.   Use what ever combination works easiest for you.   Use one method to check the other method.

Graphing Paper

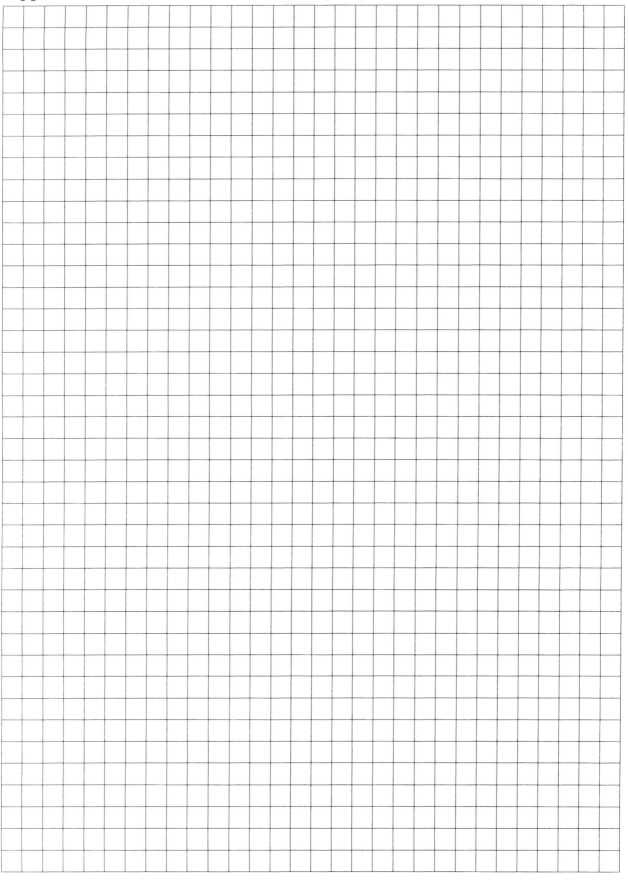

Appendix - D
Answers to Pretest, Story Poles, Objective Practice Problems, and Post Test:

Objective Practice Problems for Module #1, page 23 and 24

1. 185 **2.** 2481 **3.** 18 **4.** 6103 **5.** 2278 **6.** 195965 **7.** 12.083 **8.** 298 **9.** 23/32 **10.** 33/64 **11.** 9/32 **12.** 7/12
13. 3/64 **14.** 7 ½ **15.** 3 ¼ **16.** 7/32 **17.** 9 9/16 **18.** 22 51/64 **19.** 13 3/16 **20.** 15 7/8 **21.** 10 5/8 **22.** 38 ½
23. 4 **24.** 5/8 **25.** 20′ 7 11/16″ **26.** 24′ 4 11/32″ **27.** 5′ 0 7/8″ **28.** 6′ 8 1/2″ **29.** 3612 sq. in. **30.** 164 linear in.
31. 17″ **32.** 1′ 4″ **33.** 48.2 **34.** 11.6921 **35.** 2.87 **36.** 43.37 **37.** 2.850 **38.** 2.47135 **39.** 3.939 **40.** 16.5

Pretest, page 25

1. 3344 **2.** 8,879 **3.** 364,014 **4.** 2,084 **5.** 17/32 **6.** 7/32 **7.** 5/8 **8.** 9/16 **9.** 9 5/8 **10.** 4 15/16
11. 8 **12.** 25/32 **13.** 7 ft. 6 5/16 in. **14.** 14 ft. 11 17/32 in. **15.** 2280 sq. in. or 15.83 sq. ft. **16.** 20 lin. in.
17. 36.31 **18.** 52.09 **19.** 6.41957 **20.** 44

Pretest, page 26

21. 30 **22.** 82 **23.** .176 or .1765 **24.** .625′ **25.** 7′3 ½-″ **26.** 4 5/8″ **27.** 243 **28.** 145 **29.** 10
30. .085 **31.** .0075 **32.** 7.5% **33.** 25% **34.** $1.84 **35.** 171 **36.** 17

Pretest, page 27

37. 850 sq. ft. **38.** 94.44 sq. yd. **39.** 324 cu. ft. **40.** 12 cu. yd. **41.** 62° **42.** 53° **43.** 22° 22′ 30″
44. 15/16″ **45.** 1 3/4″ **46.** 2 3/8″ **47.** 2 5/8″ **48.** 3 3/16″ **49.** 4 19/32″ **50.** 6 1/8″

Pretest, page 28 (Optional)

1. .625″ **2.** 5/8″ **3.** .4804″ **4.** 31/64-″ **5.** 12.762″or 12 ¾+″ **6.** 28° **7.** 17.746″ or 1′ 5 3/4″ **8.** 16.083″
or 1′ 4 1/16+″ **9.** 32.17122° **10.** 18.312″ or 1′ 6 5/16″

Trade Trick #1, page 34 - Make a Story Pole (Problem 2: 24 3/4″ Stick – 4 Centers)

1. 24.75″ ÷ 5 = 4.95″

		or	4.95″	= 4 15/16″		14.85	
			+ 4.95			+ 4.95	
		2.	9.90	= 9 7/8+″ or 9 15/16-″	4.	19.80	= 19 13/16-″ or 19 ¾+″
			+ 4.95			+ 4.95	
		3.	14.85	= 14 13/16+″ or 14 7/8-″	5.	24.75	= 24 3/4″

Objective Practice Problems for Module #2, page 35

1. 7 1/2 **2.** 7/64 **3.** 28.2 **4.** 78 **5.** .3846 = .385 **6.** .875 inches **7.** .375 feet **8.** 4′- 10 7/8+″ or
4′- 10 15/16-″ **9.** 9 9/16+″ or 9 5/8-″ **10.** 7′ 2 3/8+″ or 7′ 2 7/16-″

Trade Trick #1, page 43 - Make a Story Pole (Problem 3: 24 3/4″ Stick – 5 Centers)

1. 24.75″ ÷ 6 = 4.125″

		or	4.125″	= 4 1/8″		16.500	
			+ 4.125			+ 4.125	
		2.	8.250	= 8 1/4″	5.	20.625	= 20 5/8″
			+ 4.125			+ 4.125	
		3.	12.375	= 12 3/8″	6.	24.750″	= 24 3/4″ OK
			+ 4.125				
		4.	16.500	= 16 1/2″			

APPENDIX-D

Answers to Objective Practice Problems, Story Poles, and Post Test (Continued)

Objective Practice Problems for Module #3, page 44

1. $3^3 = 27$ and $2^7 = 128$ **2.** 143 **3.** 22 5/8-" or 1'- 10 5/8-" **4.** 12 **5.** .0975 **6.** 3 1/8% **7.** 87 ½%
8. $1.44

Trade Trick #1, page 57 - Make a Story Pole (Problem 4: 24 3/4" Stick – 6 Centers)

1. $24.75'' \div 7 = 3.535''$ <u>or</u>   3.535"   = 3 ½+" or 3 9/16-"
                                <u>+ 3.535</u>
                        2.   7.070   = 7 1/16"
                                  <u>+ 3.535</u>
                        3.   10.605   = 10 9/16+" or 10 5/8-"
                                  <u>+ 3.535</u>
                        4.   14.140   = 14 1/8+" or 14 3/16-"
                                  <u>+ 3.535</u>
                        5.   17.675   = 17 11/16"
                                  <u>+ 3.535</u>
                        6.   21.210   = 21 3/16+" or 21 ¼-"
                                  <u>+ 3.535</u>
                        7.   24.745   = 24 3/4" Checks Out as stick is 24 3/4" long.

Objective Practice Problems for Module #4, page 58

1. 612 **2.** 186 **3.** 14 **4.** 18 **5.** 222.1875 sq, ft. **6.** 24.6875 sq. yd. **7.** 309.375 cu. ft.
8. 11.458 cu. yd. **9.** 180° **10.** 60°

Objective Practice Problems for Module #5, page 63 and 64

1. 9" **2.** 14 teeth **3.** 6-8-10 **4.** 12-16-20 **5.** 5-12-13 **6.** 23' 3 7/8+" **7.** 76.5 sq. ft. **8.** 83.851
9. 2 3/8+" **10.** 4 1/8" **11.** 10'- 0 1/4" **12.** 10' 0 1/4" **13.** 21'- 0" **14.** 21' 0" **15.** 9' 5 7/16+"
16. 2' 0 1/32" or 2' 0+" or 2' 0 1/16-" **17.** .005 **18.** 75% **19.** 7% **20.** $1.50

Trade Trick #1, page 70 - Make a Story Pole (Problem 5: 24 3/4" Stick – 7 Centers)

1. $24.75'' \div 8 = 3.093''$ <u>or</u>   3.093"   = 3 1/16+" or 3 1/8-"
                                  <u>+ 3.093</u>
                        2.   6.186   = 6 3/16"
                                  <u>+ 3.093</u>
                        3.   9.279   = 9 1/4+" or 9 5/16-"
                                  <u>+ 3.093</u>
                        4.   12.372   = 12 3/8"
                                  <u>+ 3.093</u>
                        5.   15.465   = 15 7/16+" or 15 ½-"
                                  <u>+ 3.093</u>
                        6.   18.558   = 18 9/16"
                                  <u>+ 3.093</u>
                        7.   21.651   = 21 5/8+" or 21 11/16-"
                                  <u> 3.093</u>
                        8.   24.744   = 24 3/4" Checks Out as stick is 24 3/4" long.

Answers to Objective Practice Problems, Story Poles, and Post Test (Continued)

Objective Practice Problems for Module #6, page 71 and 72

1. 153.938 sq. ft. **2.** 17.104 sq. yd. **3.** 30′ 7 9/16+″ **4.** 3.5014″ = 3 1/2″ **5.** 199.9 gal. = 200 gal. **6.** 64
7. 49.2616″ or 4′ 1 ¼+″ **8.** 4200 sq. in. or 29.169 sq. ft. **9.** 15-20-25 in whole feet or 192-256-320 in whole inches **10.** 10-24-26 in whole feet or 145-348-377 in whole inches **11.** 33′ 4 15/16+″

Trade Trick #1, page 79 - Make a Story Pole (Problem 6: 8′- 0″ Stick – 4 Centers)

1. 96″ ÷ 5 = 19.2″   or   19.2″ = 1′ 7 ¼-″ or 1′ 7 3/16+″
                                            + 19.2
                              2.   38.4   = 3′ 2 7/16-″ or 3′ 2 3/8+″
                                            + 19.2
                              3.   57.6   = 4′ 9 5/8-″ or 4′ 9 9/16+″
                                            + 19.2
                              4.   78.8   = 6′ 4 13/16-″ or 6′ 4 ¾+″
                                            + 19.2
                              5.   96.0   Checks Out as stick is 8′ 0″ long.

Or 8.0′ ÷ 5 = 1.6′

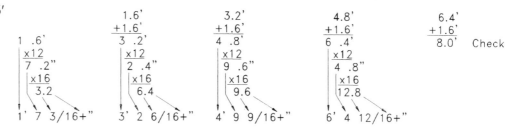

Objective Practice Problems for Module #7, page 80

1. 5′ 3 1/4″ **2.** 6′ 5 7/8″ **3.** 4′ 9 3/4″ **4.** 9′ 1 1/2″ **5.** 18′ 9 1/2″ **6.** 4′ 8 1/8″ **7.** 8′ 10 11/16″
8. 5′ 0 7/16″ **9.** 3′ 7 13/16″

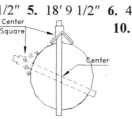 **10.**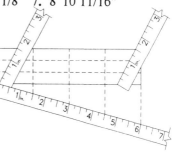

11. 27.5 sq. ft. **12.** 3960 sq. in.

Objective Practice Problems for Module #8, page 92

1. 59 3/8+″ = 4′ 11 3/8+″ **2.** 110 ¼+″ = 9′ 2 ¼+″ **3.** 10′ 8 ¼″ **4.** 5′ 7 11/16″ **5.** 11′ 6 3/4″
6.

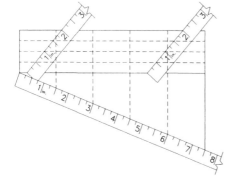

7. 48″ ÷ 5 = 9.6″   or   9.6″ = 9 5/8-″
                              + 9.6
              8.   19.2   = 19 ¼-″
                              + 9.6
              9.   28.8   = 28 13/16-″
                              + 9.6
              10.   38.4   = 38 7/16-″
                              + 9.6
                       48.0   = 48″ Checks OK

APPENDIX-D

Answers to Objective Practice Problems, Story Poles, and Post Test (Continued)

The 3-4-5 Squaring Method (Chalk Line Problem #1), page 93

1. 6 ft. 1 in. = 6.083 ft. and 10 ft. 3 in = 10.25 ft. **2.** 10 ft. 11 15/16+ in. to 11 ft. 11 1/16+ in. (1/8 in. tolerance) **3.** Diagonal = 11' 11+" or 11' 11 1/16-". Largest combination of 3-4-5 would be 6'-8'-10'.

The 5-12-13 Squaring Method (Chalk Line Problem #2), page 94

1. 6 ft. 4 in. = 6.333 ft. and 10 ft. 6 in = 10.5 ft. **2.** 12 ft. 3 1/16+ in. to 12 ft. 3 3/16+ in. (1/8 in. tolerance) **3.** Diagonal = 12' 3 1/8+" or 12' 3 3/16-". Largest combination of 5-12-13 would be 50"-120"-130".

Trade Trick #1, page 98 - Make a Story Pole (Problem 7: 8'- 0" Stick – 6 Centers)

1. 96" ÷ 7 = 13.714" or

	13.714"	= 1' 1 11/16+" or 1' 1 ¾-"
	+ 13.714	
2.	27.428	= 2' 3 7/16"
	+ 13.714	
3.	41.142	= 3' 5 1/8+" or 3' 5 3/16-"
	+ 13.714	
4.	54.856	= 4' 6 13/16+" or 4' 6 7/8-"
	+ 13.714	
5.	68.570	= 5' 8 9/16"
	+ 13.714	
6.	82.284	= 6' 10 ¼+" or 6' 10 5/16-"
	+ 13.714	
7.	95.998	= 96" Checks Out as stick is 96" long.

Or 8.0' ÷ 7 = 1.1428'

1.1428'	2.2856'	3.4284'	4.5712'	5.7140'	6.8568"
+1.1428'	+1.1428'	+1.1428'	+1.1428'	+1.1428'	+1.1428'
1 .1428'	2. 2856'	3. 4284'	4 .5712'	5 .7140'	7 .9996 = 8'- 0"
x12	x12	x12	x12	x12	Checks Okay
2856	5712	8568	11424	14280	
1428	2856	4284	5712	7140	
1.7136"	3.4272"	5.1408"	6.8544"	8.5680"	
1' 1 3/4-"	2' 3 7/16"	3' 5 1/8+"	4' 6 13/16+"	5' 8 9/16"	6' 10 1/4+"

6 .8568
x12
17136
8568
10.2816"→ Multiply by 16 or use a decimal of in. equivalent chart.

Objective Practice Problems for Module #9, page 99 and 100

1. 12 in. or 1 ft. **2.** 21.21" or 21 ¼-" or 1' 9 ¼-" **3.** 46.662" or 46 5/8+" or 3'- 10 5/8+" **4.** 101.808", 101 13/16", or 8' 5 13/16" **5.** .208' **6.** .047' **7.** 7' 0 3/4" **8.** 8' 11 13/16" **9.** .0025 **10.** 1.25 **11.** 212.5%

12. 295.5" ÷ 7 = 42.214" = 3' 6 ¼-"   or   24' 7 1/2" = 24.625' " ÷ 7 = 3.517'

	+ 42.214	
2.	84.428	= 7' 0 7/16"
	+ 42.214	
3.	126.642	= 10' 6 5/8+"
	+ 42.214	
4.	168.856	= 14' 0 13/16+"
	+ 42.214	
5.	211.070	= 17' 7 1/16"
	+ 42.214	
6.	253.284	= 21' 1 ¼+"
	+ 42.214	
7.	295.498	= 295.5" Checks Out as stick is 295.5" long.

3.517'	7.034'	10.551'
	+3.517'	+3.517'
3 .517'	7 .034'	10 .551'
x12	x12	x12
1034	68	1102
517	34	551
6.204"	0.408"	6.612"
3' 6 1/4-"	7' 0 7/16-"	10' 6 5/8"

10.551'
+3.517'
14 .068'
x12
136
68
0.816"
14' 0 13/16"

14.068'	17.585'	21.102
+3.517'	+3.517'	+3.517'
17 .585'	21 .102'	24.619' = 24.62'
x12	x12	Checks Okay
1170	204	
585	102	
7.020"	1.224"→	
17' 7 1/16-"	21' 1 1/4-"	

Multiply by 16 or use a decimal of in. equivalent chart.

Answers to Objective Practice Problems, Story Poles, and Post Test (Continued)

Objective Practice Problems for Module #9, page 100 (Continued)

19. 27-36-45 in ft. & 336-448-560 in in. **20.** 20-48-52 in feet & 260-624-676 in in. **21.** 59′ 0 11/16+″ or 59′ 0 ¾-″

Objective Practice Problems for Module #10, page 105 and 106

1. 471.486 sq. in. and 3.2742 sq. ft. **2.** 2547.031 sq. in. and 17.688 sq. ft. **3.** .7071 **4.** .9563 **5.** .2679
6. .4226 **7.** 11.43 **8.** .8386 **9.** .1736 **10.** .7660 **11.** 27° **12.** 52° **13.** 25° **14.** 42° **15.** 22° **16.** 22°
17. 22° **18.** 4° **19.** 52 13/16+″ and 4′ 4 13/16+″ **20.** 111 11/16+″ and 9′ 3 11/16+″

Objective Practice Problems for Module #11, page 115 and 116

1. .0625″ **2.** 1/16″ **3.** .625″ **4.** 5/8″ **5.** .2104″ **6.** 13/64+″ **7.** .4804″ **8.** 15/32+″ **9.** .368″
10. 23/64+″ **11.** .625″ **12.** 5/8″ **13.** .886″ **14.** 57/64″ **15.** 1.150″ **16.** 1 9/64+″ **17.** .563″ **18.** 9/16″

Objective Practice Problems for Module #12, page 127

Job #1 - 1. Dowel jig, center punch, ruler, scribe or marker, and cutting oil **2.** Measure and center mark for the hole **3.** Center punch the hole **4.** Set up the dowel jig **5.** Drill 3/16″ pilot hole **6.** Drill the 1/2″ hole
Job #2 – 1. Drill press and/or magnetic drill motor, center punch, wing divider, ruler, small square, and cutting oil **2.** Measure hole and mark **3.** Center punch the hole **4.** Scribe a 1″ diameter circle with wing dividers, and center punch around circle scribe mark **5.** Drill a 3/16″ or 1/4″ pilot hole **6.** Drill a larger hole and watch for drift **7.** Drill the 1″ hole and guide to coincide with the circle scribe punch marks

Objective Practice Problems for Module #12, page 128

Draw Circles with a Square:

Copy Angles:

Shimming Tricks:

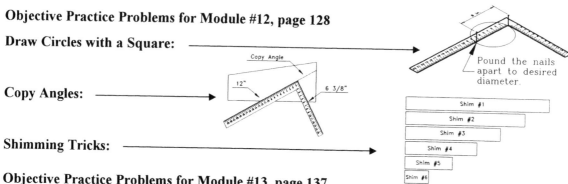

Objective Practice Problems for Module #13, page 137

1. Blade 12″, Tongue 4.368 or 4 3/8″, and 70° **2.** Blade 12″, Tongue 9.208 or 9 3/16+″, and 52.5°
3. Blade 12″, Tongue 12″, and 45° **4.** Blade 12″, Tongue 5.596 or 5 9/16+″, and 25°
5. 175.5″ ÷ 7 = 25.071″ = 2′ 1 1/16″ or 14′ 7 1/2″ = 14.625′ ÷ 7 = 2.089′

+25.071		
2. 50.142	= 4′ 2 1/8+″	
+25.071		
3. 75.213	= 6′ 3 1/4-″	
+25.071		
4. 100.284	= 8′ 4 1/4+″	
+25.071		
5. 125.355	= 10′ 5 3/8-″	
+25.071		
6. 150.426	= 12′ 6 7/16″	
+25.071		
7. 175.497	= 175.5″ Check Out	

2.089′
+2.089′
2 .089′
×12
178
89
1.068″
2′ 1 1/16″

4.178′
+2.089′
4 .267′
×12
356
178
2.136″
4′ 2 1/8+″

6.267′
+2.089′
6 .267′
×12
534
267
3.204″
6′ 3 1/4-″

6.267′
+2.089′
8 .356′
×12
712
356
4.272
8′ 4 1/4+″

8.356′
+2.089′
10 .445′
×12
890
445
5.340
10′ 5 3/8-″

10.445′
+2.084′
12 .534′
×12
1068
534
6.408″
12′ 6 7/16-″

12.534′
+2.089′
14.623′ = 14.625′
Checks Okay

Multiply by 16 or use a decimal of in. equivalent chart.

APPENDIX-D

Answers to Objective Practice Problems, Story Poles, and Post Test (Continued)

Objective Practice Problems for Module #13, page 138 (Continued)

1. Blade 12", Tongue 4.971 or 4 15/16+", and 67.5° **2.** Blade 12", Tongue 6.928 or 6 15/16", and 60°
3. Blade 12", Tongue 3.441 or 3 7/16", and 74°

Objective Practice Problems for Module #14, page 143 and 144

1. Angle A = 22.620° and angle B = 67.38° **2.** 36.870° **3.** Angle A = 59.967° and angle B = 30.033°
4. 34.624° **5.** .29237 **6.** .89101 **7.** 3.73205 **8.** .35837 **9.** .5 **10.** 1 **11.** 1 **12.** .74314 **13.** 57.995 or
58° **14.** 44° **15.** 51.999 or 52° **16.** 30.996 or 31° **17.** 27.995 or 28° **18.** 66.002 or 66° **19.** 8.995 or 9°
20. 9.997 or 10° **21.** Blade 12", Tongue 2.992 or 3", and 76° **22.** Blade 12", Tongue 1.0498 or 1 1/16",
and 85° **23.** Blade 12", Tongue 3.215 or 3 ¼-", and 15° (use the tangent of 15° × 12)

Objective Practice Problems for Module #15, page 159 and 160

1. Common Rafter = 11' 2 1/4", Hip Rafter = 15' 0", Total Rise = 5' 0", Jack difference = 17 7/8", and Slope
Angle = 26.565 **2.** Common Rafter = 7' 2 5/8", Hip Rafter = 9' 9 15/16", Total Rise = 2' 9 5/16+", Jack
difference = 26", and Slope Angle = 22.6198° **3.** Com. (Shed) Rafter = 13' 2 7/16+", Total Rise = 44 5/16",
and Slope Angle = 16.26° (the hypotenuse of 3 ½ and 12 = 12.5") **4.** 23° **5.** 12° **6.** 36° **7.** 53° **8.** 25°
9. 89° **10.** 82° **11.** 19° **12.** Angle A = 20.556° or 20 1/2° and Angle B = 69.444° or 69 1/2° **13.** 26.565
or 26 1/2° **14.** Angle A = 30.033 or 30° and Angle B = 60° **15.** Stair Angle A = 36.409 or 36.5°

Objective Practice Problems for Module #16, page 167

1. 5 risers at 7.4 or 7 7/16-", 4 treads at 10" or 10 1/2", total run 40" or 42", and Stair Angle = 36.5°
2. 8 risers at 7.125 or 7 1/8", 7 treads at 10" or 10 1/2", total run 70" or 73.5", and Stair Angle = 35.469°
3. Common Rafter = 16' 7 1/4-", Hip Rafter = 22' 10 5/8+", Total Rise = 5' 3", Jack difference = 16 7/8", and
Slope Angle = 18.4349°

Objective Practice Problems for Module #16, page 168

1. Blade 12", Tongue 8.666 or 8 5/8+", and 54.16235°
2. Blade 12", Tongue 2.116 or 2 1/8", and 80°

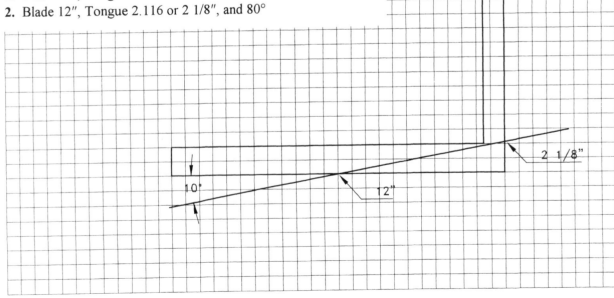

Answers to Objective Practice Problems, Story Poles, and Post Test (Continued)

Objective Practice Problems for Module #17, page 179

1. **14 risers** at 7.536 or 7 9/16″ height, **13 treads** at 10″, **Rise #1** = 9 risers (67.824″ or 67 13/16″) and **Run #1** = 8 treads (80″), and **Rise #2** = 5 risers (37.68″ or 37 11/16″) and Run #2 = 4 treads (40″ not shown). The Stair Angle = 37°

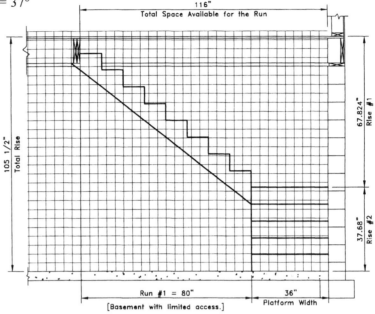

Objective Practice Problems for Module #17, page 180

2. **12 risers** at 7.958″ or 7 15/16+″ height, **11 treads** (width of 8 treads 9.25″, width of 3 treads are wedges) **Run #1** = 64.75″ or 64 3/4″, **Run #2** = 32″ × 32″ platform plus 9.25″. The Stair Angle is 40.706°

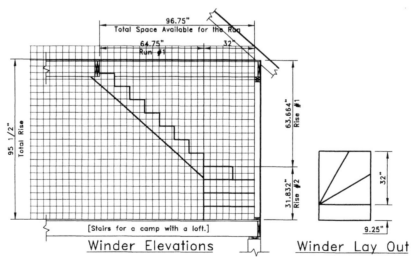

3. **12 risers** at 7.958″ height, **11 treads** at 36″ width, Center-Line Arc Length = 8″, Large Tread Length = 14 1/4″, Tread Angle = 19.929°

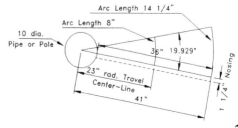

APPENDIX-D

Answers to Objective Practice Problems, Story Poles, and Post Test (Continued)

Objective Practice Problems for Module #18, page 189 and 190

1. Solve with SOH, Angle B = 57°, Opp. = 5.651 or 5 5/8+″, and Adj. = 8.702 or 8 11/16+″ (formula: $b^2 = c^2 - a^2$) **2.** Formula: CAH, Angle B = 50°, Hyp. = 15.665 or 15 5/8+″, and Opp. = 10.069 or 10 1/16″ (solve with $a^2 = c^2 - b^2$) **3.** Solve with SOH, Angle B = 52°, Hyp. = 21.115 or 21 1/8-″, and Adj. = 16.639 or 16 5/8+″ (formula: $b^2 = c^2 - a^2$) **4.** Formula: TOA, Angle A = 23.126°, Opp. = 13.048 or 13 1/16-″

5. Lay out an octagon from a 6 inch square:

Hold 1″ for greater accuracy, in this case

Measure 1 ¼-″ both sides of of all center "marks" as shown.

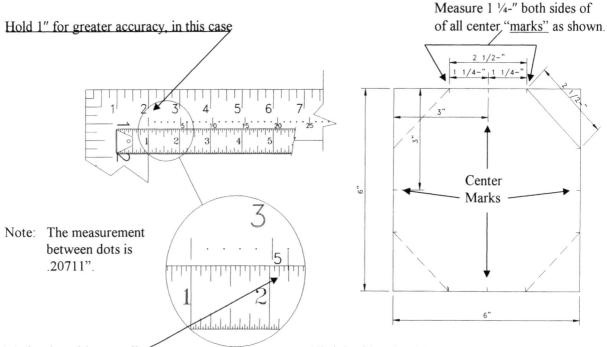

Note: The measurement between dots is .20711″.

Mark ruler with a pencil, exactly as you see. Just a little under 1 ¼-″ (6 × .20711 = 1.243″).

All eight sides should measure very close to 2 ½-″, if care was taken when measuring.

Trade Trick #1, page 196 – Story Pole [Problem 8: 2 Meter Stick (MM and Inches) – 5 Centers]

1. 2000mm ÷ 6 = 333.3mm __or__ 13.122″ = 1′ 1 1/8-″ (333.3 × .03937 = 13.122″)
+ 333.3mm + 13.122

2. 666.6mm __or__ 26.244 = 2′ 2 ¼-″ (666.6 × .03937 = 26.244″)
+ 333.3mm + 13.122

3. 999.9mm __or__ 39.366 = 3′ 3 3/8″ (999.9 × .03937 = 39.366″)or 1 meter
+ 333.3mm + 13.122

4. 1333.2mm __or__ 52.488 = 4′ 4 7/16+″ (1333.2 × .03937 = 52.488″)
+ 333.3mm + 13.122

5. 1666.5mm __or__ 65.610 = 5′ 5 5/8-″ (1666.5 × .03937 = 65.610″)
+ 333.3mm + 13.122

6. 1999.8mm __or__ 78.732 = 78.732″ × 25.4mm = 1999.7928mm or 2000mm = 2 meters OK
6′ 6 ¾-″   Answer Reduced

Objective Practice Problems for Module #19, page 197

1. 10mm (.393 × 25.4 = 9.982mm), **2.** 6mm (.236 × 25.4 = 5.994), **3.** 22mm (.866 × 25.4 = 21.996), **4.** 14mm (.551 × 25.4 = 13.995) **5.** 1 5/16″ = 33.3375mm **6.** 3 3/8″ = 85.725mm **7.** 5 11/32″ = 135.73125mm

Answers to Objective Practice Problems, Story Poles, and Post Test (Continued)

Objective Practice Problems for Module #19, page 197 (Continued)

8. 7/16″ (11.11 × .03937 = .4374) **9.** 1/4″ (6.35 × .03937 = .2499) **10.** 15/16″ (23.81 × .03937 = .93739) **11.** 5/8″ (15.88 × .03937 = .62519) **12.** 51mm = 2″ **13.** 89mm = 3 1/2″ **14.** 123mm = 4 13/16+″

Objective Practice Problems for Module #19, page 198

1. Angle B = 70°, Hyp. = 17.707 or 17 ¾-″, and Adj. = 16.639 or 16 5/8+″ **2.** Angle B = 60°, Hyp. = 13.856 or 13 13/16+″, and Adj. = 6.927 or 6 15/16″ **3.** Angle B = 51°, Opp. = 8.501 or 8 1/2″, and Adj. = 10.499 or 10 1/2″ **4.**

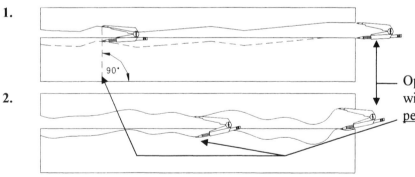

Note: The measurement between dots is .20711″.

Mark ruler with a pencil, exactly as you see.
Just a little under 5/8″ (3 × .20711 = .621)

Trade Trick #1, page 207 – Story Pole [Problem 9: 2.032 Meter Stick (MM and Inches) – 6 Centers]

1. 290.285mm **2.** 580.570mm **3.** 870.855mm **4.** 1161.140mm **5.** 1451.425mm **6.** 1741.710mm **7.** 2031.995mm
1. 11 7/16″ **2.** 22 7/8″ **3.** 34 ¼+″ **4.** 45 ¾-″ **5.** 57 1/8+″ **6.** 68 9/16+″ **7.** 80″

Objective Practice Problems for Module #20, page 208

1.

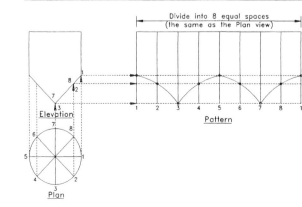

2.

Open compass (scriber) to the widest point and follow through <u>perpendicular</u> to the base as shown.

3.

APPENDIX-D

Answers to Objective Practice Problems, Story Poles, and Post Test (Continued)

Objective Practice Problems for Module #21, page 222

Job #1 – 1. 7.4235 or 7 7/16″ **2.** 10.5 or 10 1/2″
Job #2 – 3. 10.5166 or 10 ½+″ **4.** 14.875 or 14 7/8″

5. Make a story pole of dimensions:

$$
\begin{array}{ll}
1^{st} & 11'\text{-}8\ 1/4'' \\
& +\ 5'\text{-}3\ 1/2'' \\
2^{nd} & 16'\text{-}11\ 3/4'' \\
& +\ 9'\text{-}8\ 1/4'' \\
3^{rd} & 25'\text{-}19\ 4/4'' = 26'\text{-}8''\ \text{Answer OK}
\end{array}
$$

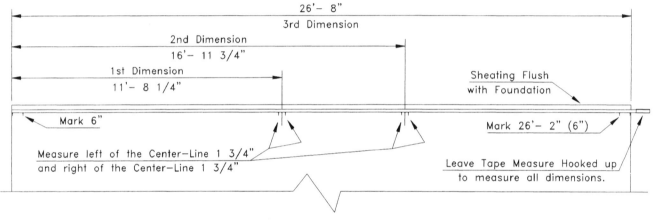

Blank Floor

Post Test, page 243

1. 3389 **2.** 9,088 **3.** 314,340 **4.** 698 **5.** 7/8 **6.** 15/64 **7.** 9/16 **8.** 1 ½ **9.** 13 13/16 **10.** 4 7/8 **11.** 6
12. 9 **13.** 7 ft. 7 11/32 in. **14.** 6 ft. 11 3/16 in. **15.** 4960 sq. in. or 34.4 sq. ft. **16.** 1 ft. 3 in. **17.** 12.263
18. 7.79 **19.** 29.1810 **20.** 19

Post Test, page 244

21. 3 **22.** 61 **23.** .857 **24.** .166′ **25.** 9′-7 7/16″ **26.** 6 13/16″ **27.** 729 **28.** 156 **29.** 25.33 **30.** .0225
31. .0033 **32.** 27 1/2% **33.** 75% **34.** $.70 **35.** 568 **36.** 41″

Post Test, page 245

37. 513 sq. ft. **38.** 57 sq. yd. **39.** 560 cu. ft. **40.** 20.74 cu. yd. **41.** 31° **42.** 37° **43.** 35°37′30″
44. 1 3/16″ **45.** 1 5/8″ **46.** 2 13/16″ **47.** 3 11/32″ **48.** 4 3/8″ **49.** 5 7/16″ **50.** 6 13/32″

Post Test, page 246 (Optional)

1. .4375″ **2.** 7/16″ **3.** .3593″ **4.** 23/64″ **5.** 16.208″ or 16 ¼-″ **6.** Angle A = 42° **7.** 15.870″ or 1′ 3 7/8″
8. 9.103″ or 9 1/8-″ **9.** 22.5° **10.** 21.107″ or 1′ 9 1/8-″

DIRECTIONS: Calculate the problems listed below and reduce all fractions to their lowest terms.

WHOLE NUMBERS A1

1. Task No.→ A2

$$\begin{array}{r} 647 \\ 988 \\ 1409 \\ + \ 345 \end{array}$$

2. A3

$$\begin{array}{r} 16{,}285 \\ - \ 7{,}197 \end{array}$$

3. A4

$$\begin{array}{r} 372 \\ \times \ 845 \end{array}$$

4. A5

$26\overline{)18{,}148}$

COMMON FRACTIONS B1

5. B2

$$\begin{array}{r} \frac{3}{4} \\ + \ \frac{1}{8} \end{array}$$

6. B3

$$\begin{array}{r} \frac{47}{64} \\ - \ \frac{1}{2} \end{array}$$

7. B4

$\frac{27}{32} \times \frac{2}{3} =$

8. B5

$\frac{33}{64} \div \frac{11}{32} =$

MIXED NUMBERS C1

9. C2

$$\begin{array}{r} 11\frac{5}{16} \\ + \ 2\frac{1}{2} \end{array}$$

10. C3

$$\begin{array}{r} 7\frac{1}{4} \\ - \ 2\frac{3}{8} \end{array}$$

11. C4

$1\frac{1}{8} \times 5\frac{1}{3} =$

12. C5

$10\frac{1}{8} \div 1\frac{1}{8} =$

DENOMINATE NUMBERS D1

13. D2

$$\begin{array}{r} 6 \text{ ft. } 2\frac{5}{32} \text{ in.} \\ + \ 1 \text{ ft. } 5\frac{3}{16} \text{ in.} \end{array}$$

14. D3

$$\begin{array}{r} 16 \text{ ft. } 5\frac{3}{8} \text{ in.} \\ - \ 9 \text{ ft. } 6\frac{3}{16} \text{ in.} \end{array}$$

15. D4

$$\begin{array}{r} 5 \text{ ft. } 2 \text{ in.} \\ \times \ 6 \text{ ft. } 8 \text{ in.} \end{array}$$

_____ sq. in.
_____ sq. ft.

16. D5

$7 \text{ ft. } 6 \text{ in.} \div 6 =$

DECIMAL FRACTIONS E1

17. E2

$$\begin{array}{r} 2.071 \\ 8.735 \\ 1.082 \\ + \ .375 \end{array}$$

18. E3

$$\begin{array}{r} 27.67 \\ - \ 19.88 \end{array}$$

19. E4

$$\begin{array}{r} 10.65 \\ \times \ 2.74 \end{array}$$

20. E5

$.375\overline{)7.125}$

243

Task No. | **B6** COMPLEX FRACTIONS

21.

$$\dfrac{\frac{3}{4} \times 64}{6 \div \frac{3}{8}}$$

E8 FIND AVERAGES

22. Find the average of 66, 84, 56, and 38 = _____.

E6 CHANGE FRACTIONS TO DECIMALS

23. Change $\frac{6}{7}$ to a decimal fraction = _____.

24. Change 2" to decimals of a foot = _____.

(Carry decimals 3 places)

E7 CHANGE DECIMALS TO FRACTIONS

Change the two figures below so you can read the dimensions on an American (English) tape measure.

25. 9.62 ft. = _____.

26. 6.81 in. = _____.

H1 POWERS

27. 9^3 = _____

H2 SQUARE ROOTS

28. $\sqrt{24,336}$

I1 RATIO AND PROPORTION

I3 DIRECT PROPORTION

29. 12:19 = 16:X

X = _____

G1 PERCENTAGE

30. Write 2 1/4% as a decimal = _____. **G1**

31. Write 1/3% as a decimal = _____. **G1**

32. Write .275 as a percent = _____. **G2**

33. Write 3/4 as a percent = _____. **G3**

34. Find 4% of $17.50 = _____. **G4**

J1 BASIC ALGEBRA

J2 ADDITION AND EQUATIONS

35. X + 275 = 843

X = _____

J4 MULTIPLICATIONS AND EQUATIONS

36. A = lw
1066 = (l)26
l = _____

26" width

A = 1066 sq. in.

? length

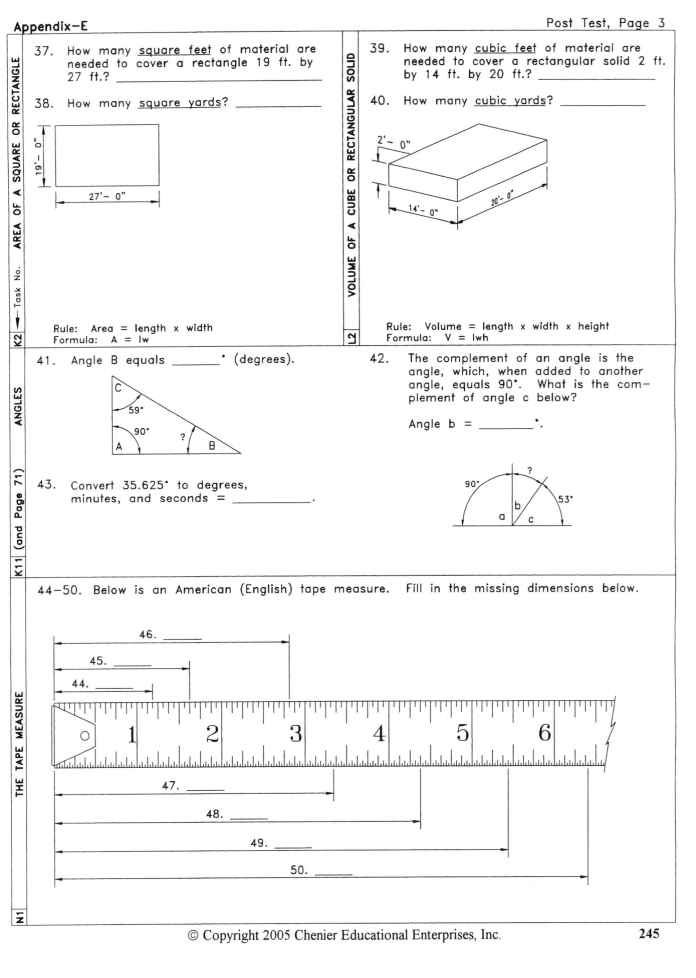

AREA OF A SQUARE OR RECTANGLE

Task No. — **K2**

37. How many <u>square feet</u> of material are needed to cover a rectangle 19 ft. by 27 ft.? _____

38. How many <u>square yards</u>? _____

19'– 0"   27'– 0"

Rule: Area = length x width
Formula: A = lw

VOLUME OF A CUBE OR RECTANGULAR SOLID

L2

39. How many <u>cubic feet</u> of material are needed to cover a rectangular solid 2 ft. by 14 ft. by 20 ft.? _____

40. How many <u>cubic yards</u>? _____

2'– 0"   14'– 0"   20'– 0"

Rule: Volume = length x width x height
Formula: V = lwh

ANGLES

K11 (and Page 71)

41. Angle B equals _____° (degrees).

C 59° 90° A ? B

43. Convert 35.625° to degrees, minutes, and seconds = _____.

42. The complement of an angle is the angle, which, when added to another angle, equals 90°. What is the complement of angle c below?

Angle b = _____°.

90° ? 53° a b c

THE TAPE MEASURE

N1

44—50. Below is an American (English) tape measure. Fill in the missing dimensions below.

46. _____
45. _____
44. _____

1   2   3   4   5   6

47. _____
48. _____
49. _____
50. _____

MICROMETER (.001") ← Task No. **N2**

Fill in the missing micrometer readings below.
Change the fraction to the nearest 64th inch.

1. _____ Ten–Thousandths

2. _____ Fraction of an inch

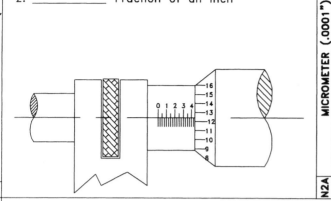

MICROMETER (.0001") **N2A**

Fill in the missing micrometer readings below.
Change the fraction to the nearest 64th inch.

3. _____ Ten–Thousandths

4. _____ Fraction of an inch

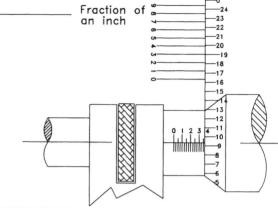

THE RULE OF PYTHAGORAS　K5A　and　SOH–CAH–TOA　FORMULAS:　Page 179 (textbook)　M1

Find the length of the missing right triangle <u>side a</u> shown on the right.

5. Side a = _____ (decimal 3 places)

_____ (ft., in., and ±16ths.)

6. Angle A = _____°.

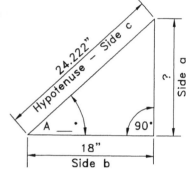

Use a scientific calculator and/or the Trig Tables in the textbook to solve the unknown right triangle angles and sides shown on the right.

7.　Hyp. = _____ (dec. 3 places) <u>or</u> _____ ft., in., & ±16ths.

8.　Side Opp. = _____ (dec. 3 places) <u>or</u> _____ ft., in., & ± 16ths.

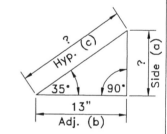

Calculate <u>angle A</u> and the <u>hypotenuse</u> of the right triangle on the right.

9.　Angle A = _____°.

10.　Hyp. = _____ (dec. 3 places) <u>or</u> _____ ft., in., & ±16ths.

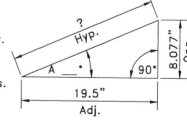

Formulas:　$a^2 + b^2 = c^2$, and SOH–CAH–TOA　(Use extra paper, if needed)

INDEX

A

INDEX

D

E

INDEX

INDEX

Polygons (Radius of 1 Unit Inscribed in Circle)
(Also see, pages 298–308 in the textbook)

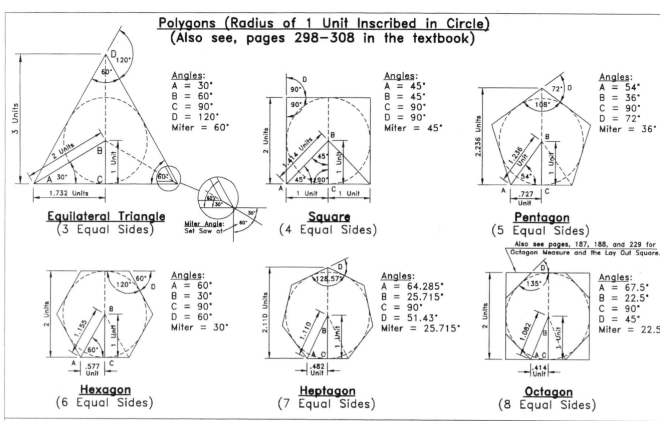

Equilateral Triangle (3 Equal Sides)

Angles:
A = 30°
B = 60°
C = 90°
D = 120°
Miter = 60°

Miter Angle: Set Saw at:

Square (4 Equal Sides)

Angles:
A = 45°
B = 45°
C = 90°
D = 90°
Miter = 45°

Pentagon (5 Equal Sides)

Angles:
A = 54°
B = 36°
C = 90°
D = 72°
Miter = 36°

Hexagon (6 Equal Sides)

Angles:
A = 60°
B = 30°
C = 90°
D = 60°
Miter = 30°

Heptagon (7 Equal Sides)

Angles:
A = 64.285°
B = 25.715°
C = 90°
D = 51.43°
Miter = 25.715°

Octagon (8 Equal Sides)

Also see pages, 187, 188, and 229 for Octagon Measure and the Lay Out Square.

Angles:
A = 67.5°
B = 22.5°
C = 90°
D = 45°
Miter = 22.5°

Largest Combination of 3-4-5

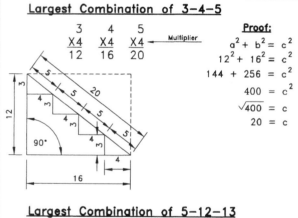

3	4	5
X4	X4	X4
12	16	20

← Multiplier

Proof:

$$a^2 + b^2 = c^2$$
$$12^2 + 16^2 = c^2$$
$$144 + 256 = c^2$$
$$400 = c^2$$
$$\sqrt{400} = c$$
$$20 = c$$

Largest Combination of 5-12-13

5	12	13
X3	X3	X3
15	36	39

← Multiplier

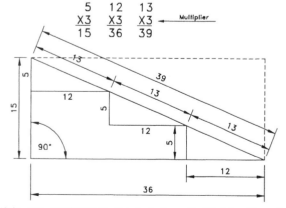

[Note any combination for 3-4-5 or 5-12-13 will work as long as the <u>same multiplier</u> is used for a specific combination. The units can be feet, inches, meters, etc.]

Brace Measure and Tubing Bend at 45°: [Multiply Side x 1.414 = Brace]

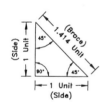

Proof:

$$a^2 + b^2 = c^2$$
$$1^2 + 1^2 = c^2$$
$$1 + 1 = c^2$$
$$2 = c^2$$
$$\sqrt{2} = c$$
$$1.414 = c$$

Find the Side from the Brace: [Multiply Brace x .707 = Side]

Proof:

$$1.414 \times .707 = .99969 \text{ or } 1$$

Brace Measure and Tubing Bend at 30°: [Multiply Offset x 2 = Brace or Tubing Bend]

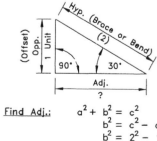

Proof:

$$SOH = [Sin. = \frac{Opp.}{Hyp.}]$$

$$Sin. (30°) = \frac{1}{Hyp.}$$

$$(Hyp.)(.5) = \frac{1}{Hyp.} (Hyp.)$$

$$Hyp. \frac{(.5)}{(.5)} = \frac{1}{(.5)}$$

$$Hyp. = \frac{1}{.5}$$

$$Hyp. = 2$$

<u>Find Adj.:</u>

$$a^2 + b^2 = c^2$$
$$b^2 = c^2 - a^2$$
$$b^2 = 2^2 - 1^2$$
$$b^2 = 4 - 1$$
$$b = \sqrt{3}$$
$$b = 1.732 \text{ Units}$$